# GENERAL CHEMISTRY PROBLEM SOLVING

# I

Math Review, Moles, Stoichiometry,
Nomenclature, Solutions, Enthalpy, Gas Laws,
Atomic Structure, Lewis Structures,
Oxidation-Reduction, Colligative Properties

## RUSSELL S. DRAGO

Professor of Chemistry
University of Florida, Gainesville

D.C. Heath and Company
Lexington, Massachusetts/Toronto

International Standard Book Number: 0-669-08214-7

# CONTENTS

# PREFACE

The only way to master the concepts and to become proficient in solving the problems encountered in general chemistry is to practice. Accordingly, this book on problem solving has been prepared to provide the student with the opportunity to practice. A systematic approach to problem solving is presented that unifies this subject and minimizes the number of equations and facts that must be memorized in order to do well in a general chemistry course. The task is further simplified by emphasizing the similarity in the logic that is used to solve the many apparently different types of problems.

The same basic format is used in this text to treat the various topics. First the concepts involved in a particular problem type are discussed, and a large number of sample problems involving these concepts are worked out and discussed. Next the reader is led through a step by step solution of the problem using a programmed exercise format. These are referred to as Tests in the book, and they serve several important functions that can be achieved only if the reader works them out as they are encountered in her or his reading. The Tests make the reader an active participant in the development of a topic. As such they tend to discourage simply reading words without getting the ideas. The tests are used to evaluate your comprehension of what has been read and also to lead you into the discovery of new ideas and relations. (Over 175 problems are presented in this way in the text.)

When working the Test, it is recommended that you check the answer to each step before proceeding. This is conveniently done by inserting a sheet of paper between the pages of the back of the text that contain the answers. The sheet should cover the answers, and you can uncover the ones you have done to check each step. If you cannot provide an answer to a test question, reread the appropriate section and try again. It is often necessary to read scientific writing several times to obtain the meaning, because the ratio of ideas to words is large compared to that encountered in other kinds of writing. If you still have trouble coming up with an answer, look it up in the back to determine if you now understand the problem. If your answer is wrong, reread the appropriate section if you do not understand why it is wrong. Discovery is the most fascinating part of chemistry, and the tests should enable you to experience this satisfaction.

At the end of each chapter a large number of problems (over 700 total in the book) are given, and the answers are provided in the back of the book. The questions are arranged topically. Most of these are basically drill, but in addition each chapter contains a selection of challenging problems. A series of questions are also provided that require you to verbalize certain concepts. This is a very important skill to develop. A selection of multiple choice questions is given with each chapter. These are not subdivided topically and are best worked after the whole chapter has been studied. If multiple choice exams are given in your course, the purchase of this book could easily improve your performance by a letter grade. Practice with questions in this format will decrease the chances for misinterpretation on an exam and will increase the speed of taking an exam. For example, the importance of reading all the possible answers to a question is illustrated by including problems with two correct answers and the option to check "two of the above." We have intentionally included questions whose answers are given in an earlier question. Practice will show that common sense is usually worth a few points on any exam.

Even though the answers are given to most of the exercises in this text, an instructor can still assign them for homework and check to be sure the problem is worked correctly. The student must consider homework as the chance to practice for the exam.

A good deal of effort has been spent to make this a clear and accurate book. The material has been extensively reviewed by Professors Jerry Atwood, Roger Cramer, Richard De Simone, and Dr. Richard Middaugh. The helpful comments provided by these individuals are greatly appreciated.

I am sure that some errors will be introduced in the publication of this manuscript and students will find some sections unclear. The author will greatly appreciate having any errors or unclear sections called to his attention. Feel free to write him directly at the Chemistry Department, University of Florida, Gainesville, FL 32611. Any suggestions that will help the student master this material will be welcomed.

# 1

# MATHEMATICS REVIEW AND THE METRIC SYSTEM

## Chapter Objectives

### (Begin each of the following with "You should master . . .")*

1. the use of the proper number of significant figures in arithmetic problems.
2. the use of exponents.
3. the rearrangements that can be carried out on an equation without changing its meaning.
4. a systematic approach to the solution of "story problems."
5. the names of the units and prefixes used in the metric system of measurement.
6. problems involving interconversion between the metric and English systems.
7. the concept of percent and the solution of problems involving this concept.
8. the concept of density and the solution of problems using this concept.

In this chapter we will review the operations that are essential to the solution of "story problems."† In general, we will review the mathematical operations needed to solve a chemistry problem as we encounter that kind of problem. In this chapter, conversions between the English and metric systems will be used as a vehicle to teach the approach to problem solving that will be used throughout most of this book.

One of the major traps in solving problems arises from the existence of "gimmick methods" that enable the student to obtain the correct answer to a *particular type* of problem without thinking the problem through. Very similar problems may appear very different, and problem solving then becomes burdensome. I will begin, therefore, by asking you to follow the logic of the approach outlined here, even though you may know quicker and easier routes to the answer. You will be rewarded in the end because the similarity of many apparently different kinds of problems will become obvious and the task of problem solving will be simplified.

---

*If you do not know some of the terms used in this list of Chapter Objectives or in the lists in other chapters, do not be concerned. Hopefully, you will know and understand them by the time the chapter is completed. This list is presented at the beginning so you will have some appreciation for the goals of the chapter. Consult these lists again when you have completed the chapter.
†A story problem is one in which the numerical information is given in the form of a word statement. To solve the problem, one must figure out how to combine the given information.

## 1–1    SIGNIFICANT FIGURES

Some numbers which we encounter in everyday living are exact quantities by definition. For example, there are exactly 100 cents in a dollar. This is 100.000000 . . . . . etc., to as many decimal places as are needed. The counting of discrete objects also result in exact numbers. However, many of the quantities that we encounter result from measurements in which some error always exists. As a result, many of the numbers we use are approximate. The concept of significant figures, which we shall discuss in this section, is an important means of indicating the accuracy of a number. For example, the weight of a turkey could be crudely measured and reported as 12 pounds. On the other hand, using a more accurate scale, the turkey could be found to weigh 12.5 pounds. Accuracy in the measurement to a tenth of a pound would be implied by a report of 12.5 pounds. This number has two certain digits (12) and one uncertain digit, the 5. *The first uncertain digit* is always recorded, and that digit *plus the certain digits in a number are called* **significant figures.** The report of 12 pounds contains two significant figures, while that of 12.5 pounds contains three significant figures. There is usually an uncertainty of at least one unit in the last digit reported for a measured quantity, but this digit is reasonably reliable and is counted as a significant figure. The following rules concerning significant figures must be remembered:

1. All nonzero numbers are significant figures.

2. Zeros that do not appear after some other digit are called **leading zeros** and are never significant;* these zeros simply locate the decimal point. For example, both 0.023 and 0.00023 have two significant figures.

3. Zeros that are surrounded by nonzero digits are called **captive zeros** and are significant. For example, 0.002002 has four significant figures, three leading zeros, and two captive zeros.

4. Zeros following a nonzero digit in a number that has a decimal point are called **trailing zeros** and are significant. For example, 0.200 has three significant figures including two trailing zeros, while 2000. has four significant figures including three trailing zeros. If the zeros are not intended to be significant in a number larger than ten, the decimal point is omitted; if they are significant, the decimal point is used. For example, we may state that a town has a population of 133,000 to the nearest thousand and imply only three significant figures. The zeros only mark the decimal point. However, if the figure were written with a decimal point after it, as 133,000., then a count to the nearest person is implied and all six figures are significant. This problem with large numbers is more satisfactorily solved by the use of exponents, and we will return to a further discussion of this topic in the next section.

Our next concern is what happens to significant figures when mathematical operations are carried out on numbers. *In addition or subtraction, the answer should be reported to the same number of decimal places as are contained in the number in the data set that has the fewest decimal places.*

---

*The choice of the word "significant" to describe this idea is in some ways unfortunate. The location of a decimal place with a zero is by no means insignificant. We should emphasize that what we are indicating with this term is how large the error is compared to the number itself.

## Sample Problem 1–1

Carry out the following addition, being sure to express your answer to the proper number of significant figures:

$$36.123 + 9.01 + 117.2 = ?$$

## Solution

| | |
|---|---|
| 36.123 | (thousandths place uncertain) |
| 9.01 | (hundreths place uncertain) |
| 117.2 | (tenths place uncertain) |
| 162.3 | (tenths place uncertain) |

Since 117.2 has only one decimal place, the answer can have only one digit after the decimal.

---

This rule for determining the number of significant figures is a logical one. The sum is not known any more accurately than the most poorly measured number. For example, no information was obtained about the hundredths place of 117.2. Accordingly, there is no way we can know the sum reliably to more than the tenths place.

In carrying out mathematical operations, at least one more significant figure should be kept than will appear in the answer. At the end of the calculation the answer is *rounded off* to the proper number of significant figures according to the following rules:

*Rule 1.* If the first digit to the right of the last significant figure is less than five, the preceding digit remains unchanged.

*Rule 2.* If this digit is more than five, the preceding digit is increased by one.

*Rule 3.* If this digit is five, the preceding digit is not changed if it is an even number but is increased by one if it is odd.*

In adding the numbers in Sample Problem 1–1, we obtain 162.333. Following Rule 1 above, we round off the answer to four significant figures by dropping the two threes farthest to the right. The number 278.561 would be rounded off to four significant figures by following Rule 2, giving 278.6. Depending upon the number of significant figures carried along in mathematical operations, rounding off can produce answers that differ slightly in the last significant figure from those given in this book. However, as mentioned above, there is always some uncertainty in the last significant figure, so these small differences should be ignored when you compare your answers to those given in the text.

*In multiplication or division, the answer is rounded off to the same number of significant figures as in the number in the data set having the fewest significant figures (regardless of the position of the decimal point.)*

---

*This rule prevents a bias in one direction or the other when dealing with a large amount of data.

## Sample Problem 1–2

Carry out the following mathematical operation and be sure to report an answer with the correct number of significant figures:

$$769.2 \div 13.6 = \;?$$

## Solution

Division yields 56.5588. However, there can be only three significant figures in the answer, because 13.6 contains the least number of significant figures and it has only three of them. Rounding off as described in Rule 3 gives 56.6 as the answer. (The number to be dropped is a 5, and the preceding number—also 5—is odd, so it is increased by one.)

Most of you own at least an inexpensive calculator. In using it, care must be taken to obtain and report the proper number of significant figures. Some calculators will round off all answers to contain two or three significant figures after the decimal point unless you set it up to do otherwise. You can determine in advance how many decimal places you will need before you begin the calculation by looking at the given information and set your calculator up accordingly. Other calculators will give a great many more significant figures than you will need. The answer should be rounded off to the correct number. In carrying out sequential operations that require you to reenter a result from a previous calculation, carry one more significant figure in the operation than you will need in the answer. Do not be concerned if your answer differs from one reported in this book in the last significant figure.

### TEST 1–1

In using these tests, each question is to be worked out in the provided space. It is important to understand each step before proceeding to the next. Your answer to each question should be compared to the one given at the end of the text before proceeding to the next question. If your answer is wrong and you do not understand why, reread the appropriate section before continuing. In reading scientific material, it is often necessary to read it several times to master all the important points. For further practice, you will find exercises on this material at the end of the chapter.

A. 1. In subtracting 18.23 from 456.7, which factor determines the number of significant figures in the answer?

2. Perform the subtraction in A(1) and round off the answer to the correct number of significant figures.

B. 1. In multiplying 82.44 times 4.92, which factor determines the number of significant figures in the answer?

2. Perform the operation in B(1) and round off the answer to the correct number of significant figures.

C. 1. Divide 4.233 by 0.0131.

2. Add 4.233 and 0.0013.

In the future, we will (without requesting it) require all answers to be expressed in the proper number of significant figures.

## 1–2  EXPONENTS

Exponents are convenient for expressing and carrying out mathematical operations involving very large or very small numbers. Some calculators do not contain enough digits to handle operations involving numbers of this kind. We will show how these numbers can be converted to exponential notation, so that the math can be performed on your calculator and the decimal place will be taken care of by manipulation of the exponents. Other calculators solve this problem by automatically converting to exponential notation when all of the display digits available are used up. You must understand exponential notation to use these calculators.

A number expressed in exponential form has the general form of:

$$K \times 10^n$$

where $K$ is called the **coefficient** and $n$ is the **exponent.** We are, in effect, multiplying the coefficient by ten raised to a power. In **scientific exponential notation**, $K$ is a number between 1 and 10 and may be either positive or negative. The exponent can also be positive or negative. A **positive exponent** *indicates the number of times that a number must be multiplied by ten to produce the number in expanded form.* For example,

$$3.3 \times 10^7 = 3.3 \times 10 \times 10 \times 10 \times 10 \times 10 \times 10 \times 10 = 33,000,000$$

In general, to convert an exponential number with a positive exponent to expanded form, we move the decimal point to the right by the number of places indicated by the exponent, adding zeros as we proceed to locate the decimal point:

$$3.3 \times 10^5 = 3.\underset{1\ 2\ 3\ 4\ 5}{3\ 0\ 0\ 0\ 0}.$$

We proceed in the reverse fashion to convert an expanded number greater than one to exponential form; the decimal point is moved to the left, and the exponent of ten is increased by one for each place moved. In this notation, $10^0 = 1$, $10^1 = 10$, $10^2 = 100$, $10^3 = 1000$ and so forth. The following equalities illustrate the discussion:

$$33,000,000 = 33,000,000 \times 10^0 = 3,300,000 \times 10^1 = 330,000 \times 10^2 =$$
$$33,000 \times 10^3 = 3,300 \times 10^4 = 330 \times 10^5 = 33 \times 10^6 = 3.3 \times 10^7$$

A **negative exponent** *tells us how many times we must divide a number by ten to obtain the expanded form of the number.* For example,

$$3.3 \times 10^{-4} = \frac{3.3}{10 \times 10 \times 10 \times 10} = 0.00033$$

Thus, to convert a number with a negative exponent to expanded form, we move the decimal as many places to the left as the number in the exponent:

$$3.3 \times 10^{-4} = 0.\underset{4\ 3\ 2\ 1}{0\ 0\ 0\ 3}.3 = 0.00033$$

To convert a number smaller than one in expanded form to exponential notation, we decrease the exponent of ten by 1 for each place moved; that is:

$$0.00033 = 0.00033 \times 10^0 = 0.0033 \times 10^{-1} = 0.033 \times 10^{-2} = 0.33 \times 10^{-3} = 3.3 \times 10^{-4}$$

All of these operations can be remembered if you remember one simple rule. *If the decimal point is moved to the right the exponent is decreased by 1 for each place moved, and if the decimal point is moved to the left the exponent is increased by 1 for each place moved.*

With large numbers, zeros are used to indicate the decimal place and do not necessarily indicate significant figures. For example, we may say that the population of a city is 250,000 even though we do not know this figure to the nearest person. This ambiguity can be removed by using exponential notation, in which *all* of the digits in the coefficient are significant figures. If the number is known to the nearest 1000 people, we would write $2.50 \times 10^5$, while $2.5 \times 10^5$ indicates accuracy to the nearest 10,000.

The following rules govern the use of exponents in carrying out mathematical operations. If the reason for one of the rules is not obvious, expand a number in exponential notation to its long form, carry out the operation and convert back to exponential form.

(1) To multiply exponential numbers, the coefficients are multiplied and the exponents are added.

$$3.3 \times 10^2 \text{ times } 4.5 \times 10^3 \text{ times } 3.0 \times 10^1 = 4.4 \times 10^7$$

(2) To divide exponential numbers, the coefficients are divided and the exponents subtracted.

$$7.6 \times 10^4 \text{ divided by } 1.8 \times 10^2 = 4.2 \times 10^2$$

(3) To raise an exponential number to a power, the exponent is multiplied by that power and the coefficient is raised to that power.

$$(3.33 \times 10^3)^3 = (3.33)^3 \times 10^9 = 36.9 \times 10^9 = 3.69 \times 10^{10}$$

(4) To take the root of an exponential number, take the root of the coefficient and divide the power by the number corresponding to the root. This is easier if you expand the number until the exponent is evenly divisible by the number corresponding to the root.

$$\sqrt{3.6 \times 10^7} = \sqrt{36 \times 10^6} = \sqrt{36} \times 10^3 = 6.0 \times 10^3$$

or

$$(3.6 \times 10^7)^{1/2} = (36 \times 10^6)^{1/2} = (36)^{1/2} \times 10^3 = 6.0 \times 10^3$$

(5) To add or subtract exponential numbers, the exponents must be the same. The numbers can be expanded so that this is the case.

$$6.66 \times 10^2 + 6.66 \times 10^3 = 6.66 \times 10^2 + 66.6 \times 10^2 =$$
$$73.3 \times 10^2 = 7.33 \times 10^3$$

## TEST 1–2

A.  Express the following numbers in scientific exponential notation:

1. 63,477

2. 0.000230

3. 3,302

4. 0.011

B.  Expand the following exponential numbers to expanded form:

1. $6.54 \times 10^4$

2. $5.55 \times 10^{-3}$

3. $3.666 \times 10^{-5}$

C.  Carry out the following computations without using the exponential notation feature of a calculator:

1.  $6.54 \times 10^4$ times $3.3 \times 10^{-7}$

2.  $(5.2 \times 10^{-3})^4$

3.  $7.77 \times 10^{-5}$ divided by $3.22 \times 10^4$*

# 1–3    OPERATIONS ON AN EQUATION

*Both sides of any equation can be multiplied or divided by the same quantity without changing the equality.* For example,

$$\frac{6}{8} = \frac{3}{4} \qquad\qquad (1\text{–}1)$$

If we multiply both sides of the equation by 2 we obtain

$$\frac{12}{8} = \frac{6}{4} \qquad\qquad (1\text{–}2)$$

which is also true. If we divide both sides of equation (1–1) by 3, we obtain

$$\frac{2}{8} = \frac{1}{4} \qquad\qquad (1\text{–}3)$$

which is also true. If we multiply both sides of equation (1–1) by 8, the answer is

$$6 = \frac{(3)\,(8)}{4}$$

which is obviously true. We can perform the same operations using symbols instead of numbers. For example,

$$ax = by \qquad\qquad (1\text{–}4)$$

If we divide both sides of equation (1–4) by $a$, we obtain

$$x = \frac{by}{a} \qquad\qquad (1\text{–}5)$$

If we wished to obtain from equation (1–4) an equation of the form $y = $ , then we would divide both sides of equation (1–4) by $b$ to obtain

$$y = \frac{ax}{b} \qquad\qquad (1\text{–}6)$$

We may also take the square root of both sides of an equation without changing its meaning or raise both sides of an equation to a given power without changing its meaning; e.g., if $x^2 = 9$ then $x$ must equal $+3$ or $-3$. In general, any legitimate mathematical operation may be carried out on both sides of any equation, without changing the equality represented by that equation. Some of you will recognize this as being a quick review of **basic algebra.**

---

*If you obtained, or at least now understand, all these answers, proceed to the next section. If not, read this section again. This instruction should be followed for all future self-testing exercises, i.e., read the appropriate section again, if you have trouble.

**TEST 1-3**

A. Solve $ax = by$ for

1. $a =$ _____

2. $b =$ _____

# 1-4    PROBLEM SOLVING AND THE METRIC SYSTEM

Let us quickly review the relation between the mathematical operations and their word descriptions. All of you know that addition corresponds to words like "sum" or "plus" and subtraction is associated with words like "minus" and "take away." Most of you realize that multiplication corresponds to "times as much." However, many people cannot explain what division is. Division is a process that converts the denominator of a fraction to one. Thus division gives "how many *per one* of something." For example, if 4 apples cost 20¢ and you wish to know the price of one apple, put 4 apples in the denominator; that is, the division 20¢/4 apples gives 5¢/1 apple. If you wish to know the number of apples you can purchase for 1¢, put 20¢ in the denominator; that is, 4 apples/20¢ gives 0.2 apple/¢.

The first step in problem solving involves reading the question carefully to determine what is being asked. Then you must identify the given facts and determine how they can be combined to yield the answer. Using a systematic approach, let us solve the problem, "How many apples can be purchased for 60¢ if 4 apples can be purchased for 20¢ ?" Bear with this even though you know the answer is twelve, because the *approach* is the essential feature of this discussion.

Step 1: Ask, "What is the question?"

Answer: How many apples? We shall abbreviate this as ? apples.

Step 2: Ask, "What do we have to begin with that is in some way equivalent to the question's answer?"

Answer: 60¢

Step 3: Ask, "How do we go from 60¢ to ? apples?"

Answer: To do this we need a **conversion factor** relating ¢ and apples. This information must be given in the problem somewhere. Reread it if necessary to find that

$$4 \text{ apples} = 20¢$$

There are two conversion factors that can be derived from this information. First, you can divide both sides of this equation by 20¢, using the ideas in the previous section to obtain

$$\frac{4 \text{ apples}}{20\cent} = 1$$

If instead you divide both sides of the equation by 4 apples, you obtain the conversion factor

$$\frac{20\cent}{4 \text{ apples}} = 1$$

The question now becomes, "Which of these two conversion factors will convert 60¢ to ? apples?" If we write

$$60\cent \times \frac{4 \text{ apples}}{20\cent}$$

we have in effect multiplied 60¢ by 1 because we have shown that the conversion factor equals one. Simplifying this equation gives

$$60\cent \times \frac{4 \text{ apples}}{20\cent} = 12 \text{ apples} = ? \text{ apples}$$

Note that in simplifying this equation the ¢ in the numerator cancels the ¢ in the denominator, leaving us with the proper units to answer the question. Slashes have been added to the equation to indicate the cancellation of units. The units can be used to select the proper conversion factor. Another approach is to divide 4 apples by 20¢ to give the number apples per one cent; there are 60 times that many in 60¢.

Had you selected the "wrong" conversion factor to do this problem, you would have obtained:

$$60\cent \times \frac{20\cent}{4 \text{ apples}} = 300\cent^2/\text{apple}$$

The failure to obtain proper units for the answer signals incorrect mathematics. The correct setup must give the units to answer the question ? apples.*

Next we shall discuss problems involving conversion between the English and metric systems. The metric system is used almost exclusively in chemistry and is the most common system in most parts of the world. Mass, length, and volume are expressed in different units in the two systems. The meter (m) in the metric system has as its counterpart in the English system the yard (yd). The liter (l) is employed as a volume unit in the metric system and the quart (qt) in the English, while grams (g) and pounds (lb) are mass units in the two systems respectively. The simplicity of the metric system arises from the fact that the metric units just described are combined to form other metric units that are multiples of ten of the original unit. For example, there are 1000 meters in a kilometer and 1/100th of a meter in a centimeter. Contrast this to the English system, where one must remember that there are 12 inches in a foot, 3 feet in a yard, 1760 yards in a mile and so forth.

---

*The only thing wrong with the "incorrect" conversion factor used in this problem is that it fails to fit the problem; that is, it gives the wrong units. As a conversion factor it is correct in an algebraic sense.

Volume and mass units are equally irregular in the English system. The names and symbols for various multiples in the metric system are summarized in Table 1–1.

| Table 1–1 | The Meaning and Abbreviations of Prefixes in the Metric System | |
|---|---|---|
| **Prefix** | **Meaning** | **Abbreviation** |
| giga | $1 \times 10^9$ | g |
| mega | $1 \times 10^6$ | M |
| kilo | $1 \times 10^3$ | k |
| deci | $1 \times 10^{-1}$ | d |
| centi | $1 \times 10^{-2}$ | c |
| milli | $1 \times 10^{-3}$ | m |
| micro | $1 \times 10^{-6}$ | $\mu$ |
| nano | $1 \times 10^{-9}$ | n |
| pico | $1 \times 10^{-12}$ | p |

The abbreviations in Table 1–1 are combined with those for the basic units to describe measurements. For example, the centimeter is abbreviated cm and indicates 1/100 meter or $1 \times 10^{-2}$ meter, while the kilogram, kg, indicates 1000 or $1 \times 10^3$ grams.

In order to give you an appreciation for the magnitudes of the units in the metric and English systems, conversion factors are summarized in Table 1–2.

| Table 1–2 | The Relation Between Common Units in the Metric and English Systems | |
|---|---|---|
| **Length** | **Volume** | **Mass** |
| 1 inch = 2.54 cm | 1 quart = 0.946 liter | 1 lb = 453.6 g |
| 1 mile = 1.609 km | 1 ft$^3$ = 28.32 liter | 1 kg = 2.205 lb |

The conversion factors need not be memorized, but you should know the meanings of the prefixes in Table 1–1. It may help you to remember the prefixes by noting that there is a decrease by a factor of $10^3$ between the first three and last four prefixes listed in Table 1–1.

Now that we know some facts about these systems of measurement, we are in a position to work some problems. We shall use the same general approach that we used previously in working the apples and cents problem. In so doing, the similarity of the two types of problems should become obvious.

---

## Sample Problem 1–3

If you had a friend from Germany, he (or she) may not know how large a foot is. You would have to use centimeters to indicate your height. Convert 5 ft 10 in to centimeters, given that there are 2.54 cm in 1.00 in.

## Solution

Step 1. The question is "How many cm," which we abbreviate as "? cm."

Step 2. The next step is to recognize that 5 ft 10 in is equivalent to ? cm. We write this as 70 in and label this the "begin with" step.

Step 3. Next we look for the relation between inches and cm.

$$2.54 \text{ cm} = 1.00 \text{ in}$$

Then we determine the proper conversion factor so that the units work out correctly:

$$? \text{ cm} = (70 \text{ in}) (X)$$

In order for inches to cancel, inches must appear in the denominator of our conversion factor $X$, so we divide both sides of the equation in step 3 by 1.00 in, giving

$$\frac{2.54 \text{ cm}}{1.00 \text{ in}} = 1$$

Thus, multiplying 70 in by this conversion factor is the same as multiplying it by one.

Step 4. Next we put it all together and solve the problem:

$$Asked = \begin{matrix} Begin \\ with \end{matrix} \times \begin{matrix} Conversion \\ factor \end{matrix} = Answer$$

$$? \text{ cm} = 70. \cancel{\text{in}} \times \frac{2.54 \text{ cm}}{1.00 \cancel{\text{in}}} = 1.8 \times 10^2 \text{ cm}$$

Step 5. Note that inches cancel and the answer has the proper units when this equation is solved.

---

With practice you will soon write the last equation immediately and check the unit cancellation to be sure you have set up the problem properly. To understand the math involved you simply need to realize that if there are 2.54 cm in one inch, there are 70 times as many in 70 inches.

---

## Sample Problem 1–4

You are in a European grocery store and would like to purchase 0.250 pound of cheese. How many grams of cheese do you ask for?

## Solution

1.  Question Asked: ? grams

2.   Begin with: 0.250 pound (lb)

3.   The relation of pounds to grams is given by: 453.6 g = 1 lb (from Table 1–2)
     To convert lb to grams we write the conversion factor

$$\frac{453.6 \text{ g}}{1 \text{ lb}} = 1$$

The conversion factor is written so that the units of the denominator will cancel the units of the number to be converted.

4.   Putting it all together,

$$? \text{ grams} = 0.250 \, \cancel{\text{lb}} \times \frac{453.6 \text{ g}}{1 \, \cancel{\text{lb}}} = 113 \text{ g}$$

5.   Note that the units cancel.

## Sample Problem 1–5

How many pounds are there in 250. grams? (The decimal point after 250 indicates three significant figures.) There are 453.6 g in one pound.

## Solution

1.   Asked: ? pounds
2.   Begin with: 250. g
3.   A conversion factor is needed which, when multiplied by grams, gives pounds; that is, 1 lb/453.6 g.

4.   $$? \text{ pounds} = 250. \, \cancel{\text{g}} \times \frac{1 \text{ lb}}{453.6 \, \cancel{\text{g}}} = 0.551 \text{ lb}$$

5.   Note that the units cancel. Had we set the problem up incorrectly, we would get

$$? \text{ pounds} = 250. \text{ g} \times \frac{453.6 \text{ g}}{1 \text{ lb}} = 114,000 \text{ g}^2/\text{lb}$$

This is an obvious goof because the units do not work out to pounds but instead give $\text{g}^2/\text{lb}$.
    To understand the math carried out, recall that division converts the denominator to one. In this case 1 lb ÷ 453.6 g gives us the number of pounds per gram. To complete the problem, we note that there are 250 times as many pounds in 250 grams as there are in 1 g, and we carry out the required multiplication.

## Sample Problem 1–6

There are 2.54 cm in one inch; 12 inches in one foot, and 5,280 feet in one mile. How many miles are there in 1.00 kilometer?

## Solution

1. Asked: ? miles
2. Begin with: 1.00 km
3. The conversion factor required depends upon the information available. For example, if we had the conversion factor from km to miles we could complete the problem in one step, as in sample problem 1–5. However, since we are not given this conversion factor directly, *we must carry out the following series of conversions: km to cm, then cm to inches, then inches to feet and finally feet to miles.* This is necessary because the only English to metric conversion unit that we have is cm to inches. In doing these problems we will assume you know the information in Table 1–1.

4. $\text{? miles} = 1.00 \text{ km} \times \dfrac{1000 \text{ m}}{1 \text{ km}^*} \times \dfrac{100 \text{ cm}}{1 \text{ m}} \times \dfrac{1 \text{ in}}{2.54 \text{ cm}} \times \dfrac{1 \text{ ft}}{12 \text{ in}} \times \dfrac{1 \text{ mi}}{5,280 \text{ft}} = 0.621 \text{ mile}$

5. Note that the units cancel.

Recall that each of the conversion factors written in the above equation equals 1, so we are in effect multiplying

$$1.00 \text{ km} \times 1 \times 1 \times 1 \times 1 \times 1$$

Each multiplication changes the number and the units but does not change the length represented. Note once again the unit cancellation in solving the problem.

### TEST 1–4

A. The United States is in the process of converting from the English to the metric system. We shall examine some of the problems this might cause Howard Cosell, announcing a football game, if the size of the field and the rules are kept the same. On receiving the ball a team has four tries (called downs) to make at least ten yards. It is fourth down (final try) and the Chicago Bears have two inches to go, Howard is waiting for you to convert inches to centimeters so he can tell America.

---

*We have not indicated significant figures on those quantities that are known exactly by definition and thus have an unlimited number of significant figures. Remember these quantities do not limit the number of significant figures in the answer. Alternately, we can determine the number of significant figures in the answer and use this many in the defined quantities.

1. What is asked?

2. What do you begin with?

3. What conversion needs to be made?

4. Using the data in Table 1–2, set up and solve this problem.

5. Do the units cancel out properly?

B.  On this rare occasion the Bears made it. Now it is first down and ten yards to go for another. You must now convert ten yards to meters as Howard stalls and awaits your answer. You know that there are 2.54 cm per inch, 12 inches to the foot, and 3 feet in a yard.
    1. What is asked?

    2. What do you begin with?

    3. What sequence of conversions needs to be made?

    4. Using conversion factors, set up the equation to bring about these conversions and solve the problem.*

    5. Do the units check out?

C.  The understanding of concepts can be measured by asking one to generalize and apply them to an abstract situation. We shall define the abstract concept of a pididdle and define it as equal to 3.33 daddles. We shall answer questions involved in calculating: "How many pididdles are there in 7.00 daddles?"

    1. What is asked?

    2. What do you begin with?

    3. What conversion needs to be made?

    4. Set up the equation, solve this problem, and check the unit cancellation.

    5. What did you determine when you divided 1 pididdle by 3.33 daddles?

---

*The quantity 2.54 cm per inch is the only quantity that is not an exact integer by definition, so it determines the number of significant figures in the answer.

An International System of Units (SI units) has been proposed by an international group of chemists. This system begins with fundamental metric units and derives units for other quantities from these base units and from fundamental laws. Some of the base units are the metre (m), the kilogram (kg), and the second (s) for length, mass, and time. We shall describe other base units as we encounter them. The prefixes in Table 1–1 are used in the SI system. Volume is not a base unit in this system because it can be derived from the product of measurements of the three dimensions of a container. Accordingly, volume has the units of cubic metres, m³. A liter is exactly equal to a **cubic decimetre**, and this latter term should be substituted for liter wherever liter appears in this text for those who wish to adhere to the SI system. The beauty of the SI system is seen with the volume unit. The unit m³ immediately indicates the relation of volume to length. The word liter does not. This advantage exists for all SI units. The problem with introducing any new units is that both the old and new units must be recognized, because the older literature uses the older units. For this reason, acceptance of the SI system has not been universal. As we proceed, we shall introduce more SI base units and derived units. We shall set these paragraphs in different type so you can emphasize or delete them as you or your instructor see fit.

## 1–5    DENSITY

Each substance has a characteristic physical property called its density. Density, $d$, is defined as the mass, $m$, of material per unit volume, $v$, at a specific temperature.

$$d = \frac{m}{v} \tag{1–7}$$

The mass is usually expressed in grams and the volume in milliliters (ml). For a given sample, the mass is independent of temperature but the volume changes with temperature. (Most substances expand on heating.) Therefore, the density (that is, the mass-volume ratio) changes with temperature because the denominator changes with temperature. Unless specified otherwise, a temperature of 25°C should be assumed for any values of density given in this text.

---

**Sample Problem 1–7**

If 25.00 ml of a substance weighs 23.55 g at 25°C, what is its density?

**Solution**

We wish to know the number of grams per ml, and since division converts the denominator to one, we write:

$$\frac{23.55 \text{ g}}{25.00 \text{ ml}} = 0.9420 \text{ g/ml} = \text{density}$$

Density is a conversion factor that interconverts the mass and volume of a substance. For example, suppose you had available apparatus to weigh something accurately but nothing with which to measure volume. Furthermore, suppose you needed 25.0 ml of a substance whose density is known. By using the density to convert the volume to mass, you can figure out the mass needed to give 25.0 ml. We shall illustrate this in sample problem 1–8.

## Sample Problem 1–8

Ethyl alcohol has a density of 0.804 g/ml. What mass of alcohol would have to be weighed out to obtain 25.0 ml?

### Solution

The question is, "What is the mass of 25.0 ml if the density is 0.804 g/ml?"
  1.  ? g
  2.  Begin with 25.0 ml
  3.  We need to convert ml to g, so a g/ml conversion factor is needed.

4.
$$? \text{ g} = 25.0 \text{ ml} \times \frac{0.804 \text{ g}}{1 \text{ ml}} = 20.1 \text{ g}$$

  5.  Note that the units cancel.

## Sample Problem 1–9

Assume that you have very accurate means available for measuring volume but no way of measuring mass. What volume of ethyl alcohol (density = 0.804 g/ml) should be measured to obtain 50.0 g?

### Solution

The question is, "What is the volume of 50.0 g of alcohol?"
  1.  ? ml
  2.  Begin with 50.0 g
  3.  We need to convert g to ml, so a ml/g conversion factor is required.

4.                          $? \text{ ml} = 50.0 \not{g} \times \dfrac{1 \text{ ml}}{0.804 \not{g}} = 62.2 \text{ ml}$

5. Note that the units cancel.

---

## 1–6    PERCENT

Percent is the amount of something in one hundred total parts of material.

$$\%A = \dfrac{\text{part A}}{\text{part A} + \text{rest}} \times 100 \qquad \qquad (1\text{–}8)$$

Where part A plus the rest is the total amount of material.

Note that part A divided by total in equation 1 – 8 gives us parts of A per one part of the total. To convert to parts A per 100 parts of the total (that is, percent) we must multiply by 100.* For example, if one states that a uranium ore (a mixture of uranium oxide, sand, and other materials) is 3% uranium by weight, this means that for every 100 g of ore (that is, total material) three grams of uranium are present.

In practice we can calculate percent using various units for the parts. Above we used weight units. If you prepared a drink by mixing 15 ml of alcohol with 55 ml of soda water, the mixture could be described in terms of percent alcohol by volume† as

$$\% \text{ alcohol (volume)} = \dfrac{\text{part alcohol}}{\text{total}} \times 100 = \dfrac{15 \text{ ml}}{15\text{ml} + 55 \text{ ml}} \times 100 = 21\%$$

If we knew the density of alcohol and the density of the soda, we could describe this mixture in terms of percent by weight.

---

## Sample Problem 1–10

At 25°C the density of alcohol is 0.78 g/ml. Assuming that the density of soda water is one (1.0) g/ml, calculate the weight percent of the alcohol solution described above.

## Solution

15 ml × 0.78 g/ml = 12 g of alcohol

55 ml × 1.0 g/ml = 55 g of soda water

---

*Units are taken care of as in the following example,
$$0.21 \times \dfrac{100}{100} = \dfrac{21}{100} = 21\%$$
†The assumption that the volumes are additive will be made in problems of this type; masses are always additive.

$$\frac{12 \text{ g of alcohol}}{12 \text{ g} + 55 \text{ g}} \times 100 = 18\%$$

---

We see by comparing 21% by volume and 18% by weight for the above solution that, even though percent has dimensions of parts in one hundred total parts, it matters very much which units we use to describe the parts. In general it will be assumed that we are employing units of mass (that is, that we mean percent by weight) unless otherwise specified.

Since 18% describes parts per 100 total, dividing the numerator (18) by the denominator (100) would give 0.18 parts per unit total. A quantity obtained in this manner can be immediately recognized as a conversion factor for obtaining the parts of something in a total amount of material. For example, carbon dioxide is a molecule which is 27% by weight carbon:

$$\frac{27 \text{ g C}}{100 \text{ g total}} = \frac{0.27 \text{ g C}}{1 \text{ g total}}$$

This can be recognized as a conversion factor for converting g total into grams carbon. If we had 88 g of carbon dioxide, we could calculate the amount of carbon in it as follows:

$$88 \text{ g total} \times \frac{27 \text{ g C}}{100 \text{ g total}} = 24 \text{ g C}$$

or

$$88 \text{ g total} \times \frac{0.27 \text{ g C}}{1 \text{ g total}} = 24 \text{ g C}$$

**TEST 1–5**

A.   A sample of an oxide of uranium is found to contain 48.0 g of oxygen and 238 g of uranium. We shall answer some questions to determine the precent uranium.

   1. Define % uranium.

   2. What is the total mass in the problem?

   3. Calculate the percent uranium in this oxide.

B.  How many grams of uranium are there in a 25.0 g sample of the oxide described in part A?

C.  A 500 g sample of an ore consists of 8.00 g of $UO_2$, 5.00 g of $UO_3$, and the rest sand. The percent uranium in $UO_2$ is 88.1% and the percent uranium in $UO_3$ is 83.2%. We shall answer a series of questions about this system that relate to percent.

1.  What is the total mass of material to be used in determining the percent $UO_2$ in the sample?

2.  Calculate the percent $UO_2$ in the ore.

3.  Calculate the percent $UO_3$ in the ore.

4.  What is the percent uranium in this sample? (Hint: we must combine the uranium in $UO_2$ and $UO_3$.)

5. If we had 48.0 grams of the ore described above, how much uranium could we obtain from it, assuming that we could somehow get it all out?

There are some other ways in which percent is employed, leading to definitions that are different from that in equation 1 – 8. One often discusses a percent yield. For example, in question C–5 we calculated the amount of uranium that we could obtain from 48.0 g of ore as 1.08 g. In practice, we could lose some material in the workup, or for some other reason end up obtaining less uranium than calculated. We would define our percent yield as:

$$\% \text{ yield} = \frac{\text{amount actually obtained}}{\text{amount calculated}} \times 100 \qquad (1-9)$$

Here the amount calculated represents the total amount which one could possibly obtain, while the amount actually obtained is usually something less. Thus, if in our workup of 48.0 g of ore we actually obtained 0.950 g of uranium, our percent yield would be

$$\frac{0.950 \text{ g}}{1.08 \text{ g}} \times 100 = 88.0\%$$

Percent change, a third way to use percent, is used to describe the extent of change in a quantity. One may speak of a percent increase or a percent decrease. For example, suppose I invested $475 in the stock market and after a year (a good year for me) this stock was worth $322; this is a decrease of $153. Suppose my wife invested $975 and after a year her stock was worth $682, for a loss of $293. The size of the percent decrease indicates which of us lost the greater fraction of the money. The percent change is defined as

$$\% \text{ change} = \frac{\text{change in initial amount}}{\text{initial amount}} \times 100 \qquad (1-10)$$

---

## Sample Problem 1–11

Calculate the percent decrease in the two stock market investments described above to determine who lost the greater percentage of their money.

## Solution

Using the definition in equation 1 – 10 we obtain:

$$\frac{\$153}{\$475} \times 100 = 32.2\% \text{ decrease} \qquad \frac{\$293}{\$975} \times 100 = 30.0\% \text{ decrease}$$

Thus I lost a larger fraction of my investment than my wife lost of hers, and as usual I can only take consolation in the fact that I did not invest more money.

## Exercises

(You will find the answers to many of the exercises at the back of the book.)

**Significant Figures and Conversions**
1. Using the approach described in this chapter, solve the following problems:
    (a) If a car travels 250 miles in 7.00 hr, how far can it travel, at the same rate, in 13.0 hr?
    (b) At the speed described in (a), how long would it take the car to travel 50.0 miles?
    (c) There are 13.0 pididdles in 7.00 daddles. How many pididdles are there in 12.0 daddles?
    (d) Using the information in (c), how many daddles are there in 3.00 pididdles?

2. How many significant figures are there in each of the following?
    (a) 2.450
    (b) 0.10007
    (c) 0.00023
    (d) 2.01
    (e) 50.00

3. Express the answers to the following in the correct number of significant figures:
    (a) $21.2 + 9.7654 + 312.22$
    (b) $0.91765 - 0.9012$
    (c) $231.22 - 9.16$
    (d) $4.81 \times 1.2$
    (e) $6.72 \times 0.32$
    (f) $0.100012 \times 9.4378$
    (g) $12.316 \div 2.3$
    (h) $(4.22)^2$

4. In a chemical reaction, 15.6 g of copper (Cu) combined with 3.90 g of sulfur (S).
    (a) How many grams of S combine with 1.00 g of Cu?
    (b) How many grams of Cu combine with 1.00 g of S?

(c) How many grams of Cu combine with 32.0 g of S?

(d) Which of the above can be considered to be conversion factors and what do they convert?

5.  Carry out the following conversions using the data in Table 1–2 (1 ft = 12 in, 32 oz = 1 qt).

(a) 30. ft to cm

(b) 30. cm to in

(c) 6 ft 6 in to m

(d) 50 lb to kg

(e) 1358 g to lb

(f) 4.4 qt to liters

(g) 1.0 oz to ml

## Exponents

6.  Express the following numbers* in scientific notation using exponents:

(a) 100.

(b) 356,000.

(c) 0.330

(d) 12,158

(e) 0.0256

(f) 0.00000032

(g) 0.00687

(h) 955.43

7.  Expand the following exponential numbers:

(a) $1.44 \times 10^3$

(b) $6.33 \times 10^{-4}$

(c) $2.556 \times 10^2$

(d) $5.55 \times 10^{-10}$

8.  Carry out the following calculations:

(a) $7.22 \times 10^3$ times $3.4 \times 10^6$

(b) $6.22 \times 10^5$ divided by $4.6 \times 10^3$

(c) $5.66 \times 10^{-3}$ divided by $2.22 \times 10^3$

(d) $5.49 \times 10^{-6}$ times $4.33 \times 10^3$

(e) $4.4 \times 10^{-5}$ times $3.44 \times 10^{-5}$

(f) $4.33 \times 10^{-4}$ minus $3.62 \times 10^{-5}$

(g) $7.246 \times 10^5$ plus $4.444 \times 10^3$

(h) $(1.00 \times 10^3)^4$

(i) $(3.5 \times 10^6)^3$

---

*If a decimal point is found after a number larger than 1.0 that ends in a zero, the zero should be considered a significant figure. If a decimal point is not given, the non-zero number farthest to the right is the last significant figure.

**Manipulations of an Equation**

9. If $\dfrac{x}{y} = \dfrac{g}{r}$

    (a) What does $g$ equal?
    (b) What does $r$ equal? (Hint: First multiply both sides by $r$.)
    (c) What does $x$ equal?
    (d) What does $y$ equal?

10. If $\dfrac{ax^2}{b} = \dfrac{cd}{e}$

    (a) What does $a$ equal?
    (b) what does $d$ equal?
    (c) What does $e$ equal?
    (d) What does $x$ equal?

11. If $ab = \dfrac{cd}{ef}$

    (a) What does $a$ equal?
    (b) What does $c$ equal?
    (c) What does $f$ equal?

**Density**

12. A piece of copper having a volume of 13.0 ml (cubic centimeters) weighs 116 grams. Calculate its density.

13. A container of unknown volume is filled with liquid bromine, $Br_2$. The bromine weighs 58.6 grams and has a density of 3.10 g/ml. Calculate the volume of the container.

14. A sample of mercury is found to weigh 55.0 grams. If the density of mercury is 13.6 g/ml, what is the volume of this sample?

15. A sample of bromine has a volume of 25.0 ml. With a density of 3.10 g/ml, what is the weight of this sample?

**Percent**

16. A substance is found to contain 10.0 g of calcium, 3.0 g of carbon, and 12.0 g of oxygen in a 25.0 g sample. Calculate the percentage of each element in the sample.

17. An ore consists of 66.6% iron oxide. The iron oxide contains 70.0% iron. How much iron could be obtained from a 50.0 g sample of the ore?

18. A pure material weighing 1.335 g picks up 0.333 g of water on being exposed to moist air. What is the percent increase in the weight?

19.   In the course of carrying out an experiment, a chemist obtains 22.5 g of a substance, but he calculated that he should have obtained 73.0 g. What is the percent yield?

20.   If a sample of iron oxide contains 70.0% iron, how many grams of iron oxide would be needed to produce 75.0 g of iron in a process with a 100% yield?

21.   A 5.00 g sample of pure chromium oxide is found to contain 3.45 g of chromium. Calculate the percentages of chromium and oxygen.

**Verbalizing General Concepts**
22.   In your own words, answer each of the following.
      (a) In a number less than one, how do you determine the number of significant figures?
      (b) When two numbers are added, how do you determine the number of significant figures in the sum?
      (c) When you divide two numbers, how do you determine the number of significant figures in the answer?
      (d) When two numbers in exponential notation are divided, what do you do with the exponents?
      (e) If you take the cube root of a number in exponential form, what do you do to the exponent?
      (f) What is the metric system prefix for:
          (1) $10^9$?
          (2) $10^{-6}$?
          (3) $10^{-12}$?
      (g) In general terms, what is a conversion factor?
      (h) Define density and describe how it can be considered to be a conversion factor.
      (i) Define:
          (1) percent by weight.
          (2) percent yield.
          (3) percent increase.
      (j) Describe how the decimal equivalent of percent (that is, percent divided by 100) can be used as a conversion factor.

**Challenging Problems**
23.   What would be the percentage increase in length if a 100 yard football field were changed to 100 meters? A mercenary professional football player wants his salary increased in proportion to the increase in the length of the field. If his salary were $88,000 per year, what is he asking to be paid?

24.   A sample of lead has a density of 11.3 g/ml. What is the density in units of pounds/gallon? (There are four quarts in a gallon.)

25.   Suppose you are able to purchase $UF_6$, a substance containing 67.6% uranium, for 50¢ per gram. You have a process for converting $UF_6$

to uranium metal with a yield of 86.4%. What would you have to charge for uranium (in dollars per gram) if you wished to make a profit of 55.0% above the cost of the $UF_6$?

26. This is a difficult problem, so do not be concerned if you cannot figure it out. A sample consisting of $UO_2$ (88.1% uranium) and $UO_3$ (83.2% uranium) is found to contain 84.5% uranium. What is the percentage of $UO_2$ in the sample?

## Multiple Choice Questions

Each multiple choice question has only one correct answer. You are to check the one answer that is the best one.

27. The number 0.00340 contains the following number of significant figures: (a) one, (b) two, (c) three, (d) five, (e) none of these.

28. Division of 78.600 by 4.00 gives (a) 19.65, (b) 0.0509, (c) 19, (d) 0.05, (e) none of these.

29. The product of $2.33 \times 10^4$ times $5.2 \times 10^{-2}$ is (a) $1.2116 \times 10^2$, (b) $1.2 \times 10^2$, (c) $1.2 \times 10^1$, (d) $1.2 \times 10^3$, (e) none of these.

30. The prefix "mega" refers to (a) $10^9$, (b) $10^6$, (c) $10^3$, (d) $10^{-9}$, (e) $10^{-12.}$

31. A nanometer corresponds to the following number of centimeters: (a) $10^{-9}$, (b) $10^{-7}$, (c) $10^{-11}$, (d) $10^{-8}$, (e) none of these.

32. To purchase 0.400 lb of meat in Europe, you would have to ask for the following number of kilograms (454 g = 1 lb): (a) 182 kg, (b) 1.13 kg, (c) 0.182 kg, (d) 11.3 kg, (e) none of these within 0.1 kg.

33. The density of ethyl alcohol is 0.804 g/ml. A sample weighing 25.0 g would have a volume of (a) 31.1 ml, (b) 20.1 ml, (c) 25.0 ml, (d) 0.804 ml, (e) none of these.

34. Iron has a density of 7.8 g/ml, and copper has a density of 8.9 g/ml. Which of the following is true? (a) 1.0 g of copper weighs more than 1.0 g of iron, (b) 1.0 g of iron weighs more than 1.0 g of copper, (c) 1.0 ml of copper weighs more than 1 ml of iron, (d) 1.0 ml of iron weighs more than 1.0 ml of copper, (e) two of the above are correct.

35. Given the densities in the above question, 5.0 ml of iron weighs (a) 1.6 g, (b) 39 g, (c) 1.8 g, (d) 44 g, (e) none of these.

36. A substance is exposed to water and undergoes an 18.3% increase in weight. If the initial weight of the substance was 25.0 grams, the final weight will be (a) 4.58 g, (b) 458 g, (c) 29.6 g, (d) 43.3 g, (e) none of these within 1.0 g.

37.  If $x = wy/z$, then $z$ equals:
     (a) $wy$, (b) $wy/x$, (c) $wxy$, (d) $x/wy$, (e) none of these.

38.  If $xy = w + z$, then $w$ equals:
     (a) $xy/z$, (b) $xy + z$, (c) $xy - z$, (d) $z/xy$, (e) none of these.

39.  Density is defined as (a) the mass of material per unit volume at a given temperature, (b) the mass of material at a given temperature, (c) the volume of a unit mass at a given temperature, (d) the volume of a substance in the metric system, (e) none of these.

40.  The product of $4.66 \times 10^5$ and $2.4 \times 10^{-3}$ is
     (a) $1.1184 \times 10^2$      (d) $1.1 \times 10^3$
     (b) $1.118 \times 10^3$      (e) none of these
     (c) $1.12 \times 10^2$

41.  A substance is exposed to water and undergoes a 16.5% increase in weight. If the initial weight of the substance were 25.0 grams, the final weight will be
     (a). 4.13 g      (d) 41.5 g
     (b) 413 g      (e) none of these within 1.0 g
     (c) 29.1 g

42.  Iron has a density of 7.80g/ml. Given this density, 25.0ml of iron weighs
     (a) 0.312 g      (d) 1.40 g
     (b) 195 g      (e) none of these
     (c) 3.21 g

# 2

# MOLES AND EMPIRICAL FORMULAE

## Chapter Objectives

## (Begin each of the following with "You should master . . .")

1. the definitions of compound, element, chemical change, physical change, atom, molecule, atomic weight, and molecular weight.
2. the concept of a mole (this is a very important idea).
3. problem solving involving the mole concept.
4. problem solving involving percent composition and empirical formula determination.
5. the ideas involved in obtaining a chemical analysis of a substance.

In this chapter, we shall attempt to bridge the gap between macroscopic (bulk) properties of substances that chemists can observe or measure, like mass, and the concepts of atoms and molecules that they use to explain these properties. We shall begin by reviewing some simple definitions.

## 2–1    SOME SIMPLE DEFINITIONS

**Chemistry** is the study of matter and the changes it undergoes. An appreciation for the scope of this science can be obtained by considering **matter** as anything that occupies space and has mass. One of the first problems in studying chemistry is to divide matter into various categories. (If any term used in the following discussion is not familiar, its definition can be found in the Glossary of the Appendix section, or in a standard dictionary.) As indicated in Figure 2–1, matter is divided into two general categories: **pure substances** and **mixtures.** Pure substances are materials that cannot be separated into two or more other forms of matter by physical means. Mixtures are materials that consist of two or more pure substances. If, on a macroscopic scale, a mixture is uniform in composition throughout, such as a solution of salt in water, the mixture is said to be **homogeneous.** If it is not uniform, but consists of two or more physically different portions, such as a mixture of salt and pepper, the mixture is said to be **heterogeneous.**

Pure substances are always homogeneous. They can be subdivided into **compounds**

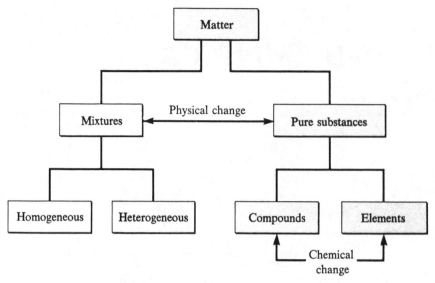

**Figure 2–1**   Schematic classification of matter.

and **elements.** A **compound** is a substance with a definite and constant composition that can be broken down by chemical reactions into simpler pure substances. For example, water can be broken down into dihydrogen and dioxygen. Simple, pure substances that can never be further decomposed by ordinary chemical reactions* are called **elements.**

The best definitions of compounds and elements can be made in terms of atoms and molecules. These definitions also provide the basis for a molecular explanation of the macroscopic classification just described. The following postulates of the atomic theory define atoms and molecules.

1. The elements are made up of minute, discrete, indivisible, and indestructible particles called **atoms.** An appreciation for the very small size of an atom can be obtained from the following statement: It would take approximately 100 million iron atoms to make a line 1 inch long. These atoms maintain their identity through all physical and chemical changes.

2. Atoms of the same element are identical in physical and chemical properties and have the same mass.† Atoms of different elements differ in properties and have different masses.

3. Chemical combination between two or more elements is a union of the atoms of these elements in simple numerical ratios to form **molecules,** the smallest possible unit of a compound.

4. Atoms of the same elements can unite in more than one ratio to form more than one compound; e.g., both CuCl and $CuCl_2$ can be prepared.

*An element is a substance that is composed of a single kind of atom. A compound is a substance that is composed of molecules that are made up of two or more kinds of*

---

*Elements are indestructible in chemical reactions. However, it is now known that, via various nuclear reactions, many elements can be converted into other elements.

†It is now known that a given element may consist of different atoms that differ in mass. The two atoms are said to be isotopes. This topic will be discussed in detail shortly.

*atoms.* All of the atoms have names and chemical symbols to abbreviate the names. These symbols are listed alphabetically in the Appendix and their names are also indicated there. Molecules are described by combining the symbols of the atoms that compose the molecule. Elements can consist of atoms [for example, helium (He)] or molecules [for example, dihydrogen ($H_2$)]. Compounds are made up of molecules. The chemical symbols are used both to refer to the macroscopic compounds and elements, and to refer to the individual atoms and molecules.

In the above discussion, and in Figure 2–1, we indicated that compounds could be made to undergo decomposition into elements. This is one kind of chemical change. A **chemical change** corresponds to the rearrangement of the atoms in a molecule or to the combination or rearrangement of the atoms in two or more molecules, to produce new molecules. The starting materials are known as **reactants,** and the materials obtained after chemical change (that is, after **reaction**) are known as **products.**

When matter undergoes a change in state (e.g., melting solid ice to form water) without undergoing a change in composition, the change is said to be a **physical change.** In a physical change, there is no change in the composition of the molecules that make up the sample, but rather a change in the relationships of the molecules to each other. Mixtures can be separated into pure substances by employing physical changes. For example, if one of two substances in a mixture could be melted while the other substance remained a solid, the solid could be filtered from the liquid and the pure substances obtained. Properties of matter such as melting point, density (weight per unit volume), solubility, and color are called **physical properties.** Chemistry is the study of the chemical reactions and physical properties of compounds and elements and the laws accounting for their behavior.

The table inside the back cover contains an alphabetical listing of all the elements with their symbols and their *atomic weights.* The atomic weights used by the chemist are *relative* weights of the atoms, compared to an arbitrary standard. This standard was established by defining the atomic weight of the most commonly occurring carbon atom to be equal to precisely 12. You should not attempt to memorize all these elements and their symbols. You will learn them through use of the symbols. Whenever you encounter an unknown symbol, look it up.

## 2–2     THE CONCEPT OF THE MOLE

The mass of an atom relative to the standard (that is, the atomic weight) has units called **atomic mass units**, amu. For example, the atomic weight of oxygen is 16.0 amu. The **molecular weight** of a compound, which is simply the relative weight of the molecule compared to the standard (carbon atom equals 12), is obtained by summing the atomic weights of all of the atoms that compose the molecule. The molecular weight is also expressed in atomic mass units.

---

## Sample Problem 2–1

Calculate the molecular weight of ethyl alcohol, $C_2H_5OH$.

**Solution**

$$
\begin{array}{rclclcl}
C_2 & = & 2 & \times & 12.01 & = & 24.02 \text{ amu} \\
H_6 & = & 6 & \times & 1.01 & = & 6.06 \text{ amu} \\
O & = & 1 & \times & 16.00 & = & 16.00 \text{ amu} \\
& & & & & & \overline{\phantom{00000000}} \\
& & & & MW & = & 46.08 \text{ amu}
\end{array}
$$

---

You can well imagine that a chemical company manufacturing aspirin does not keep its records in terms of individual pills. Instead, it operates in terms of cartons, each of which contains thousands of aspirins. If one ever needed to know the number of aspirins for some reason, one could multiply the number of cartons by the number of aspirins in a carton to find out the answer. The chemist operates in the same way with molecules as described above for aspirin, except that he uses **moles** instead of cartons. A mole is a collection of $6.02 \times 10^{23}$ molecules, and *this number of molecules of any substance has a mass in grams equal to the value of the molecular weight of the substance.* For example, the molecular weight of carbon dioxide is 44.0 amu and that of water is 18.0 amu. The molecules have a ratio of mass given by 44.0/18.0. If we multiplied the numerator by $6.02 \times 10^{23}$, the quantity of $CO_2$ molecules would be a mole, and its mass would be 44.0 grams. Proceeding to multiply the denominator by $6.02 \times 10^{23}$ molecules, we find that the mass of a mole of water is 18.0 grams. Since multiplying both numerator and denominator by $6.02 \times 10^{23}$ is the same as multiplying the whole ratio by 1, we see that the ratio of the mass of a mole of $CO_2$ to the mass of a mole of water is also given by 44.0/18.0. The ratio of the mass of a mole of each of any two substances is the same as the ratio of the masses of the molecules of the two substances. Since $6.02 \times 10^{23}$ molecules of water have a mass of 18.0 grams, the mass of one molecule can be calculated as:

$$
\frac{18.0 \text{ g}}{\text{mole}} \times \frac{1 \text{ mole}}{6.02 \times 10^{23} \text{ molecules}} = 2.99 \times 10^{-23} \text{ g/molecule}
$$

Table 2–1 summarizes the actual masses and relative masses of various molecules as an illustration of the above discussion.

In the laboratory, we cannot count molecules, but we can weigh substances. In view of the above discussion, we know that 2.0 g of $H_2$, 32 g of $O_2$, 44 g of $CO_2$, and 36.5 g of HCl all contain the same number of molecules ($6.02 \times 10^{23}$). Each mass given represents the mass of one mole. The mass of one mole in grams is called a *gram molecular weight,* because every mole has a mass in grams whose value equals the molecular weight. Equal numbers of moles of various substances all contain equal numbers of molecules.

The word "mole" is used interchangeably for quantities of molecules or atoms. A mole of $H_2$ consists of $6.02 \times 10^{23}$ molecules of dihydrogen, but it contains $12.04 \times 10^{23}$ atoms of hydrogen. A mole of hydrogen atoms contains $6.02 \times 10^{23}$ atoms. Thus, a mole of $H_2$ consists of two moles of hydrogen atoms and a molecule of $H_2$ consists of two hydrogen atoms.

The mole is a base unit for the amount of substance in the SI system.

Table 2–1   **Actual and Relative Weights for Various Quantities of $O_2$, $CO_2$, and HCl.**

|  | $O_2$ | $CO_2$ | HCl |
|---|---|---|---|
| Actual weight in grams of 1 molecule | $5.32 \times 10^{-23}$ | $7.31 \times 10^{-23}$ | $6.06 \times 10^{-23}$ |
| Relative weight | 32.0 | 44.0 | 36.5 |
| Actual weight in grams of 2 molecules | $10.6 \times 10^{-23}$ | $14.6 \times 10^{-23}$ | $12.1 \times 10^{-23}$ |
| Relative weight of this group | 32.0 | 44.0 | 36.5 |
| Actual weight in grams of 100 molecules | $5.32 \times 10^{-21}$ | $7.31 \times 10^{-21}$ | $6.06 \times 10^{-21}$ |
| Relative weight of this group | 32.0 | 44.0 | 36.5 |
| Actual weight in grams of $6.02 \times 10^{23}$ molecules | 32.0 | 44.0 | 36.5 |
| Relative weight of this group | 32.0 | 44.0 | 36.5 |

## TEST 2–1

A.  Calculate the molecular weight of:

1. $H_2SO_4$ (sulfuric acid)

2. $C_{21}H_{30}O_2$ (the active ingredient in marijuana)

3. $SO_2$ (sulfur dioxide)

B.   How many moles are there in 64 g of $SO_2$?

C.   How many molecules are there in 64 g of $SO_2$?

D.   What mass of $H_2SO_4$ contains the same number of molecules as 64 g of $SO_2$?

E.   What is the mass ratio of a molecule of $H_2SO_4$ to a molecule of $SO_2$?

F.   How many grams are there in a mole of $H_2SO_4$?

G.   If a certain number of carbon atoms weighed 0.0066 g, what would be the mass of the same number of $SO_2$ molecules?

With the mass of a mole being given by the gram molecular weight, GMW, we can write:

$$GMW = 1 \text{ mole}$$

Dividing both sides by 1 mole produces the conversion factor:

$$\frac{MW \text{ (grams)}}{1 \text{ mole}} = 1 \qquad (2\text{--}1)$$

This factor gives the number of grams per mole and can be multiplied by any number of moles to give their mass. The reciprocal gives the number of moles in a gram and can be multiplied by any number of grams to give the number of moles in a given mass of material;

that is, the left-hand side of equation 2–1 converts moles to grams, and the reciprocal of this quantity converts grams to moles. There are four essentially different kinds of problems that can be posed relating to the above discussion, and these are illustrated below.

## Sample Problem 2–2

Given that the molecular weight of ethyl alcohol, $C_2H_5OH$, is 46.1, calculate the mass of 3.33 moles.

### Solution

GMW = 46.1 g
Asked: ? mass (g)
Begin with: 3.33 moles
A mole-to-grams conversion factor is needed, g/mole (46.1 g = 1 mole)
? g = (3.33 moles)(46.1 g/mole) = 154 g

## Sample Problem 2–3

Given a molecular weight of 46.1 for ethyl alcohol, calculate the number of moles in 15.0 grams.

### Solution

Asked: ? moles
Begin with: 15.0 g
A grams-to-moles conversion factor is needed, mole/gram.

$$? \text{ moles} = (15.0 \text{ g}) \left( \frac{1 \text{ mole}}{46.1 \text{ g}} \right) = 0.325 \text{ mole}$$

By now, we should be ready to skip a few steps and set up our problems directly in the form:

$$\text{asked} = (\text{begin with})(\text{conversion factor})$$

## Sample Problem 2–4

Given that 0.666 mole of a substance weighs 82.3 g, calculate the mass of one mole and the molecular weight (MW).

## Solution

$$? \, g = (1.00 \, \cancel{mole}) \frac{82.3 \, g}{0.666 \, \cancel{mole}} = 124 \, g \text{ (this is the GMW)}$$

The conversion factor was obtained from the given information, namely, that 0.666 moles = 82.3 g.

The problem also asks for the molecular weight. The answer expressed in atomic mass units instead of grams is the molecular weight, that is,

$$MW = 124 \, amu$$

---

## Sample Problem 2–5

If 0.725 mole of a substance weighs 66.6 g, how many moles are there in 75.0 g?

## Solution

This problem should be recognized as a combination of problems 2–3 and 2–4. A conversion factor is needed to convert g to moles and is derived from the equality:

$$0.725 \, mole = 66.6 \, g$$

$$? \, moles = (75.0 \, \cancel{g}) \frac{0.725 \, mole}{66.6 \, \cancel{g}} = 0.816 \, mole$$

---

## Sample Problem 2–6

Calculate the number of molecules in a 0.000222 gram sample of ethyl alcohol, $C_2H_5OH$.

## Solution

We know that $6.02 \times 10^{23}$ molecules = 1 mole. Furthermore, we can calculate the number of moles in 0.000222 g from the molecular weight, which we can obtain from the formula by summing the atomic weights.

$$MW \, (C_2H_5OH) = (2 \times 12.01) + (6 \times 1.008) + (1 \times 16.0) = 46.1$$

Thus, we can convert from grams to moles, as we did in problem 2–3, and then from moles to molecules.

In summary,

? asked = begin with × conversion factor × conversion factor
         (g to moles)      (moles to molecules)

$$? \text{ molecules} = 2.22 \times 10^{-4} \cancel{g} \times \frac{1 \cancel{\text{mole}}}{46.1 \cancel{g}} \times \frac{6.02 \times 10^{23} \text{ molecules}}{1 \cancel{\text{mole}}}$$

$$= 2.90 \times 10^{18} \text{ molecules.}$$

---

### TEST 2–2

Set up all of the problems in this test as in the sample problems above, that is, ? asked = begin with × conversion factor(s).

A.  If 1.00 mole of a substance weighs 33.4 g, calculate the mass of 5.27 moles.

B.  If 0.227 mole of a substance weighs 11.3 g, calculate its molecular weight.

C.  If a substance has a molecular weight of 55.5, calculate the number of moles in 13.3 g.

D.  If 0.456 mole of a substance weighs 84.3 g, how many moles are there in 17.5 g?

E.  How many molecules are there in $3.00 \times 10^{-6}$ grams of the substance in question D above?

## 2–3    PERCENT COMPOSITION AND EMPIRICAL FORMULAS

As stated above, we can obtain the molecular weight of a substance from its formula by summing the atomic weights of the elements that make up the molecule. For example, the molecular weight of $KClO_3$ is the sum $39.1 + 35.5 + (3 \times 16.0) = 122.6$. We calculate the weight percent oxygen in this material by obtaining the mass of oxygen in 1 mole, dividing it by the total mass of the mole, and multiplying by 100 to convert it to percent. The mass of oxygen ($3 \times 16$) is 48 grams.

$$\frac{48.0 \text{ g}}{122.6 \text{ g}} \times 100 = 39.2\%$$

(In this case, weight percent means parts by weight of oxygen per 100 parts by weight of $KClO_3$.)

In the laboratory it is relatively simple to determine the weight percent of any element in a compound by experiment. Thus we are often confronted with the reverse problem; determining a formula from weight percent. If we know the weight percent, we also know the number of grams of that atom in 100 grams of the compound. We must convert grams to moles of atoms in order to go from percent to the formula of the compound. In this way we calculate the **empirical formula,** which is the simplest whole-number ratio of the atoms in a molecule. Sample problem 2–7 illustrates the logic required to solve this type of problem.

---

## Sample Problem 2–7

Find the empirical formula of a compound containing 22.7% sodium, 21.6% boron, and 55.7% oxygen.

## Solution

It is convenient to think of this as a 100 g sample containing 22.7 g of Na, 21.6 g of B, and 55.7 g of O.* We convert these weights to moles by dividing by the atomic weights. The relative number of moles of each element indicates the relative number of atoms.

| Atom | Moles | = | Relative Number of Atoms | Atomic Ratios |
|------|-------|---|--------------------------|---------------|
| Na | 22.7 g/23.0 g mole$^{-1}$ | = | 0.99 | 1.0 |
| B | 21.6 g/10.8 g mole$^{-1}$ | = | 2.00 | 2.0 |
| O | 55.7 g/16.0 g mole$^{-1}$ | = | 3.48 | 3.5 |

To obtain the ratios of atoms, we divide the relative number of atoms of each kind by the smallest number (0.99) to produce 1 Na : 2 B : 3.5 O atoms. Since 3.5 is not a whole number and is not close enough to a whole number to round off, it is necessary to double

---

*For example, (100 g sample)(0.227 g Na/g total) = 22.7 g Na. Thus % is simply converted to grams. The final answer will be the same regardless of the sample size selected.

all of the atomic ratios to produce whole numbers. Accordingly, the simplest **whole-number ratio** for the compound is 2 Na : 4 B : 7 O and the empirical formula for the compound is $Na_2B_4O_7$. A reasonable amount of rounding off is allowed to account for experimental error.

There are several relatively straightforward methods of determining the molecular weight of a substance without knowing or determining its identity or formula. The percent composition and molecular weight of new or unknown substances are often obtained by practicing chemists. We shall repeat the above type of problem but, in addition, give the molecular weight to illustrate how this permits calculation of the molecular formula.

## Sample Problem 2–8

A compound consisting of only sulfur (S) and chlorine (Cl) contains 47.5% sulfur and has a molecular weight of 135.1. What is the molecular formula?

## Solution

Again we select a 100 g sample. It will consist of 47.5 g of S. Since the sample contains only S and Cl, the remainder of the mass must be Cl, so there is 100 g − 47.5 g = 52.5 g of Cl. We convert these masses to moles by dividing by the respective atomic weight.

$$\frac{47.5\ g}{32.06\ g/mole\ S} = 1.48\ moles\ of\ S\ atoms$$

$$\frac{52.5\ g}{35.45\ g/mole\ Cl} = 1.48\ moles\ of\ Cl\ atoms$$

This gives a simple whole-number ratio of 1 to 1, i.e., SCl. The mass of a mole of SCl molecules is 67.51 g, but the molecular weight given in this problem is 135.1. The ratio 135.1/67.51 is 2. The molecule must be twice as heavy as SCl, so the molecular formula is $S_2Cl_2$. Note that the atom ratio of S to Cl is still 1:1 and that the formula is written as $S_2Cl_2$ and not 2SCl. The latter would imply two molecules with one atom of S and one atom of Cl in each molecule, giving a molecular weight of only 67.51 amu.

A summary of the steps involved in the empirical and molecular formula types of problems follows:
1. If the weight composition is given in percent, convert the percent of each element to grams in a 100 g total.
2. Convert the mass in grams of each element to moles by dividing by the atomic weights.
3. Divide the number of moles of each of the elements in the starting mass of

compound by the smallest value to get the simplest whole-number ratio, i.e., the empirical formula. In some cases it will be necessary to multiply by a factor to obtain whole numbers. This gives the empirical formula.
4. If the molecular weight is known, calculate the molecular formula by first dividing the molecular weight by the empirical formula weight. Then multiply the subscripts in the empirical formula by the value obtained from this division.

## TEST 2–3

A.   1. Calculate the molecular weight of $SO_3$.

2. What is the percent S in $SO_3$?

B.   1. A compound consisting of only P and O is found to contain 56.34% O. What is the mass of P(_____ g) and O(_____ g) in a 100 g sample?

2. What is the mass of P (and O) in an 18.0 g sample?

3. How many moles each of P and O atoms are there in 100 g of this compound?

4. What is the ratio of moles of O atoms per mole of P atoms?

5. What is the empirical formula?

6. Given a molecular weight of 284 for this compound, what is the molecular formula?

## 2–4   CHEMICAL ANALYSIS*

How are the percent compositions, which enable us to calculate the empirical formulas of unknown substances, determined? This is accomplished by converting the substance to a known material by a chemical reaction and then weighing the known material. For example, suppose we had a given mass of a substance containing carbon that could be burned to produce $CO_2$. We would then weigh the $CO_2$ formed; since we know the percent carbon in $CO_2$, we can calculate the amount of carbon in the original material. Knowing the mass of the original material, we could calculate the percent carbon in the sample.

### Sample Problem 2–9

A substance consisting of carbon, hydrogen, and oxygen is converted, by burning with oxygen, to carbon dioxide ($CO_2$) and water ($H_2O$). A 5.00 g sample produced 9.55 g of $CO_2$ and 1.04 g of water. Calculate the percent carbon and hydrogen in the sample.

---

*If necessary, review Section 1–6 on percent.

## Solution

All of the carbon in the carbon dioxide came from the carbon in the sample. We can calculate the percent carbon in $CO_2$.

$$\% \text{ C in } CO_2 = \left( \frac{12.0 \text{ g C}}{44.0 \text{ g total}} \right) (100) = 27.3\% \text{ C}$$

The amount of carbon in 9.55 g of $CO_2$ is calculated as:

$$(9.55 \text{ g } CO_2) \left( \frac{0.273 \text{ g of C}}{1.00 \text{ g of } CO_2} \right) = 2.61 \text{ g C}$$

The percent carbon in the original sample is obtained by dividing 2.61 g of carbon that we determined was in the original sample by the mass of the original sample and multiplying by 100.

$$\left( \frac{2.61 \text{ g C}}{5.00 \text{ g sample}} \right) (100) = 52.2\% \text{ C}$$

Similar reasoning can be used to calculate the percent hydrogen.

$$\% \text{ H in } H_2O = \left( \frac{2.02 \text{ g H}}{18.0 \text{ g total}} \right) (100) = 11.2.\%$$

1.04 g of $H_2O$ contains

$$(1.04 \text{ g } H_2O) \left( \frac{0.112 \text{ g H}}{1.00 \text{ g } H_2O} \right) = 0.116 \text{ g H}$$

$$\left( \frac{0.116 \text{ g H}}{5.00 \text{ g total}} \right) (100) = 2.32\% \text{ H}$$

We cannot use this approach to calculate the percent oxygen in the sample, because in the course of burning the sample in air some of the oxygen in the $CO_2$ and $H_2O$ came from the dioxygen in the air. However, if we know that the sample contains only carbon, hydrogen, and oxygen we can calculate the oxygen in the sample by difference:

|        |       |
|--------|-------|
| 100%   | total |
| − 52.2% | C     |
| − 2.3% | H     |
| 45.5%  | O     |

You are now in a position to calculate the empirical formula of the substance if desired.

## TEST 2–4

We shall work a series of problems designed to answer the question, "What is the % Cl in a compound if 7.500 g of an unknown substance reacts completely with a chlorine-free silver compound to produce 23.48 g of AgCl?"

A.   Calculate the % chlorine in AgCl.

B.   Calculate the mass of chlorine in 23.48 g of AgCl.

C.   What is the mass of chlorine in 7.500 g of the unknown substance?

D.   Calculate the % chlorine in the unknown.

## Exercises

### Simple Definitions
1.   Indicate whether the following are compounds, mixtures, or elements.
     (a) water
     (b) oxygen
     (c) air
     (d) salt water
     (e) Dry Ice (solid $CO_2$)

2. Indicate whether the following are physical or chemical changes, and explain why.
   (a) evaporation of water
   (b) rusting of iron
   (c) burning of a match
   (d) lighting a light bulb
   (e) cooking an egg

3. Determine the molecular weight of the following.
   (a) KF
   (b) $NH_4Cl$
   (c) $(NH_4)_2SO_4$
   (d) $Cu(NH_3)_4Cl_2$
   (e) $K_2PtCl_6$
   (f) $CH_3CO_2H$.

4. How many moles are there in each of the following?
   (a) 25 g of KF
   (b) 30 g of $NH_4Cl$
   (c) 80 g of $K_2PtCl_6$
   (d) 3.00 lb of $NH_4Cl$

5. How many grams of material are there in each of the following?
   (a) 0.750 mole of KF
   (b) 3.00 moles of $NH_4Cl$
   (c) 0.100 mole of $Cu(NH_3)_4Cl_2$

6. If there are 12 g of a substance in 0.17 mole, what is its molecular weight?

7. If 2.17 g of a substance constitute 0.0250 mole, what is the molecular weight?

8. Calculate:
   (a) the number of molecules in 12.0 g of $C_6H_6$ (benzene).
   (b) the weight of 1,000 molecules of $C_6H_6$.
   (c) the number of molecules in 0.00010 mole of $C_6H_6$.
   (d) the number of grams of $CO_2$ that would contain the same number of moles as 44.4 g of $C_6H_6$.

9. What is the mass of a sample of $C_2H_6$ that contains the same number of molecules as 7.0 g of $CO_2$?

10. What mass of $C_6H_6$ would contain the same number of molecules as 11.0 g of $O_2$?

11. What is the mass percent H in $H_2O_2$?

12. What is the mass percent Cu in $CuCl_2$?

13. A compound consists of 46.66% N and 53.34% O. What is the empirical formula?

14. What is the mass percent N in $NH_4NO_3$?

15. A compound consists of 30.43% N and 69.57% O. Its molecular weight is 92. What is the molecular formula?

16. A compound consists of 2.25% H, 34.83% P, and 62.92% O. Its molecular weight is 178. What is the molecular formula?

17. A compound contains 85.7% C and 14.3% H. Its molecular weight is 28.05. What is the molecular formula?

18. A compound is produced by 2.00 g of S combining with 3.00 g of O. What is the empirical formula?

19. A compound weighing 2.685 g is formed when 2.500 g of Ag reacts with O at elevated temperatures. What is the empirical formula of the product?

20. How many g of P are there in 250. g of $H_3PO_4$?

21. An oxide of tin contains 88.1% Sn. What is the empirical formula?

**Chemical Analysis**

22. A 1.023 g sample of a compound containing sulfur is converted to 1.509 g of $BaSO_4$. Calculate the percent sulfur in the original compound.

23. A compound consists of carbon and hydrogen. Combustion of 5.500 g of the material produced 17.25 g of $CO_2$. Calculate the empirical formula.

24. An oxide of chlorine (a compound consisting of oxygen and chlorine) is converted into AgCl. A 0.9035 g sample of this oxide gives 1.920 g of AgCl. Calculate the empirical formula.

**Challenging Problems**

25. A metal M forms an oxide $M_2O_3$ containing 68.4% of the metal by weight. Calculate the atomic weight of M.

26. A 5.00 g sample of a compound with the formula $MgSO_4 \cdot x H_2O$ (where $x$ is a whole number) is heated and 2.56 g of water is lost. Calculate the value of $x$.

27. How many moles of copper could be obtained from 25.0 g of CuO?

### Verbalizing General Concepts

28. In your own words, answer each of the following:
    (a) Explain the difference between a pure substance and a mixture.
    (b) Explain the difference between a compound and an element.
    (c) Describe the relation between the molecular weight and the mass of a mole.
    (d) What is meant by the statement that molecular weights are relative masses?
    (e) How many molecules are there in a mole?
    (f) Why was the concept of a mole invented?
    (g) Explain the difference between the formulae $3C_2H_2$ and $C_6H_6$.
    (h) How do you convert grams of a substance to moles?
    (i) Given the number of grams and the number of moles of a substance, how do you calculate the molecular weight?
    (j) If a sample consists of 66% carbon and 34% of some other element, how many grams of carbon are there in a 100 g sample?
    (k) How do you convert the gram ratio of the various elements in a compound to the mole ratio?
    (l) What is the empirical formula?
    (m) What information is needed to determine the molecular formula of a compound?

### Multiple Choice Questions

(When necessary use the atomic weights inside the back cover.)

29. One mole of a substance (a) contains $6.02 \times 10^{23}$ molecules, (b) has a mass in grams equal to the molecular weight, (c) none of the above, (d) both of the above.

30. If a certain quantity of $H_2O$ has a mass of 6.00 g, the quantity of $C_2H_5OH$ containing the same number of molecules will have a mass of (a) 9.22 g, (b) 6.00 g, (c) 12.0 g, (d) 26.3 g, (e) none of these within 0.1 g.

31. The mass of a mole of $CS_2$ is (a) $6.02 \times 10^{23}$ g, (b) 44.07 g, (c) 76.13 g, (d) 64.12 g, (e) none of these within 0.1 g.

32. The ratio of the mass of a molecule of $CS_2$ to the mass of a molecule of $CO_2$ is given by (a) 1.00, (b) 0.58, (c) 0.58 g, (d) 1.7, (e) none of the above.

33. The ratio of the mass of a mole of $CS_2$ to the mass of a mole of $CO_2$ is given by (a) 1.00, (b) 0.58, (c) 1.7, (d) 1.7 g, (e) none of the above.

34. If you had a 76.1 g sample of $CS_2$ and a 44.0 g sample of $CO_2$, (a) they would both contain the same number of molecules, (b) the $CS_2$ sample would contain more molecules, (c) each corresponds to a mole, (d) two of the above, (e) none of the above.

35.   A sample of water weighs 5.00 g and a sample of $H_2S$ weighs 5.00 g.
      (a) They both contain the same number of molecules. (b) There are
      more molecules in the $H_2O$ sample. (c) There are more molecules in
      the $H_2S$ sample. (d) We cannot tell which sample has more molecules.

36.   How many moles of sulfur molecules are there in 80.3 g of sulfur if
      the molecular formula is $S_8$? (a) 0.399, (b) 2.51, (c) 3.20, (d) 0.313,
      (e) none of these within 0.05.

37.   A substance contains 40.0 g of potassium, 35.5 g of chlorine, and
      48.0 g of oxygen. How many grams of chlorine would there be in
      100. g of material? (a) 88.7 g, (b) 74.0 g, (c) 28.7 g, (d) 35.5 g, (e)
      none of these are within 1.0 g of the correct answer.

38.   How many moles are there in 2.0 g of $CO_2$? (a) $4.5 \times 10^{-2}$, (b) 88.,
      (c) 22, (d) $12 \times 10^{23}$, (e) none of these.

39.   Malachite is an ore of copper with the empirical formula $Cu_2CO_5H_2$.
      How much copper could be obtained from 340. g? (a) 127 g, (b) 63.5
      g, (c) 57.5 g, (d) 195 g, (e) none of these within 2 g.

40.   Vitamin C consists of 40.9% C, 4.58% H, and 54.5% O. The empirical
      formula is: (a) $C_8H_9O_{11}$, (b) $C_3H_4O_3$, (c) $C_4H_5O_5$, (d) $C_{3.4}H_{4.5}O_{3.4}$, (e)
      none of these.

41.   The percentage carbon in a compound consisting of only carbon and
      oxygen is 27.29%. Calculate the empirical formula. (a) CO, (b) $CO_2$,
      (c) $C_2O_3$, (d) $CO_3$, (e) none of these.

42.   A certain compound has the empirical formula $CH_2O$. Which of the
      following molecular weights is possible? (a) 15, (b) 45, (c) 75, (d)
      none of those in a to c, (e) all of those in a to c.

43.   If 0.225 moles of a compound weigh 66.3 g, the molecular weight is:
      (a) 295 amu, (b) 295 grams, (c) 14.9 amu, (d) 14.9 grams, (e) impossible
      to calculate because there is not enough information.

44.   If a certain quantity of $H_2O$ has a mass of 12.0 g, the quantity of
      $C_2H_5OH$ containing the same number of molecules will have a mass of
      (a) 3.84 g          (d) 69.1 g
      (b) 12.0 g          (e) none of these within 0.1 g
      (c) 24.0 g

45.   Malachite is an ore of copper with the empirical formula $Cu_2CO_5H_2$.
      How much copper could be obtained from 98.0 g of malachite?
      (a) 127 g          (d) 56.3 g
      (b) 28.1 g          (e) none of these within 0.5 g
      (c) 63.5 g

46. If 0.405 moles of a compound weigh 101 g, the molecular weight is
    (a) 249 amu          (d) 40.9 grams
    (b) 249 grams        (e) impossible to calculate because
    (c) 40.9 amu             there is not enough information

# 3

# CHEMICAL EQUATIONS AND STOICHIOMETRY

## Chapter Objectives

## (Begin each of the following with "You should master . . . ")

1. an understanding of all the information conveyed in a balanced chemical equation.
2. the balancing of chemical equations.
3. the solving of mole-mole, mole-mass, and mass-mass types of problems. The limited reactant problem is a problem of this type. These problems in effect measure whether or not you have a true understanding of the meaning of a mole and the meaning of a chemical equation. The arithmetic is the same as that discussed in our earlier problems using conversion factors.
4. the calculation of percent yield.

The chemical equation is the chemist's shorthand way of describing a chemical reaction in terms of masses, molecules, and moles. A very considerable amount of effort must be spent in the laboratory to determine the compositions of all the substances involved in a chemical reaction. This information and more is contained in the balanced chemical equation. Our goal in this chapter is to gain an appreciation for all the information presented in a balanced equation.

## 3–1    THE MEANING OF AN EQUATION

The **Haber process,** discovered in 1908, is now used to convert dinitrogen, $N_2$, and dihydrogen, $H_2$, into ammonia, $NH_3$. Ammonia is a very important chemical that is used, for example, in huge quantities in agriculture as a fertilizer. The following equation describes this very important chemical reaction:

$$N_2 + 3H_2 \rightarrow 2NH_3 \qquad \text{(3–1)}$$

This equation states that 1 molecule of dinitrogen reacts with 3 molecules of dihydrogen to produce 2 molecules of ammonia. Since we can multiply both sides of the equation by 2 without changing its meaning, it also indicates that 2 molecules of dinitrogen will react with 6 molecules of dihydrogen to give 4 molecules of ammonia. To be completely general, any number of molecules of dinitrogen and dihydrogen in a 1:3 ratio will yield twice as many ammonia molecules as dinitrogen molecules used. Accordingly, if we multiply both sides of the equation (read in terms of molecules) by $6 \times 10^{23}$, the equation then reads: 1 mole of dinitrogen reacts with 3 moles of dihydrogen to produce 2 moles of ammonia.

As discussed in Chapter 2, we can convert from moles to grams. Upon doing so, we find that the equation also means that 28 g of dinitrogen plus 6 g of dihydrogen yield 34 g of ammonia. Note that the ratio of the weights is not in the ratio 1:3:2 because moles of different substances usually have different masses; e.g., a mole of dinitrogen weighs 28 g, whereas a mole of dihydrogen weighs only 2 g. To be completely general (since both sides of the equation can be multiplied by any quantity), any masses in the mass ratio of 14 $N_2$: 3 $H_2$: 17 $NH_3$ could be involved. In summary, the ratios of molecules or moles involved in a chemical reaction are given by the coefficients of the equation. The ratios of masses (in any units, such as g, lb or tons) are given by the masses of the moles multiplied by these coefficients.

## 3–2   BALANCING SIMPLE EQUATIONS

Before we can obtain information about mole and mass ratios from a chemical equation, the equation must be balanced. The following conditions and rules apply in balancing chemical equations.

1. Formulae for all starting materials (reactants) and for all products must be known from experiment. This information will be given for all problems in this chapter.
2. The number of atoms of each element in the reactants must equal that in the products. This is because atoms are never destroyed or created in chemical reactions. They are simply arranged differently in the molecules of the reactants and products.
3. The coefficients in the formulas must be reduced to the smallest possible whole numbers.

We shall see how these rules apply to the reaction of dinitrogen and dihydrogen to produce ammonia. If we examine equation (3–1), we see that there are 2 atoms of nitrogen on the left-hand side of the equation and 2 atoms of nitrogen (one in each molecule of ammonia) on the right-hand side of the equation. There are 6 atoms of hydrogen in the 3 molecules of $H_2$ on the left-hand side of the equation *and* in the 2 molecules of ammonia on the right-hand side of the equation. Consequently, this equation is balanced, and Rule 2 has been satisfied. It is conceivable that in the course of attempting to balance this equation you would have obtained

$$2N_2 + 6H_2 \rightarrow 4NH_3$$

Rule 2 would be satisfied but Rule 3 would not be. Each of the coefficients could be divided by 2 to produce 1 dinitrogen molecule plus 3 dihydrogen molecules to yield 2 ammonia molecules. Only when this has been done is Rule 3 satisfied. If, in the course of balancing the above equation, the subscripts in the product were changed to produce the balanced equation.

$$N_2 + H_2 \rightarrow N_2H_2$$

the equation would now be incorrect. The product of the reaction is ammonia (a molecule containing 1 atom of nitrogen and 3 atoms of hydrogen). It is not $N_2H_2$ (a molecule containing 2 atoms of nitrogen and 2 atoms of hydrogen). Consequently, to balance the equation we must know the formulas of all starting material and products. Changing the subscripts changes the composition of the molecule, but changing the coefficient in front merely changes the number of molecules involved in the chemical equation. This is an illustration of the importance of Rule 1.

Just like shooting a basketball or playing a piano, the only way to become skilled at balancing equations is to practice. Fortunately, balancing equations is the easiest of the three tasks to do well. We shall illustrate the balancing of equations with sample problems and a test.

## Sample Problem 3–1

When aluminum reacts with dioxygen, aluminum oxide is formed:

$$Al + O_2 \rightarrow Al_2O_3$$

Balance this equation.

## Solution

It is a good idea to balance one kind of atom at a time and to begin with that atom that looks least straightforward. Select this atom from the most complicated-looking molecule. If this does not lead to an an obvious solution, start all over again with another kind of atom. In the equation above, we begin with oxygen. With three oxygens on the right-hand side and two on the left, the common denominator is seen to be six, leading to:

$$Al + 3O_2 \rightarrow 2Al_2O_3$$

We have four aluminum atoms on the right-hand side of the equation, so we will also need four on the left; that is,

$$4Al + 3O_2 \rightarrow 2Al_2O_3$$

Presto, we have balanced the equation. As the final step, make a quick check to be sure the coefficients are not divisible by a whole number.

## Sample Problem 3–2

The gas nitric oxide, NO, reacts with dioxygen in air to form $NO_2$:

$$NO + O_2 \rightarrow NO_2$$

Balance this equation.

## Solution

The oxygens again look most difficult. The number of oxygen atoms on the right-hand side will always be even, so we must get an even number on the left-hand side. Multiplying NO by two does this: $2NO + O_2 \rightarrow NO_2$. Then multiplying the $NO_2$ by two also balances the oxygens.

$$2NO + O_2 \rightarrow 2NO_2$$

The above operations also balance the nitrogens, so we are finished.

There is a useful trick that can be illustrated with this equation. Returning to our original unbalanced equation, we note that the equation could be balanced very easily if we wrote $\frac{1}{2} O_2$.

$$NO + \frac{1}{2} O_2 \rightarrow NO$$

We can get rid of the fraction by multiplying both sides of the equation by two:

$$2NO + O_2 \rightarrow 2NO$$

The equation is now balanced, and the answer is the same as before.

---

Note that in a balanced equation, the numbers of *molecules* on the two sides of the equation can differ, but the number of *atoms* must be the same on both sides. No new atoms are made in a chemical reaction. A chemical reaction corresponds to rearranging the atoms of the reactants to form different molecules for products.

### TEST 3–1

In this test we shall systematically balance equations using the three rules given above. All products and reactants shall be presented in the form of an unbalanced equation.

A. We shall answer some questions that illustrate the steps in balancing the equation:
$$CH_4 + O_2 \rightarrow CO_2 + H_2O$$

1. Select H and adjust the coefficients of $H_2O$ and $CH_4$ to balance this element.

2. Is the equation balanced? If not, balance the element that is not balanced.

3. Are the coefficients reduced to the simplest whole number set (Rule 3)?

B.   Balance the equation

$$C_4H_{10} + O_2 \rightarrow CO_2 + H_2O$$

1. Select H and balance the compounds containing this element.

2. Is the equation balanced? If not, balance the carbons.

3. Is the equation balanced? If not, balance the oxygens.
   (Hint: Remember, if you can use ½ $O_2$ you can multiply by two to balance.)

4. Carry out Rule 3.

Often the physical states of the reactants and products are indicated in the chemical equation by adding the symbols g, s, l, and aq in parentheses after the symbols of the molecules to indicate the gaseous, solid, liquid, and aqueous (water) solution conditions, respectively.

## 3-3    MOLE RELATIONS IN A REACTION (MOLE-MOLE PROBLEMS)

**Photosynthesis** is a process whereby plants store energy from the sun by converting carbon dioxide ($CO_2$) and water ($H_2O$) into energy-rich materials; that is, materials that can be burned to release energy. In photosynthesis, $CO_2$ and $H_2O$ (the usual products of complete combustion) are converted into a sugar ($C_6H_{12}O_6$, glucose) and dioxygen ($O_2$).

$$CO_2(g) + H_2O(l) \rightarrow C_6H_{12}O_6(aq) + O_2(g)$$

Since sugar can be burned to produce energy, the sun's energy is stored in glucose by the process of photosynthesis. We shall use this reaction to illustrate the solution of problems that involve mole relationships between products and reactants.

1.  The first step in deducing the mole relationships in a chemical reaction is to write the balanced chemical equation if it is not given! To accomplish this for the photosynthesis reaction, we write:

$$6CO_2 + 6H_2O \rightarrow C_6H_{12}O_6 + 6O_2$$

   Recall that this equation reads:

   6 moles of $CO_2$ + 6 moles of $H_2O$ yields 1 mole of $C_6H_{12}O_6$ + 6 moles of $O_2$.

2.  We are in a position to write a whole series of conversion factors based upon the following equations that can be written directly from the balanced equation:

$$6 \text{ moles } CO_2 \equiv 1 \text{ mole } C_6H_{12}O_6; \quad 6 \text{ moles } H_2O \equiv 1 \text{ mole } C_6H_{12}O_6;$$
$$6 \text{ moles } CO_2 \equiv 6 \text{ moles } O_2; \quad 6 \text{ moles } H_2O \equiv 6 \text{ moles } O_2$$

These are not strict equalities, as indicated by the symbol $\equiv$.* They can be considered to state, for example, that 6 moles of $CO_2$ are required to form one mole of $C_6H_{12}O_6$ and so forth. Furthermore, we can write 6 moles $CO_2 \equiv 6$ moles $H_2O$ and 1 mole $C_6H_{12}O_6 \equiv 6$ moles $O_2$. These latter two equations can be considered to state respectively that 6 moles of $CO_2$ need 6 moles of water to react completely, and that if one mole of $C_6H_{12}O_6$ is formed then so are 6 moles of $O_2$. From these various equations we can write any conversion factor needed to solve for mole relationships in the chemical reaction. We can, for example, convert from moles of $CO_2$ to moles of glucose with the factor 1 mole glucose/ 6 moles $CO_2$. You now know all the chemistry you need to know to do mole-mole problems. The remainder of the task involves applying the concepts in the section on problem solving (Section 1–4).

---

*This symbol $\equiv$ means "equivalent to."

## Sample Problem 3–3

If 0.327 mole of $C_6H_{12}O_6$ is formed by reaction of $CO_2$ with water, how many moles of $CO_2$ would be needed?

## Solution

Step 1.   Write the balanced equation.

$$6CO_2 + 6H_2O \rightarrow C_6H_{12}O_6 + 6O_2$$

Step 2.   ? moles of $CO_2$

Step 3.   Begin with 0.327 mole $C_6H_{12}O_6$.

Step 4.   Write the conversion factor for changing moles of $C_6H_{12}O_6$ to moles of $CO_2$.

$$1 \text{ mole } C_6H_{12}O_6 \equiv 6 \text{ moles } CO_2 \quad \text{so} \quad \frac{6 \text{ moles } CO_2}{1 \text{ mole } C_6H_{12}O_6} = 1$$

Step 5.   Solve the problem:

$$? \text{ moles } CO_2 = 0.327 \text{ mole } C_6H_{12}O_6 \times \frac{6.00 \text{ moles } CO_2}{1.00 \text{ mole } C_6H_{12}O_6} = 1.96 \text{ moles } CO_2.$$

Note the format:

$$? \text{ Asked} = \text{Begin With} \times \text{Conversion Factor}$$

## Sample Problem 3–4

How many moles of $O_2$ are formed if 0.349 mole of $CO_2$ is consumed in photosynthesis?

## Solution

Step 1.   See the balanced equation in sample problem 3–3.

Step 2.   ? moles $O_2$

Steps 3 and 4. "Begin with" moles $CO_2$.

$$6 \text{ moles CO}_2 \equiv_1 6 \text{ moles O}_2$$

$$\frac{6 \text{ moles O}_2}{6 \text{ moles CO}_2} = 1$$

Step 5.

$$? \text{ moles O}_2 = 0.349 \ \cancel{\text{mole CO}_2} \times \frac{6.00 \text{ moles O}_2}{6.00 \ \cancel{\text{moles CO}_2}} = 0.349 \text{ mole O}_2$$

---

## TEST 3–2

A. The Haber process is described by the following equation:

$$N_2 + H_2 \rightarrow NH_3$$

We shall answer a series of questions designed to illustrate the logical approach to answering the question, "How many moles of $H_2$ (dihydrogen) are needed to produce 0.889 mole of $NH_3$ (ammonia)?"

1. What is the first thing to do? Do it.

2. What is asked?

3. What do you begin with?

4. Derive the conversion factor that is needed.

5. Solve the problem.

B. In this problem we shall put all the steps in part A together and set up the problem in the form:

? Asked = Begin With × Conversion Factor

How many moles of ammonia could be obtained in the Haber process by completely reacting 0.369 mole of dinitrogen? Set up the problem as described above, making sure that the units cancel, and solve.

C.  How many moles of dinitrogen would be required to react completely with 0.577 mole of dihydrogen?

# 3–4    MASS-MOLE PROBLEMS

Since we can calculate the mass of any number of moles from the molecular weight, we can determine the mass relationships involved in a chemical reaction from the mole relationships discussed in the previous section. Returning to photosynthesis:

$$6CO_2 + 6H_2O \rightarrow C_6H_{12}O_6 + 6O_2,$$

we shall illustrate sample problems that involve mass and mole relations.

## Sample Problem 3–5

How many grams of $C_6H_{12}O_6$ can be obtained from 0.131 mole of $CO_2$ in photosynthesis?

## Solution

We calculate the number of moles of $C_6H_{12}O_6$ as in the previous section and then convert this number of moles to grams.

$$? \text{ moles } C_6H_{12}O_6 = 0.131 \text{ mole } CO_2 \times \frac{1 \text{ mole } C_6H_{12}O_6}{6 \text{ moles } CO_2} = 0.0218 \text{ mole } C_6H_{12}O_6$$

The molecular weight of $C_6H_{12}O_6$ is 180.2. Therefore, 0.0218 mole has a mass of:

$$0.0218 \text{ moles } C_6H_{12}O_6 \times \frac{180.2 \text{ g } C_6H_{12}O_6}{1 \text{ mole } C_6H_{12}O_6} = 3.93 \text{ g } C_6H_{12}O_6$$

Instead of two steps, the problem could be done in one step by writing both conversions into the one equation:

$$? \text{ grams} = 0.131 \text{ mole } CO_2 \times \frac{1 \text{ mole } C_6H_{12}O_6}{6 \text{ moles } CO_2} \times \frac{180.2 \text{ g } C_6H_{12}O_6}{1 \text{ mole } C_6H_{12}O_6} = 3.93 \text{ g } C_6H_{12}O_6$$

## Sample Problem 3–6

How many moles of $CO_2$ are required to produce 11.3 g of $O_2$?

## Solution:

Convert g $O_2$ to moles $O_2$ and moles $O_2$ to moles $CO_2$.

$$? \text{ moles } CO_2 = 11.3 \text{ g } O_2 \times \frac{1 \text{ mole } O_2}{32.0 \text{ g } O_2} \times \frac{1 \text{ mole } CO_2}{1 \text{ mole } O_2} = 0.353 \text{ mole } CO_2$$

## Sample Problem 3–7

If 0.222 mole of $C_6H_{12}O_6$ is produced by photosynthesis, how many grams of $O_2$ would be obtained?

## Solution:

Convert moles $C_6H_{12}O_6$ to moles $O_2$ and moles $O_2$ to g $O_2$.

$$? \text{ g } O_2 = 0.222 \text{ mole } C_6H_{12}O_6 \times \frac{6 \text{ mole } O_2}{1 \text{ mole } C_6H_{12}O_6} \times \frac{32.0 \text{ g } O_2}{1 \text{ mole } O_2} = 42.6 \text{ g } O_2$$

## 3–5    MASS-MASS PROBLEMS

Since we can calculate the mass of a mole, we can write the following relationships from the equation for photosynthesis:

$$6CO_2 + 6H_2O \rightarrow C_6H_{12}O_6 + 6O_2$$

$$264.1 \text{ g CO}_2 + 108.1 \text{ g H}_2\text{O} \rightarrow 180.2 \text{ g C}_6\text{H}_{12}\text{O}_6 + 192 \text{ g O}_2$$

We can write the same relationships involving grams that we wrote earlier for moles, for example,

$$264.1 \text{ g CO}_2 \equiv 108.1 \text{ g H}_2\text{O} \quad \text{or} \quad 264.1 \text{ g CO}_2 \equiv 192 \text{ g O}_2$$

and so forth. (Note that mass is conserved in the balanced equation: 264.1 g + 108.1 g = 180.2 g + 192.0 g.)

## Sample Problem 3–8

How many grams of $O_2$ can be obtained from 65.0 g of $CO_2$ by photosynthesis?

## Solution

From the above relationships we note that the conversion factor from g of $CO_2$ to g of $O_2$ is

$$\frac{192 \text{ g O}_2}{264.1 \text{ g CO}_2} = 1$$

In one step we write:

$$? \text{ g O}_2 = 65.0 \text{ g CO}_2 \times \frac{192 \text{ g O}_2}{264.1 \text{ g CO}_2} = 47.2 \text{ g O}_2$$

## Sample Problem 3–9

How many grams of water would be needed to make 110. g of $C_6H_{12}O_6$ by photosynthesis?

## Solution

In one step:

$$? \text{ g H}_2\text{O} = 110. \text{ g C}_6\text{H}_{12}\text{O}_6 \times \frac{108.1 \text{ g H}_2\text{O}}{180.2 \text{ g C}_6\text{H}_{12}\text{O}_6} = 66.0 \text{ g H}_2\text{O}$$

**TEST 3–3**

The following problems will all involve the Haber process:

$$N_2 + H_2 \rightarrow NH_3.$$

A. How many grams of ammonia can be obtained by complete reaction of 0.267 mole of dinitrogen?  Hint: Be sure to balance the equation first. Then convert moles $N_2$ (begin with) to moles $NH_3$ and then moles $NH_3$ to grams ammonia.

B. How many grams of $H_2$ are needed to produce 0.275 mole of ammonia?

   1. First write out a statement comparable to that given in the hint in problem A.

   2. Set up and solve this problem in one step.

C. How many moles of dihydrogen are required to produce a kilogram of ammonia?

D.  Write an equation that indicates the mass relationships of all the substances involved in the Haber process.

E.  How many grams of ammonia could be produced by complete reaction of 66.6 g of $H_2$?

F.  How many grams of $H_2$ would be required for complete reaction of 88.8 grams of $N_2$?

## 3-6  LIMITED REACTANT PROBLEMS

Whenever there are two or more reactants in an equation, the amount of products that can be obtained will be determined by whichever reactant is used up first or, as we say, present in limited amount. For example, consider the reaction

$$O_2 + 2H_2 \rightarrow 2H_2O$$

$$1 \text{ mole of } O_2 + 2 \text{ moles of } H_2 \rightarrow 2 \text{ moles of } H_2O$$

or

$$32 \text{ g of } O_2 + 4 \text{ g of } H_2 \rightarrow 36 \text{ g of } H_2O$$

If we allowed 32 g of $O_2$ and 8 g of $H_2$ to react, only 36 g of $H_2O$ could be obtained. Because of insufficient oxygen, an excess of 4 g of $H_2$ would remain unreacted. The amount of water produced is determined by the reactant not in excess — in this case, $O_2$. 

You can instantly recognize a **limited reactant** problem because, instead of a "begin with" statement involving one reactant, the quantities of two or more reactants will be given; that is, there will be ambiguity in selecting the "begin with" fact. You must first determine which reactant is present in limited amount in order to pick the "begin with" quantity. After this has been determined, the remainder of the problem will be identical to the types discussed in Sections 3-3 to 3-5.

## Sample Problem 3–10

How many moles of Cu will be produced by passing 0.75 mole of $NH_3$ over 1.55 moles of CuO?

$$3CuO + 2NH_3 \rightarrow N_2 + 3H_2O + 3Cu$$

### Solution

Since the quantities of two reactants are given, we must determine which one is present in a limited amount, for it will determine the quantity of product obtained. We begin by determining the amount of CuO needed to react completely with 0.75 mole of $NH_3$:

$$0.75 \text{ mole } NH_3 \times \frac{3 \text{ moles CuO}}{2 \text{ moles } NH_3} = 1.1 \text{ moles CuO}$$

We have more CuO than that required for complete reaction, so the $NH_3$ is limiting and it determines the amount of Cu formed.

$$0.75 \text{ mole } NH_3 \times \frac{3 \text{ moles Cu}}{2 \text{ moles } NH_3} = 1.1 \text{ moles Cu}$$

## Sample Problem 3–11

Given the equation:

$$H_2 + O_2 \rightarrow H_2O,$$

how many grams of water ($H_2O$) can be produced by the reaction of 77.7 grams of $O_2$ with 15.0 grams of $H_2$?

### Solution

First we balance the equation.

$$2H_2 + O_2 \rightarrow 2H_2O$$

Then we note that we have two quantities that are candidates for the "begin with" statement, grams of $H_2$ and grams of $O_2$. The mass relations for this equation tell us that we need

$$\frac{32.0 \text{ g } O_2}{4.03 \text{ g } H_2} = \frac{7.94 \text{ g } O_2}{1.00 \text{ g } H_2} \text{ (read as 7.94 g } O_2 \text{ per g of } H_2)$$

The problem states that we have

$$\frac{77.7 \text{ g O}_2}{15.0 \text{ g H}_2} = \frac{5.18 \text{ g O}_2}{1.00 \text{ g H}_2}$$

Therefore we do not have as much $O_2$ as we need. The 77.7 g of $O_2$ is the limiting reagent.

$$? \text{ g H}_2\text{O} = 77.7 \text{ g O}_2 \times \frac{36.0 \text{ g H}_2\text{O}}{32.0 \text{ g O}_2} = 87.4 \text{ g H}_2\text{O}$$

## Sample Problem 3–12

How many grams of $H_2$ will be left over after complete reaction of the $O_2$ in sample problem 3–11?

## Solution

We can calculate the amount of $H_2$ needed to make 87.4 g of $H_2O$ and, by difference, determine how much is left.

$$? \text{ g H}_2 = 87.4 \text{ g H}_2\text{O} \times \frac{4.03 \text{ g H}_2}{36.0 \text{ g H}_2\text{O}} = 9.78 \text{ g H}_2$$

If we started with 15.0 g of $H_2$ and used 9.78 g, we will have 15.0 g $H_2$ − 9.78 g $H_2$ = 5.2 g of $H_2$ left.

Other "begin with" statements and conversion factors could have been selected to solve this problem. For example, 77.7 g of $O_2$ could have been converted to 9.78 g of $H_2$ with the factor 4.03 g $H_2$/32.0 g $O_2$

In summary, whenever we have two or more reactants, we must first determine which one is not in excess, i.e., which one is the limiting reagent. When the quantities of all the reactants are exactly those specified in the equations, these are said to be the **stoichiometric amounts**. Problems that involve the calculation of mass and mole relationships in a chemical reaction are called problems in **stoichiometry**.

## 3–7   PERCENT YIELD

In some of the above problems, we have calculated the amounts of products that can be obtained from a chemical reaction if the reaction goes to completion according to the equation written. In practice, one obtains an amount that is less than this for a variety of reasons. For example, some material could be lost in the separation of the products from the reaction mixture, or another reaction could be taking place simultaneously that uses up reactants and forms undesirable products, or the reaction may not go to completion. We indicate the amount of material that is actually obtained by the **percent yield**:

$$\% \text{ Yield} = \frac{\text{Actual amount}}{\text{Theoretical amount}} \times 100$$

The **theoretical amount** is that quantity calculated from the equation for the reaction assuming that the reaction went to completion as written. The unit cancellation is taken care of by recalling that percent is parts per 100. Actual amount divided by theoretical amount gives parts per one (division converts the denominator to one) times 100 gives parts per hundred; that is percent.

## Sample Problem 3–13

In carrying out the reaction described for the Haber process, a chemist obtains 27.7 g of $NH_3$ by the reaction of 18.4 g of $H_2$ with excess $N_2$. What is the percent yield?

## Solution

First we determine the theoretical amount of ammonia. From the balanced equation

$$N_2 + 3H_2 \rightarrow 2NH_3$$

we note that for a complete reaction 6.05 grams of $H_2$ (3 moles) will in theory produce 34.1 grams of $NH_3$ (2 moles). Therefore, 18.4 g of $H_2$ would give

$$? \text{ g } NH_3 = 18.4 \text{ g } H_2 \times \frac{34.1 \text{ g } NH_3}{6.05 \text{ g } H_2} = 104 \text{ g of } NH_3$$

$$\% \text{ Yield} = \frac{27.7 \text{ g } NH_3}{104 \text{ g } NH_3} \times 100 = 26.6\%$$

## TEST 3–4

A. Consider the following equation in answering the exercises in this test:

$$Zn + 2HCl \rightarrow ZnCl_2 + H_2$$

1. How many moles of $H_2$ can be obtained by the reaction of 0.333 mole of HCl with excess Zn?

2. Indicate the mass in grams of all the substances involved in this reaction.

3. If 30.0 g of Zn is mixed with 25.0 g of HCl, which reactant is in excess?

4. The amount of $H_2$ formed from the amounts of material indicated in the previous question is limited to that from _____ g of _____ .

5. The amount of $ZnCl_2$ formed from the amounts of material indicated in question 3 is limited to that from _____ g of _____ .

6. Using the amounts of reactants in question 3, a chemist obtained 35.0 g of $ZnCl_2$. Calculate the percent yield.

# Exercises

### The Meaning and Balancing of Equations

1.  Given the following equation

$$KClO_3 \rightarrow KCl + O_2$$

   (a) Balance the equation.
   (b) State the mole, molecule, and mass relations of the substances involved in this reaction.

2.  Given the following equation

$$H_2O_2 \rightarrow H_2O + O_2$$

   (a) Balance this equation.
   (b) State the molecule, mole, and mass relations of the substances involved in this reaction.

3.  Balance the following equations:
   (a) $Al + N_2 \rightarrow AlN$
   (b) $Fe + O_2 \rightarrow Fe_3O_4$
   (c) $CaCO_3 \rightarrow CaO + CO_2$
   (d) $NH_4NO_3 \rightarrow N_2O + H_2O$
   (e) $KI + Cl_2 \rightarrow KCl + I_2$
   (f) $Pb(NO_3)_2 + HCl \rightarrow PbCl_2 + HNO_3$
   (g) $BaO_2 \rightarrow BaO + O_2$
   (h) $Al + H_2SO_4 \rightarrow Al_2(SO_4)_3 + H_2$
   (i) $CH_4 + Cl_2 \rightarrow CHCl_3 + HCl$
   (j) $MgCl_2 + NaOH \rightarrow Mg(OH)_2 + NaCl$
   (k) $AgNO_3 + CuCl_2 \rightarrow AgCl + Cu(NO_3)_2$
   (l) $ZnS + O_2 \rightarrow ZnO + SO_2$
   (m) $Na + H_2O \rightarrow NaOH + H_2$
   (n) $BaCl_2 + (NH_4)_2CO_3 \rightarrow BaCO_3 + NH_4Cl$

### Mass-Mass, Mole-Mole, and Mass-Mole Relations

4.  Given the equation

$$4Al + 3O_2 \rightarrow 2Al_2O_3$$

   (a) How many moles of $Al_2O_3$ could be produced from 1 mole of Al and excess $O_2$?
   (b) How many moles of Al would be needed to produce 6 moles of $Al_2O_3$?
   (c) How many moles of $O_2$ are needed to produce 6 moles of $Al_2O_3$?
   (d) Indicate the mass of $O_2$ needed and the mass of $Al_2O_3$ produced from complete reaction of 4.00 moles of Al.

5. Given the following equation:

$$S_8 + O_2 \rightarrow SO_2$$

(a) How many grams of $SO_2$ can be produced by reaction of 2.00 g of sulfur, $S_8$, with excess $O_2$?

(b) How many grams of $O_2$ are needed for complete reaction of 2.00 g of $S_8$?

(c) How many grams of $S_8$ are needed to produce 20.0 g of $SO_2$?

(d) How many grams of $O_2$ are needed to produce 20.0 g of $SO_2$?

6. Given the equation

$$Cl_2 + 2NaI \rightarrow 2NaCl + I_2$$

How many grams of $I_2$ would be produced by the reaction of 200. g of NaI with excess $Cl_2$?

7. Consider the reaction

$$MnO_2 + 4HCl \rightarrow Cl_2 + MnCl_2 + 2H_2O$$

(a) How many grams of $Cl_2$ are produced by the reaction of 50. g of $MnO_2$ with excess HCl?

(b) If 25 g of $Cl_2$ are produced in this reaction, how much $MnCl_2$ would be formed?

8. The reaction of hydrazine, $N_2H_4$, with hydrogen peroxide $H_2O_2$, has been used to propel rockets;

$$N_2H_4(l) + 2H_2O_2(l) \rightarrow N_2(g) + 4H_2O(g).$$

(a) How many moles of $N_2$ can be obtained from 1.00 kilogram of $N_2H_4$ and excess $H_2O_2$?

(b) What is the total number of moles of products produced from the reactants in 8(a)?

(c) How many grams of water are produced from complete reaction of 567 g of $H_2O_2$?

(d) How many grams of $H_2O_2$ are needed for complete reaction of 1.00 kilogram of $N_2H_4$?

9. The sugar glucose can be burned to produce $CO_2$ and $H_2O$:

$$C_6H_{12}O_6 + O_2 \rightarrow CO_2 + H_2O$$

Note that this is the reverse of the reaction for photosynthesis.

(a) How many grams of $CO_2$ can be obtained from the combustion of 593 g of $C_6H_{12}O_6$?

(b) How many grams of $O_2$ are needed to burn 593 g of $C_6H_{12}O_6$ according to the above equation?

10. A mineral source for making copper, Cu, is the ore $CuFeS_2$. The reaction involved is:

$$2CuFeS_2 + 5O_2 \rightarrow 2Cu + 2FeO + 4SO_2$$

(a) How much copper could be obtained from 1.00 kilogram of $CuFeS_2$?

(b) How much $SO_2$ would be produced from complete reaction of 1.00 kilogram of $CuFeS_2$?

11. The compound nitromethane, $CH_3NO_2$, is used as a fuel in racing cars. The products of combustion are $CO_2$, $H_2O$, and NO. How many grams of $O_2$ are needed to burn 0.555 kilogram of nitromethane?

12. The compound $KClO_3$ decomposes on heating into KCl and $O_2$.

(a) How many grams of $KClO_3$ are needed to produce 7.44 moles of $O_2$?

(b) How many grams of KCl are produced when 7.44 moles of $O_2$ are made?

**Limiting Reactant Problems and Percent Yield**

13. Consider the reaction of 33.5 g of hydrazine, $N_2H_4$, with 30.3 g of $H_2O_2$,

$$N_2H_4 + 2H_2O_2 \rightarrow N_2 + 4H_2O$$

(a) How many grams of water should be produced?

(b) If 29.0 grams of water are obtained, what is the percent yield?

(c) How many grams of the reactant in excess would remain after the reaction in part a is complete?

14. Many of the activities of man introduce $SO_2$ into the atmosphere. The $SO_2$ is then converted into sulfuric acid, $H_2SO_4$:

$$2SO_2(g) + O_2(g) + 2H_2O(l) \rightarrow 2H_2SO_4(aq)$$

(a) With excess water, how many grams of $H_2SO_4$ could be formed from 1.00 kg of $SO_2$ and 325 g of $O_2$?

(b) If 512 g of $H_2SO_4$ were obtained from the reaction in part a, what is the percent yield?

15. Consider the reaction given in problem 14. If the percent yield is 88.3%, how many grams of $SO_2$ would have to react with excess water and dioxygen to form 35.3 g of $H_2SO_4$?

16. Referring to the equation for photosynthesis given in this chapter, how many grams of glucose could be produced from the reaction of 50.0 g of $CO_2$ with 20.0 g of water?

17. If 25.3 g of glucose are obtained from the reaction described in problem 16, what is the percent yield?

18. If in the following reaction:

$$Al + Fe_2O_3 \rightarrow Al_2O_3 + Fe$$

5.00 g of Al are combined with 15.0 g of $Fe_2O_3$, then:
(a) how many grams of iron would be produced?
(b) how many moles of the material in excess would be left over?
(c) what percent yield have you assumed in answering part a?

19. (a) How many grams of $NH_3$ could be produced by causing 12.0 g of $N_2$ to react with 4.00 g of $H_2$?
(b) How many grams of excess material would remain in the problem in part a?

**Verbalizing General Concepts**
20. Answer each of the following in your own words:
(a) How would you describe the objective of balancing an equation?
(b) The coefficients of an equation state the relationship between the molecules of the substances involved. Why do the coefficients also give the relationship between the moles involved?
(c) Indicate the mass, molecule, and mole relationships implied by the following equation:

$$4Al(s) + 3O_2(g) \rightarrow 2Al_2O_3(s)$$

(d) What do the symbols in parentheses in question 20(c) indicate?
(e) Refer to the equation in question 20(c) and write as many equalities involving masses of material as you can.
(f) Describe the chemical concept involved in limited reactant problems.
(g) What is percent yield? Describe how it is similar to the grade (in percent) that you get on an examination in which 80 is the top score.

**Challenging Problems**
21. Nitric acid, $HNO_3$, is made from ammonia by the following sequence of reactions:

$$4NH_3 + 5O_2 \rightarrow 4NO + 6H_2O$$
$$2NO + O_2 \rightarrow 2NO_2$$
$$3NO_2 + H_2O \rightarrow 2HNO_3 + NO$$

(a) How many grams of $HNO_3$ could be obtained from 66.6 g of $NH_3$ if all of the above reactions proceeded to completion as written, if the NO in the last step were lost, and if $O_2$ and $H_2O$ were present in excess?

(b) Given all the conditions in part a, how much $NH_3$ would be required to produce 73.5 g of $HNO_3$?

22.  A sample of $P_4$ is burned in 32.0 g of $O_2$ according to

$$P_4 + 5O_2 \rightarrow P_4O_{10}$$

Enough $O_2$ is left over to convert 15.0 g of $S_8$ to $SO_2$. How many moles of $P_4$ were burned?

23.  A sample of $Fe_3O_4$ plus its glass container weigh 150.0 g. When the $Fe_3O_4$ is allowed to react with $H_2$ according to the equation

$$Fe_3O_4 + 4H_2 \rightarrow 3Fe + 4H_2O$$

12.5 g of $H_2O$ are produced. What is the weight of the container?

24.  The combustion of methane, $CH_4$ ($O_2$ is the other reactant in a combustion reaction), produces $CO_2$ and water. How many grams of air, which is 23% by weight dioxygen, are needed to burn 66 g of $CH_4$?

25.  Refer to the equation given in problem 23. If the sample of $Fe_3O_4$ were 88.8% pure and if the yield of iron from pure $Fe_3O_4$ were 81.0%, (a) what percentage of the impure sample could be converted to iron? (b) Calculate the mass of iron one would obtain from 133 g of impure $Fe_3O_4$.

**Multiple Choice Questions**
26.  $w\ PCl_5 + x\ H_2O \rightarrow y\ POCl_3 + z\ HCl$

The above equation is a properly balanced one when:
(a) $w = 1, x = 2, y = 2, z = 4$;
(b) $w = 2, x = 2, y = 2, z = 2$;
(c) $w = 2, x = 2, y = 2, z = 4$;
(d) $w = 1, x = 1, y = 1, z = 2$;
(e) none of these.

27.  Given the balanced equation

$$4Al(s) + 3O_2(g) \rightarrow 2Al_2O_3(s)$$

and the following statements:
(1) 2 moles Al + 3/2 moles $O_2 \rightarrow$ 1 mole $Al_2O_3$
(2) 54.0 g Al + 48.0 g $O_2 \rightarrow$ 102.0 g $Al_2O_3$
(3) 12 moles Al + 9 moles $O_2 \rightarrow$ 6 moles $Al_2O_3$
    Ignoring significant figures, which of the following is correct?
    (a) Only statements 1 and 3 above are correct.
    (b) Only statements 1 and 3 are incorrect.

(c) Only statements 1 and 2 are correct.

(d) All of the above are correct.

(e) None of the above are correct.

28. Given the balanced equation

$$2N_2H_4(l) + N_2O_4(l) \rightarrow 3N_2(g) + 4H_2O$$

Calculate the number of grams of $N_2$ formed when 2.72 moles of $N_2H_4$ react completely.

(a) 114 g of $N_2$;

(b) 228 g of $N_2$;

(c) 57.0 g of $N_2$;

(d) 76.2 g of $N_2$;

(e) none of these are correct within 2 g.

29. If 174 g of $N_2H_4$ react with 276 g of $N_2O_4$, how many g of $N_2$ will be obtained?

(a) 114 g of $N_2$;

(b) 76.2 g of $N_2$;

(c) 84.0 g of $N_2$;

(d) 252 g of $N_2$;

(e) none of these are correct within 2 g.

30. A chemist obtains 38.2 grams of material in a reaction which theoretically should have given him 55.4 grams. What is the % yield?

(a) 145%,

(b) 1.45%,

(c) 0.69%,

(d) 69.0%,

(e) none of these.

31. Assume that the reaction between dihydrogen and dioxygen goes to completion under the existing conditions. Which statement is true if 10.0 g of dihydrogen is mixed with 64.0 g of dioxygen and ignited?

(a) The limiting reagent is dioxygen.

(b) 74 g of water will form.

(c) 3 moles of dihydrogen will be left over after the reaction.

(d) 68 g of water will form.

(e) None of these.

32. Calculate the mass of dihydrogen that would be formed by the reaction of 25.0 grams of zinc with 0.250 moles of HCl.

$(Zn + 2HCl \rightarrow ZnCl_2 + H_2)$.

(a) 0.775 g,

(b) 0.388 g,

(c) 0.252 g,

(d) 0.504 g,

(e) none of these.

33.    Sulfuric acid can be made by the following process:

$$4FeS_2 + 11O_2 \rightarrow 2Fe_2O_3 + 8SO_2$$
$$2SO_2 + O_2 \rightarrow 2SO_3$$
$$SO_3 + H_2O \rightarrow H_2SO_4$$

How many grams of $H_2SO_4$ will be produced from 1.000 kg of $FeS_2$?
(a) 1.000 kg, (b) 818 g, (c) 1.635 kg, (d) 2.000 kg, (e) 3.271 kg.

34.    When the following equation is balanced

$$Zn + NaOH \rightarrow Na_2ZnO_2 + H_2$$

the sum of the coefficients is: (a) 2, (b) 3, (c) 4, (d) 5, (e) none of the above.

35.    When the following equation is balanced

$$Al(OH)_3 + H_2SO_4 \rightarrow Al_2(SO_4)_3 + H_2O$$

the sum of the coefficients is: (a) 24, (b) 22, (c) 14, (d) 11, (e) none of these.

36.    In a balanced chemical equation: (a) the number of molecules on the left-hand side must equal the number on the right; (b) the sum of the masses of the molecules on the right-hand side must equal the sum of the masses of those on the left; (c) the sum of the coefficients on the left must equal the sum on the right; (d) two of the above are correct; (e) all of the above are correct.

37.    Consider the following reactions leading to the formation of $NO_2$ from $N_2$ and $O_2$:

$$N_2 + O_2 \rightarrow 2NO$$
$$2NO + O_2 \rightarrow 2NO_2$$

If the percent yield of the first step is 60% and that of the second step 50%, the overall yield from $N_2$ to $NO_2$ is: (a) 10%, (b) 50%, (c) 55%, (d) not enough information is provided to determine, (e) none of these.

38.    In problem 37, one would need _____ moles of $O_2$ to produce 2.50 moles of $NO_2$ from $N_2$: (a) 2.00, (b) 1.25, (c) 2.50, (d) 0.500, (e) none of the above.

39. Given the equation

$$N_2(g) + H_2(g) \rightarrow NH_3(g)$$

If 0.225 moles of $N_2$ react completely with 0.225 moles of $H_2$, (a) 0.075 moles of $H_2$ will remain; (b) 0.075 moles of $N_2$ will remain; (c) 0.150 moles of $H_2$ will remain; (d) 0.150 moles of $N_2$ will remain; (e) none of the reactants will remain.

40. When the following equation is balanced,

$$H_3PO_3 \, (l) \rightarrow H_3PO_4 \, (l) + PH_3 \, (g)$$

the sum of the coefficients is
(a) 4, (b) 5, (c) 7, (d) 8, (e) none of these

41. Given the balanced equation

$$2N_2H_4 \, (l) + N_2O_4 \, (l) \rightarrow 3N_2 \, (g) + 4H_2O$$

calculate the number of grams of $N_2$ formed when 5.44 moles of $N_2H_4$ react completely.
(a) 228 g of $N_2$     (d) 152 g of $N_2$
(b) 114 g of $N_2$     (e) none of these are correct
(c) 457 g of $N_2$       within 5g

42. Sulfuric acid can be made by the following process:

$$4FeS_2 + 11 \, O_2 \rightarrow 2Fe_2O_3 + 8SO_2$$
$$2SO_2 + O_2 \rightarrow 2SO_3$$
$$SO_3 + H_2O \rightarrow H_2SO_4$$

How many grams of $H_2SO_4$ will be produced from 500.g of $FeS_2$?
(a) 500 g, (b) 409 g, (c) 818 g, (d) 102 g, (e) 1.64 kg

43. Given the equation:

$$N_2 \, (g) + H_2 \, (g) \rightarrow NH_3 \, (g)$$

If 0.450 moles of $N_2$ react completely with 0.450 moles of $H_2$, then
(a) 0.300 moles of $H_2$ will remain
(b) 0.300 moles of $N_2$ will remain
(c) 0.150 moles of $H_2$ will remain
(d) 0.150 moles of $N_2$ will remain
(e) none of the reactants will remain

44. On ignition, the salt, Al $(NH_4)_2(SO_4)_2 \cdot 6H_2O$, is converted to $Al_2O_3$. The molecular weight of $Al(NH_4)_2(SO_4)_2 \cdot 6H_2O = 299.09$ and of $Al_2O_3 = 102.00$, and the atomic weight of aluminum $= 27.00$. When 5.6000 grams of the starting material is thermally decomposed, the amount of $Al_2O_3$ formed is

    (a) 0.9549 g
    (b) 1.0111 g
    (c) 1.9098 g

    (d) 2.8647 g
    (e) 3.8196 g

45. A nickel complex on analysis gave the following percentage composition: Ni $= 18.9$, $SO_4^{2-} = 30.9$, $H_2O = 11.6$, and $(H_2NCH_2CH_2NH_2) = 38.6$. The molecular formula of the complex is

    (a) $Ni[(H_2NCH_2CH_2NH_2)_3]SO_4 \cdot 2H_2O$
    (b) $Ni[(H_2NCH_2CH_2NH_2)_3]SO_4 \cdot H_2O$
    (c) $Ni[(H_2NCH_2CH_2NH_2)_2(H_2O)_2]SO_4$
    (d) $Ni[(H_2NCH_2CH_2NH_2)_2(H_2O)_2]SO_4 \cdot H_2O$
    (e) $Ni[(H_2NCH_2CH_2NH_2)_2(H_2O)_2]SO_4 \cdot 2H_2O$

# 4

# ELEMENTARY BONDING CONSIDERATIONS AND NOMENCLATURE

## Chapter Objectives

### (Begin each of the following with "You should master . . .")

1. the determination of the number of electrons, neutrons, and protons in an atom, given the atomic number and atomic mass number.
2. the definition of isotopes.
3. the difference between ionic and covalent bonding.
4. the definitions of cation, anion, and polyatomic ion.
5. the rules given for naming simple molecules and the names for the polyatomic anions listed in rule 1d (p.80). Be able to write the name if given the formula of a compound and the formula if given the name of a compound.
6. the names of the families of elements in the periodic table.
7. the use of analogy in predicting the formulas of compounds formed by a family of elements in the periodic table.
8. the writing of the formulas of ionic compounds, given the charges on the ions.
9. the approximate masses and the charges of the proton, electron, and neutron.

## 4–1   THE NUCLEAR ATOM

An atom is composed of the fundamental particles listed and described in Table 4–1. The protons and neutrons are located in a very small nucleus which contains most of the mass of the atom. Each atom is described by an **atomic number, Z,** and an **atomic mass number, A.** The **atomic number** *indicates the number of protons in the nucleus.* The **atomic mass number** is defined as the nearest whole number to the actual **atomic mass.** *The number of neutrons in the atom is given by the difference between the atomic mass number and the atomic number:*

$$\text{number of neutrons} = A - Z \tag{4-1}$$

**TABLE 4-1**
**Some Important Fundamental Particles**

| Particle | Charge[a] | Mass[b] |
|----------|-----------|---------|
| Electron | $-1$ | 0.00055 ($9.1 \times 10^{-28}$ g) |
| Proton | $+1$ | 1.0076 ($1.67 \times 10^{-24}$ g) |
| Neutron | 0 | 1.0089 ($1.67 \times 10^{-24}$ g) |

[a]These charges are relative to the charge of a single electron ($1.6 \times 10^{-14}$ coulomb) being considered as $-1$.
[b]The mass is given in atomic mass units; the mass in grams is shown in parentheses.

Most elements are composed of more than one kind of atom, called isotopes. **Isotopes** contain the same number of protons in the nucleus but differ in the number of neutrons. For example, magnesium (atomic number = 12) consists of atoms with atomic masses of 23.98, 24.99, and 25.98 amu. The mass numbers of these magnesium isotopes are 24, 25, and 26, respectively. By using equation (4–1), we determine that these atoms contain 12, 13, and 14 neutrons, respectively.

The **atomic weight** of an element is the average atomic mass of all the naturally occurring isotopes of that element. These average atomic masses are reported for the elements in the periodic table inside the front cover and in alphabetical listing of the elements inside the back cover.

The nucleus of each atom is surrounded by a cloud of electrons that occupies most of the space which makes up the atom. *In the neutral atom, the number of electrons in this cloud is equal to the number of protons in the nucleus.*

## 4-2 BONDING

Molecules are composed of atoms that are joined together by chemical bonds. Two types of bonding interactions, **covalent** and **ionic,** can be distinguished. *In the covalent bond, the atoms are joined together by sharing a pair of electrons.* This sharing corresponds to the mutual attraction for both negatively charged electrons in the bond by both of the positively charged nuclei of the attached atoms. This sharing of electrons is illustrated in Fig. 4–1 along with common ways of representing this type of bond. In the water molecule, depicted in Fig. 4–1 (c), two bonds of this type hold the three atoms together in the molecule.

*In an ionic bond the force holding the molecule together is the electrostatic attraction of the positive and negative ions that have been formed by electron transfer from neutral atoms.* For example, when a sodium atom and a chlorine atom combine, an electron is transferred from the sodium atom to the chlorine atom. The sodium ion now has one more proton than it has electrons. Accordingly, this species has a charge of +1 and is written as $Na^+$. *Any positively charged species is called a* **cation.** The chlorine atom, on the other hand, has gained an electron and now has one more electron than there are protons in its nucleus, giving it a charge of $-1$. *This negatively charged species is called an* **anion** and is written as $Cl^-$. Solid sodium chloride consists of a large number of sodium ions, each

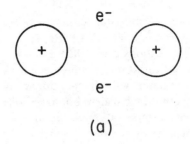

**Figure 4–1**    Ways of representing covalent bonds; (a) mutual attraction of two electrons by two nuclei, (b) ways of writing the interaction in (a), (c) representation of the two covalent bonds in water.

(a)

H:H   or   H:H   or   H–H

(b)

O
H       H

(c)

surrounded by six chloride ions. Each chloride ion in turn is surrounded by six sodium ions. The arrangement of these ions is illustrated in Fig. 4–2.

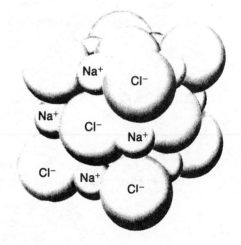

**Figure 4–2**    The arrangement of sodium ions and chloride ions in solid sodium chloride.

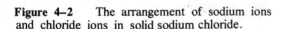

A small grain of table salt (sodium chloride) is a crystal that consists of a huge number of ions arranged in this way. There is no sharing of a pair of electrons between a given sodium ion and a single chloride ion. Rather, each ion is electrostatically interacting with many other ions. *In sodium chloride, the entire crystal is a giant molecule.* The overall composition is given by a 1:1 ratio of $Na^+$ and $Cl^-$, so *the formula is written as $Na^+Cl^-$ or simply NaCl in chemical equations.* In general, in ionic compounds there are no bonds between particular pairs of atoms; instead, a large group of ions is held together by mutual electrostatic attraction.

An ionic compound will result whenever an atom from the first two columns of the periodic table (the columns headed by lithium and beryllium) reacts with an element in the fluorine column (F, Cl, Br, I, At) or with oxygen or sulfur. Ionic compounds also result when cations other than $H^+$ are combined with more complex anions. For example, the $NO_3^-$ (nitrate) ion, called a **polyatomic anion** because it consists of several atoms, forms ionic bonds with most cations. The nitrogen and oxygen atoms in the $NO_3^-$ anion are held together by covalent bonds. Similarly, many polyatomic cations, for example, $NH_4^+$, form ionic compounds with anions. The nitrogen and hydrogen atoms in this cation are held together by covalent bonds.

The elements in the periodic table are divided into metals and nonmetals by the solid line separating boron from aluminum, aluminum from silicon, and so forth. In chemical reactions, metals often form cations and nonmetals often form anions.

For now, consider that other combinations of atoms lead to covalent bonding. Later, in the discussion of atomic structure, better rules for predicting bond types will be offered.

## TEST 4–1

A. Referring to the table inside the back cover, answer the following questions:

1. What is the atomic number of iodine, I?

2. What is the atomic mass of iodine?

3. What is the atomic mass number of iodine?

4. How many protons are there in the iodine nucleus?

5. How many neutrons are there in the iodine nucleus?

6. How many electrons surround the iodine nucleus?

7. How does an iodide ion, $I^-$, differ from an iodine atom?

B. The molecule H—I is held together with a covalent bond.
   1. What does the dash imply?

   2. What type of bonding do you expect in sodium iodide, NaI?

   3. How does the bonding in HI differ from the bonding in NaI?

C. Indicate whether you expect the following compounds to be joined by covalent or ionic bonds:
   1. MgO

   2. $SO_2$

   3. $H_2S$

   4. $BaF_2$

   5. CsCl

   6. $CCl_4$

## 4–3    NOMENCLATURE

The chemist's system of nomenclature requires the understanding of more concepts than we have covered so far. However, in order to simplify memorization of the names of the many compounds that we have mentioned already, a few of the simpler rules will be given here. We shall add to these as the required background is developed. Essentially, we would like to have a simple system of nomenclature that indicates in a systematic way the atomic composition of the molecule.

We shall begin our discussion with the nomenclature of ionic compounds.

1.  First we shall consider the names of individual ions.

    a.  Cations that consist of a single atom are named after the element; for example, $Rb^+$ is called rubidium ion and $Ca^{2+}$ is called calcium ion.

    b.  The names of polyatomic cations are more difficult and we shall name these ions as we encounter them. For example, remember that $NH_4^+$ is called ammonium ion.

    c.  Anions consisting of a single atom have the stem name of the element and a suffix -*ide* added. For example:

| Atom | Anion stem | Name | Formula |
|------|-----------|------|---------|
| boron | bor | boride | $B^{3-}$ |
| bromine | brom | bromide | $Br^-$ |
| chlorine | chlor | chloride | $Cl^-$ |
| hydrogen | hydr | hydride | $H^-$ |
| oxygen | ox | oxide | $O^{2-}$ |
| sulfur | sulf | sulfide | $S^{2-}$ |

    d.  Polyatomic anions are more difficult to name. A few that we shall encounter often are listed below, and systematic procedures for naming these anions will be given later.

| Formula | Name | Formula | Name |
|---------|------|---------|------|
| $CO_3^{2-}$ | Carbonate | $OH^-$ | Hydroxide |
| $HCO_3^-$ | Bicarbonate | $PO_4^{3-}$ | Phosphate |
| $NO_2^-$ | Nitrite | $SO_3^{2-}$ | Sulfite |
| $NO_3^-$ | Nitrate | $SO_4^{2-}$ | Sulfate |
| $ClO_4^-$ | Perchlorate | $CN^-$ | Cyanide |
| $ClO_3^-$ | Chlorate | $CH_3CO_2^-$ | Acetate |

When a given element forms *two* oxygen-containing anions (for example, sulfur forms $SO_3^{2-}$ and $SO_4^{2-}$), the one containing the larger number of oxygen atoms is usually named with the suffix -*ate* and the one with the smaller number is named with the suffix -*ite*. An exception is perchlorate ($ClO_4^-$) and chlorate ($ClO_3^-$).

2.  To name an ionic compound, the cation is named first and the anion next. For example,

$Cs_2O$ is cesium oxide

$MgCl_2$ is magnesium chloride

$Mg_3B_2$ is magnesium boride

$NH_4I$ is ammonium iodide
$KNO_2$ is potassium nitrite
$Sr(NO_3)_2$ is strontium nitrate

3. Covalent compounds are named in a similar fashion to ionic compounds. The atom in the compound located farther to the right in the periodic table is given the *-ide* suffix. If both atoms are in the same column, the one closest to the top of the table (except for hydrogen) is given the *-ide* suffix, for example,

$HCl$ is hydrogen chloride
$SO_2$ is sulfur dioxide

4. If a pair of elements form more than one compound, for example CO and $CO_2$, the different compounds are distinguished by using the prefixes mono-, di-, tetra-, penta-, hexa-, hepta-, octa-, nona-, and deca- for numbers one to ten. For example:

$CO$ is carbon monoxide
$CO_2$ is carbon dioxide
$N_2O_4$ is dinitrogen tetroxide
$N_2O$ is dinitrogen monoxide

5. Many very familiar compounds have been given common names that you probably have heard of; for example, $H_2O$ is water, $NH_3$ is ammonia, and $H_2O_2$ is hydrogen peroxide.
6. The formulas of these compounds are usually written with the element given the *-ide* suffix listed last; that is, we write CO and not OC.

## 4–4   USE OF THE PERIODIC TABLE TO PREDICT MOLECULAR FORMULAS

The elements are arranged in the periodic table in such a manner that all of the members of a vertical column, referred to as a **family of elements,** have many aspects of their chemistry in common. The families are numbered with Roman numerals and letters. The letter A refers to the **main group elements** and the letter B to the **transition elements.** The differences between these two groups will be discussed later. The families are often referred to by name. Group IA is called the alkali metal family, Group IIA the alkaline earths, Group VIIA the halogens, and Group 0 (or 8) the noble gases. The other families are often named after the first element of the group; for example, Group IVA is called the carbon family.

In forming compounds, the alkali metals usually become $+1$ ions and the alkaline earths become $+2$ ions. Often the halogens form $-1$ ions when they react, and a $-2$ ion is common for the oxygen family elements. The formulas of ionic compounds can be predicted by combining the ions in such a way that the resulting molecule is uncharged. For example, $BaCl_2$, and $Na_2O$ contain equal numbers of positive and negative charges in each formula, producing a molecule that is uncharged.

The formulas of covalent compounds can also be predicted by reference to the periodic table. For example, in analogy to the compound $H_2O$, the compounds $H_2S$, $H_2Se$, $H_2Te$, and $H_2Po$ can be formed. By analogy to $CO_2$, the molecules $SiO_2$, $GeO_2$, $SnO_2$, and $PbO_2$ can be formed.

## TEST 4-2

A.  Given the stem names of fluor and iod, name the anions $F^-$ and $I^-$.

B.  Name the following compounds:
1. NaI

2. $NH_4Br$

3. $CaF_2$

C.  The only fluoride that calcium forms is $CaF_2$. Why is this compound not named calcium difluoride?

D.  Write the formulas of the following compounds and list the numbers of the rules presented above that are used in arriving at the name:
1. magnesium sulfide

2. carbon disulfide

3. sodium hydride

4. ammonium sulfate

E.  Which rule tells you that $CS_2$ is called carbon disulfide and not disulfur carbide?

F.  Referring to the periodic table, write formulas for the compounds formed by all the elements of a given family that are analogous to the formula listed:

1.  $NH_3$

2.  $NCl_3$

3.  $CCl_4$

## Exercises

1.  Referring to the table inside the back cover, indicate the numbers of protons, neutrons, and electrons in:
    (a) Zn, (b) In, (c) $Fe^{3+}$, (d) $H^+$, (e) $S^{2-}$, (f) U.

2.  Predict whether the following will be joined by ionic or covalent bonds: (a) HI, (b) $SrBr_2$, (c) $SiCl_4$, (d) $NO_2$, (e) $Rb_2O$, (f) $CH_4$, (g) $H_2Te$, (h) SrS, (i) $NH_4Br$, (j) $NaNO_3$, (k) $K_2CO_3$, (l) $NH_4NO_3$.

3.  Write the formulas of the following compounds: (a) ammonium sulfide, (b) calcium oxide, (c) magnesium hydroxide, (d) sulfur dioxide, (e) silicon dioxide, (f) ammonium sulfate, (g) beryllium hydride, (h) sodium phosphate, (i) magnesium phosphate, (j) barium sulfate, (k) barium sulfite, (l) sodium bicarbonate.

4.  Name the compounds listed in question 2, given the fact that $Te^{2-}$ has the tellur stem, silicon forms more than one chloride, nitrogen forms more than one oxide, and $CH_4$ has the common name methane.

5.  Balance the following equations:
    (a) sodium hydroxide + carbon dioxide → sodium carbonate + water; (b) magnesium nitrate + potassium sulfate → magnesium sulfate + potassium nitrate; (c) potassium sulfite + barium nitrate → barium sulfite + potassium nitrate.

**Verbalizing General Concepts**
6.  In your own words, answer the following questions:
    (a) Given the atomic number and atomic weight, how do you determine the nuclear composition of an atom?
    (b) How does a cation differ from the neutral atom?
    (c) What is an isotope?
    (d) What is the atomic mass number and how does it differ from the atomic mass?
    (e) What is meant by the average atomic mass?
    (f) How do ionic and covalent bonds differ?
    (g) How do you determine if a combination of elements will form an ionic compound?
    (h) Anions formed by a single element have the suffix _____ added.
    (i) What information should be conveyed by our system of nomenclature?

**Multiple Choice Questions**
7.  The silver atom (atomic number = 47; atomic mass = 107.9) has _____ neutrons in the nucleus. (a) 47, (b) 60, (c) 61, (d) 108, (e) none of these.

8.  Which of the following describe isotopes?
    (a) At. No. = 7, At. Mass = 14; (b) At. No. = 8, At. Mass = 14; (c) At. No. = 7, At. Mass = 15; (d) a and b above; (e) a and c above.

9.  Which of the following is an ionic compound?
    (a) $CaBr_2$, (b) $Mg_3B_2$, (c) $SiCl_4$, (d) two of these, (e) none of these.

10. The formula of magnesium phosphate is:
    (a) $Mn_3P_2$, (b) $Mg_3P_2$, (c) $MgPO_4$, (d) $Mn_3(PO_4)_2$, (e) none of these.

11. Sodium has an atomic number of 11 and an atomic mass of 23.0. It has: (a) 11 protons and 12 neutrons in the nucleus, (b) 11 protons and 23 neutrons in the nucleus, (c) 23 protons and 11 neutrons in the nucleus, (d) 11 neutrons and 12 protons in the nucleus, (e) none of these because charged protons cannot exist in the small nuclear space.

12. Which of the following is true of isotopes?
    (a) They have the same atomic mass.
    (b) They have the same atomic mass but different atomic numbers.
    (c) They have the same atomic number but different atomic masses.
    (d) They have different numbers of electrons.
    (e) None of the above are true.

13. Which of the following is true of a cation?
    (a) It is negatively charged.
    (b) It has more protons than electrons.
    (c) It has more neutrons than electrons.
    (d) It has no electrons.
    (e) None of the above are true.

14. The correct name of the compound $SO_3$ is: (a) sulfuric acid, (b) sulfur monoxide, (c) oxyoxium sulfide, (d) trioxysulfide, (e) none of these.

# 5

# SOLUTIONS*

## Chapter Objectives

## (Begin each of the following with "You should master ...")

1. the definitions of solute, solvent, and solution.
2. the definition of molarity and the working of problems involving this concept: that is, the calculation of volume, moles, or molarity when given two of these quantities.
3. the definition of molality, ppm, and mole fraction and the solution of problems involving these concepts.
4. the concepts of strong and weak acids and bases. Begin to accumulate chemical facts about the strengths of some of the common acids and bases.
5. the behavior of solutes, leading to their classification as electrolytes or nonelectrolytes.
6. the solubility rules and the prediction of the species that exist in solution when solutes are dissolved.
7. the writing of total and net ionic equations.
8. the factors that provide driving forces for chemical reactions and the ideas concerning the coexistence of certain pairs of ions in solution.
9. calculations of stoichiometry problems that involve solutions of reactants.
10. the concept of equivalents and the calculation of normality.†

You are already familiar with solutions. A bottle of soda pop is a solution of $CO_2$ (g), sugar (s), preservatives, coloring, and flavoring dissolved in a large amount of water. For liquid solutions, the liquid present in excess (in soda pop this is the water) is referred to as the **solvent,** and the materials dissolved in this solvent are the **solutes.** A solute can be a solid, liquid, or gaseous material before it is dissolved. When a substance dissolves, it is dispersed into its constituent molecules, atoms, or ions to produce a homogeneous (uniform) mixture of these particles with the solvent molecules. *The homogeneous mixture of the solvent and the solute is called the solution.* A solution is a mixture and not a compound, because the composition of the solution can be varied continuously over a wide range depending on how much solute one dissolves in a given amount of solvent.

Since the composition of a solution is variable, one of our first problems in defining a solution quantitatively is to describe its composition by expressing its concentration.

---

*If you are using this book at the time you are attending lectures in General Chemistry, you may find that your instructor does not cover this topic as early as it is covered in this text. In that case you may omit this chapter now and return to it later. This text has been constructed so that the remaining chapters may be used in whatever order the topics are presented in your lecture. You may find that certain sections in this chapter are covered later in your lectures. They and the related problems can be omitted now and be covered later.

†This objective is often omitted by many chemistry teachers.

Concentration, which is the amount of solute in a certain amount of solvent or solution, can be specified in many different ways. One of the most common concentration units is molarity. **Molarity** *is defined as the number of moles of solute per liter of solution* and is abbreviated with the capital letter M.

## 5–1   CALCULATIONS INVOLVING MOLARITY

We can write the definition given above as

$$\text{molarity (M)} = \frac{\text{moles of solute}}{\text{volume (liters) solution}} \qquad (5\text{–}1)$$

Thus we can encounter problems involving molarity in which any two of the quantities in this equation are given and we are asked for the third. We shall illustrate how these problems are solved, using molarity as a conversion factor in the sample problems that follow.

---

### Sample Problem 5–1

A solution contains 0.161 mole of solute in 310. ml. What is the molarity?

### Solution

We are being asked to derive the conversion factor, molarity.
? molarity = ? moles liter$^{-1}$

$$0.161 \text{ mole} \ = 310 \text{ ml}$$

$$? \text{ moles liter}^{-1} = \frac{0.161 \text{ mole}}{310 \text{ ml}} \times \frac{1000 \text{ ml}}{1 \text{ liter}} = 0.519 \text{ mole liter}^{-1} = 0.519 \text{ M}$$

---

With the next two sample problems we shall illustrate the idea that molarity is a conversion factor for converting moles to liters and liters to moles.

---

### Sample Problem 5–2

How many moles are contained in 35.1 ml of a 0.879 M solution?

## Solution

? moles

$$? \text{ moles} = 35.1 \text{ ml} \times \frac{1 \text{ liter}}{1000 \text{ ml}} \times \frac{0.879 \text{ mole}}{\text{liter}} = 0.0309 \text{ mole}$$

## Sample Problem 5–3

What volume of a 0.533 M solution must be taken to obtain 0.107 mole of solute?

## Solution

? volume ; remember M = moles per liter of solution.

$$? \text{ volume} = 0.107 \text{ mole} \times \frac{1 \text{ liter}}{0.533 \text{ mole}} = 0.201 \text{ liter}$$

The three problems that were worked above constitute the three essentially different types of problems that can be worked using molarity as a conversion factor. We shall next illustrate some problems that combine these ideas with other problems you have mastered.

## Sample Problem 5–4

How many grams of barium hydroxide are needed to make 300. ml of a 0.692 M solution?

## Solution

? grams ; so we need to convert ml to moles and moles to grams.

$$? \text{ grams} = 300. \text{ ml} \times \frac{1 \text{ liter}}{1000 \text{ ml}} \times \frac{0.692 \text{ mole}}{1 \text{ liter}} \times \frac{171.3 \text{ g}}{1 \text{ mole}} = 35.6 \text{ g}$$

where 171.3 is the molecular weight of $Ba(OH)_2$. Thus, this problem is the same as sample problem 5–2 with the mole-to-gram conversion from Chapter 3 added on.

## Sample Problem 5-5

What is the molarity of a solution made by dissolving 32.2 grams of $Mg(NO_3)_2$ in 650 ml of solution?

## Solution

$$? \text{ molarity} = \frac{? \text{ moles}}{\text{liter}}$$

The molecular weight of $Mg(NO_3)_2$ is 148.3.

$$? \text{ moles } Mg(NO_3)_2 = 32.2 \, \cancel{g} \times \frac{1 \text{ mole}}{148.3 \, \cancel{g}} = 0.217 \text{ mole } Mg(NO_3)_2$$

There is 0.217 mole in 650 ml.

$$\frac{? \text{ moles}}{\text{liter}} = \frac{0.217 \text{ mole}}{650 \, \cancel{ml}} \times \frac{1000 \, \cancel{ml}}{1 \text{ liter}} = \frac{0.334 \text{ moles}}{\text{liter}} = 0.334 \text{ M}$$

## Sample Problem 5-6

A 250 ml solution of 2.11 M $H_2SO_4$ is diluted to 725 ml. What is the molarity of the diluted solution?

## Solution

We can determine the number of moles in 250 ml of 2.11 M solution as in sample problem 5-2. This number of moles will be present in the resulting 725 ml obtained by dilution. *Dilution does not change the number of moles of solute present in the original solution.* We then calculate the molarity of 725 ml of solution as in sample problem 5-1.

$$? \text{ moles} = 250 \, \cancel{ml} \times \frac{1 \, \cancel{liter}}{1000 \, \cancel{ml}} \times \frac{2.11 \text{ moles}}{1 \, \cancel{liter}} = 0.528 \text{ mole}$$

$$0.528 \text{ moles} = 725 \text{ ml in the final solution}$$

$$\frac{? \text{ moles}}{\text{liter}} = \frac{0.528 \text{ moles}}{725 \, \cancel{ml}} \times \frac{1000 \, \cancel{ml}}{1 \text{ liter}} = 0.728 \, \frac{\text{moles}}{\text{liter}}$$

## Sample Problem 5–7

In the laboratory there is available a bottle of 6.00 M $H_2SO_4$ solution. How would you prepare 325 ml of a 0.333 M solution from the 6.00 M solution?

### Solution

This can be immediately recognized as a dilution problem. We must calculate how many moles would be needed to make 325 ml of a 0.333 M solution. We then have to calculate how much 6.00 M $H_2SO_4$ to take in order to obtain the needed number of moles.

$$? \text{ moles} = 325 \text{ ml} \times \frac{1 \text{ liter}}{1000 \text{ ml}} \times \frac{0.333 \text{ mole}}{1 \text{ liter}} = 0.108 \text{ mole } H_2SO_4$$

How many liters of 6.00 M $H_2SO_4$ are needed?

$$? \text{ liters} = 0.108 \text{ moles} \times \frac{1 \text{ liter}}{6.00 \text{ moles}} = 0.0180 \text{ liter}$$

Thus, if we take 0.0180 liter (18.0 ml) of 6.00 M $H_2SO_4$ and dilute this to 0.325 liter (325 ml) of solution, we will have 325 ml of 0.333 M $H_2SO_4$ solution.

## Sample Problem 5–8

To what volume would 110 ml of 4.12 M HCl have to be diluted in order to produce a 2.88 M solution?

### Solution

This is a two-step problem like the other dilution problems. First we determine the number of moles in the starting solution. Then we determine the volume that is needed to contain this number of moles in order that the final solution be 2.88 M.

$$? \text{ moles} = 110 \text{ ml} \times \frac{1 \text{ liter}}{1000 \text{ ml}} \times \frac{4.12 \text{ moles}}{\text{liter}} = 0.453 \text{ mole}$$

$$? \text{ volume} = 0.453 \text{ mole} \times \frac{1 \text{ liter}}{2.88 \text{ moles}} = 0.157 \text{ liter}$$

In summary, 110 ml of 4.12 M HCl solution would have to be diluted to 157 ml to produce a solution that is 2.88 M.

## TEST 5–1

A.  In this part of the test we shall examine your understanding of the
    preceding discussion by introducing a new concentration unit and
    asking you to employ similar logic in working problems using this
    unit. The unit is **molality,** m, *and is defined as moles of solute per
    kilogram of solvent.*
    1. From the above definition, write an equation similar to equation
       5–1 but for molality, and label this equation 5–2.

    2. Indicate what m is a conversion factor for.

    3. We shall answer a series of questions based on the calculation of
       the molality of a solution prepared by dissolving 0.224 mole of
       $C_2H_5OH$ (ethyl alcohol) in 575 g of water.
       (a) What is asked?

       (b) Write the equality from which the conversion factor will be
           determined.

       (c) Calculate the molality.

4. We shall solve the problem, "How much water must be added to 3.75 moles of $C_2H_5OH$ to produce a 1.66 m solution?"
   (a) What is asked?

   (b) Set up the equation to convert moles to kg solvent and solve.

5. We shall solve the problem, "How many grams of water must be added to 11.5 g of $C_2H_5OH$ to produce a 0.336 m solution?"
   (a) What is asked?

   (b) Describe the conversions that need to be made.

   (c) Set up the problem and solve for the answer.

B. A series of questions will be asked about a dilution problem in molarity units. How would you prepare 675 ml of a 0.222 M solution of sodium hydroxide from a 2.00 M solution?

1. In words, state the steps you will go through to obtain the answer.

2. Calculate the number of moles needed for 675 ml of a 0.222 M solution.

3. Calculate the number of ml of a 2.00 M solution of NaOH needed to give the number of moles in part 2.

4. Complete the answer to this question.

# 5–2   OTHER CONCENTRATION UNITS (OPTIONAL)

Two other common concentration units are **mole fraction** and **parts per million** (ppm). The latter is used to describe very small amounts of solute in a large amount of solvent. It is frequently used in pollution studies, where trace amounts of materials can have profound effects. As the name implies, this unit is defined as the parts (grams or other units, which should be specified) of a minor component in $1 \times 10^6$ parts (same units) of a major component. We shall imply grams as the unit in this text unless otherwise indicated.

## Sample Problem 5–9

Methyl mercuric chloride, $CH_3HgCl$, is a toxic pollutant found in natural waters surrounding certain industrial sites. If a sample of 350 grams of water is found to contain $1.0 \times 10^{-4}$ gram of this material, what is the concentration in ppm (that is, parts per $10^6$)?

### Solution

$$\text{conc. ppm} = \frac{\text{parts minor}}{\text{parts major}} \times 10^6 \qquad \textbf{(5–3)}$$

Parts minor divided by parts major gives the parts minor per one part major, and there are $10^6$ times as many minor parts in 1 million parts major. Substituting the given information into this equation gives:

$$\text{conc. ppm} = \frac{1.0 \times 10^{-4}\,g}{350\,g} \times 10^6 = 0.29 \text{ ppm}$$

## Sample Problem 5–10

A water solution contains 1.6 ppm of a pollutant. If you drank 250 ml of this water, how much pollutant would you ingest?

(Density of water = 1.0 g/ml)

### Solution

$$250 \text{ ml} \times 1.0 \text{ g/ml} = 250 \text{ g } H_2O$$

As in previous problems, two of the three quantities in the appropriate equation are given; in this case, g major and ppm. Rearranging equation 5–3, and substituting grams for parts, we obtain

$$\text{g minor} = \frac{\text{conc. ppm} \times \text{g major}}{1 \times 10^6} = \frac{1.6 \text{ ppm} \times 250\,g}{1 \times 10^6} = 4.0 \times 10^{-4}\,g$$

The **mole fraction** concentration unit, $X$, is defined as the number of moles of one component (which we shall label A) divided by the total number of moles of all components.

$$X_A = \frac{\text{moles of A}}{\text{moles of A + moles of B + etc.}} \qquad (5-4)$$

where $X_A$ is the mole fraction of A. Mole fraction is often used to describe the concentration of solutions that contain more than two components.

---

## Sample Problem 5-11

A solution is made by mixing 115 g of $H_2O$, 31.0 g of ethanol, $C_2H_5OH$, and 11.2 g of glucose, $C_6H_{12}O_6$. Calculate the mole fraction of ethanol.

## Solution

Converting grams to moles, we obtain:

$$115 \text{ g } H_2O \times \frac{1 \text{ mole}}{18.0 \text{ g } H_2O} = 6.39 \text{ moles}$$

$$31.0 \text{ g } C_2H_5OH \times \frac{1 \text{ mole}}{46.1 \text{ g } C_2H_5OH} = 0.672 \text{ mole}$$

$$11.2 \text{ g } C_6H_{12}O_6 \times \frac{1 \text{ mole}}{180. \text{ g } C_6H_{12}O_6} = 0.062 \text{ mole}$$

Substituting into equation 5-4 we obtain

$$X_{C_2H_5OH} = \frac{0.672 \text{ mole } C_2H_5OH}{(0.672 \text{ mole } C_2H_5OH) + (6.39 \text{ moles } H_2O) + (0.062 \text{ mole } C_6H_{12}O_6)}$$

$$= \frac{0.672}{7.12} = 0.094$$

---

## 5-3    THE NATURE OF SOLUTES DISSOLVED IN WATER

Various substances differ in the extent to which they dissolve in a solvent, ranging from instances of unlimited solubility (like ethanol in water) to cases where only a few molecules will dissolve in a liter of solvent (like HgS, which dissolves in water to the extent of only $10^{-55}$ moles per liter). The latter type of substance is said to be very slightly (or poorly) soluble, while substances with appreciable solubility are said to be soluble or to have good solubility.

The nature of the species formed in solution when a solute dissolves can sometimes be inferred from the nature of bonding in the solute. For example, *soluble ionic compounds usually dissociate into ions that move independently of one another when the compound dissolves.* The solution of magnesium chloride can be represented by the following equation:

$$Mg^{2+}(Cl^-)_2(s) \xrightarrow{+ H_2O} Mg^{2+}(aq) + 2\ Cl^-(aq)$$

The species $Mg^{2+}(aq)$ indicates that the magnesium ion has water molecules that are directly bonded to the cation, but the number of water molecules is not being specified. The (aq) after $Cl^-$ also indicates that an unspecified number of water molecules are attached, and $H_2O$ is placed over the arrow to indicate an unspecified number of reacting molecules. All ionic compounds that dissolve in water form ions. Since any solution that contains ions will conduct an electric current, solutes that produce ions when dissolved in solvents are called **electrolytes.**

Some covalent molecules dissolve in water without ionizing, while others undergo reaction with water to produce ionic species when they dissolve. When ethyl alcohol dissolves in water, the $C_2H_5OH$ molecules mix with water molecules, but no reaction to form ionic species occurs. Any solution containing molecules instead of ions will not conduct electric current readily, and the solute is called a **non-electrolyte.**

The HCl molecule is an example of a covalent molecule that reacts with water to form ions:

$$HCl(g) \xrightarrow{+ H_2O} H^+(aq) + Cl^-(aq)$$

Thus, even though HCl is not an ionic compound, it ionizes when it is dissolved in water and is classified as an electrolyte. The resulting aqueous solution of hydrogen chloride is called **hydrochloric acid.** Aqueous solutions of HF, HBr, and HI behave similarly and their aqueous solutions are called **hydrofluoric, hydrobromic, and hydroiodic acids,** respectively.

Any substance that dissolves in water and ionizes nearly completely to form $H^+(aq)$ is said to be a **strong acid.** Some substances undergo ionization only to a slight extent and exist in solution mainly as unionized molecules. As an example, HCN, hydrogen cyanide, produces only a small amount of $H^+(aq)$ when it dissolves. Compounds of this type are called **weak acids** and are poor electrolytes. As we discuss more chemistry, you will learn which substances are strong acids and which are weak ones.

Bases are substances that form $OH^-(aq)$ when dissolved in water. Strong bases ionize nearly completely to form $OH^-$, and are good electrolytes. Weak bases exist in solution mostly in the unionized form. Since only small amounts of $OH^-$ form when weak bases dissolve in water, they are poor electrolytes.

As we shall see in the next sections, you will need to know the solubilities of substances in water. The following rules simplify this task:

1. Most nitrates ($NO_3^-$), perchlorates ($ClO_4^-$) and chlorates ($ClO_3^-$) are soluble.*
2. Most chlorides are soluble; exceptions are AgCl, $Hg_2Cl_2$, and $PbCl_2$.

---

*If the solute will dissolve enough to form a 0.1 M solution, we shall call it a soluble compound.

3. Most bromides and iodides are soluble; exceptions are $Hg_2^{2+}$, $Ag^+$ and $Pb^{2+}$ compounds.

4. Most fluorides are soluble; exceptions are those of $Mg^{2+}$, $Ca^{2+}$, $Sr^{2+}$, $Ba^{2+}$, and $Pb^{2+}$.

5. Most sulfates ($SO_4^{2-}$) are soluble; exceptions are $Ca^{2+}$, $Sr^{2+}$, $Ba^{2+}$, $Hg_2^{2+}$, $Pb^{2+}$, and $Ag^+$ salts.

6. Most metallic hydroxides ($OH^-$) are only slightly soluble; soluble salts include those of the elements in the first column of the periodic table as well as $Ca^{2+}$, $Sr^{2+}$, and $Ra^{2+}$.

7. Most sulfides ($S^{2-}$), carbonates ($CO_3^{2-}$) and phosphates ($PO_4^{3-}$) are only slightly soluble; soluble salts include the compounds of the elements in the first column of the periodic table (except $Li^+$), as well as their $NH_4^+$ compounds.

8. Most alkali metal compounds and the ammonium compounds are soluble.

The determination of which substances are insoluble solids and which substances are weak or strong acids (or bases) is simplified by the use of common sense. For example, any substances that are normally ingested or applied to the body of a person or animal will not be a strong acid (or base). We know that acetic acid ($CH_3CO_2H$), the principal component of vinegar, must be a weak acid, as is $H_2CO_3$, the bubbly part of beer, champagne, and soda. You also know that iron oxide (rust) is insoluble in water. We are now in a position to do solution problems in terms of the cations and anions that exist in solution. For example, if a solution of $BaCl_2$ was 2.2 M in $BaCl_2$, the solution would be 2.2 M in $Ba^{2+}$(aq) and 4.4 M in $Cl^-$(aq) because

$$BaCl_2(s) \xrightarrow{+ H_2O} Ba^{2+}(aq) + 2Cl^-(aq)$$

## Sample Problem 5–12

A solution is made by dissolving 28.0 g of $Na_2SO_4$ in 350 ml of solution. Calculate (a) the molarity of $Na_2SO_4$, (b) the molarity of $SO_4^{2-}$, and (c) the molarity of $Na^+$.

## Solution

(a)
$$28.0 \text{ g } Na_2SO_4 \times \frac{1 \text{ mole}}{142.0 \text{ g}} = 0.197 \text{ mole}$$

$$\frac{? \text{ moles}}{\text{liter}} = \frac{0.197 \text{ mole}}{350. \text{ ml}} \times \frac{1000 \text{ ml}}{\text{liter}} = 0.563 \text{ M in } Na_2SO_4$$

(b) One mole of $SO_4^{2-}$ is formed in solution for every mole of $Na_2SO_4$ (1 $Na_2SO_4 \equiv 1$ $SO_4^{2-}$), so the solution is 0.563 M in $SO_4^{2-}$.

(c) Two moles of $Na^+$ form for every mole of $Na_2SO_4$ ($Na_2SO_4 \equiv 2 Na^+$) so the solution is 1.13 M in $Na^+$.

## 5–4   TOTAL AND NET IONIC EQUATIONS

In describing reactions that occur in solution, it is often desirable to write the equation for the reaction in ionic form, indicating the ionic species that actually exist in solution. For example, if we were describing the reaction of a solution of $BaCl_2$ with a solution of $Na_2SO_4$ to form the insoluble solid $BaSO_4$, we would write the total ionic equation as:

$$2Na^+(aq) + SO_4{}^{2-}(aq) + Ba^{2+}(aq) + 2Cl^-(aq) \rightarrow 2Na^+(aq) + 2Cl^-(aq) + BaSO_4(s)$$

In writing a total ionic equation for reactions in water:

1. We indicate all soluble ionic materials as ions, followed by (aq).
2. All substances that react with water to form ions are written as ions followed by (aq).
3. All insoluble ionic solids are written with (s) following their molecular formulas.
4. All soluble unionized species are written with their molecular formula followed by (aq).

In the above equation, we note that the sodium and chloride ions are unchanged and are present on both sides of the equation. Since they are not undergoing chemical reaction, they are sometimes referred to as **spectator ions**. If we subtract the spectator ions from each side of the equation, we then have a **net ionic equation**. The net ionic equation for the above reaction is:

$$Ba^{2+}(aq) + SO_4{}^{2-}(aq) \rightarrow BaSO_4(s)$$

The net ionic equation is a statement of the chemistry that occurred, namely, $Ba^{2+}(aq)$ reacted with $SO_4{}^{2-}(aq)$ to form solid $BaSO_4$.

### Sample Problem 5–13

Write the total and net ionic equations for the reaction of barium chloride with silver nitrate ($AgNO_3$) to form silver chloride and barium nitrate.

### Solution

The solubility rules tell us that $BaCl_2$, $AgNO_3$, and $Ba(NO_3)_2$ are all soluble ionic substances, while $AgCl$ is insoluble. The total ionic equation is:

$$Ba^{2+}(aq) + 2Cl^-(aq) + 2Ag^+(aq) + 2NO_3{}^-(aq) \rightarrow Ba^{2+}(aq) + 2NO_3{}^-(aq) + 2AgCl(s)$$

The net ionic equation is:

$$Ag^+(aq) + Cl^-(aq) \rightarrow AgCl(s)$$

Note that in writing the net ionic equation, we divided both sides by two to get the smallest whole number coefficients.

## Sample Problem 5–14

Write the total ionic equation and the net ionic equation for the following reaction, given that $NaCH_3CO_2$ is a soluble ionic salt.

$$NaOH + CH_3CO_2H \rightarrow NaCH_3CO_2 + H_2O$$

## Solution:

NaOH is a soluble strong base (that is, a source of $OH^-$) while acetic acid, $CH_3CO_2H$ (the principal component of vinegar), is a soluble poor electrolyte. The total ionic equation is:

$$Na^+(aq) + OH^-(aq) + CH_3CO_2H(aq) \rightarrow Na^+(aq) + CH_3CO_2^-(aq) + H_2O$$

The net ionic equation is:

$$OH^-(aq) + CH_3CO_2H(aq) \rightarrow H_2O + CH_3CO_2^-(aq)$$

## 5–5    DRIVING FORCES FOR CHEMICAL REACTION

From the previous section, we can see that whenever ions are mixed which can combine to form a poorly soluble solid, a reaction occurs. If a solid is poorly soluble, the solution cannot tolerate large concentrations of both cation and anion simultaneously. For example, when a solution with a large concentration of barium ion is mixed with another solution containing a large concentration of $SO_4^{2-}$, the combined solution cannot tolerate these large concentrations simultaneously and solid $BaSO_4$ will precipitate.

In addition to the precipitation reaction, ions will combine if a weak electrolyte or non-electrolyte can form. For example, if a solution with a large $H^+(aq)$ concentration is mixed with another containing a large $OH^-(aq)$ concentration, the mixed solution cannot simultaneously tolerate both ions in large concentration. The two ions will combine to form the weak electrolyte water, $H_2O$, according to the net ionic equation:

$$H^+(aq) + OH^-(aq) \rightarrow H_2O(l)$$

The same idea applies to other poor electrolytes or non-electrolytes. For example, large concentrations of $H^+(aq)$ and $CH_3CO_2^-(aq)$ cannot exist simultaneously in the same solution, for they will combine to form $CH_3CO_2H$. Thus, *the combination of ions to form poorly soluble solids or weak electrolytes provides a driving force for the occurrence of many chemical reactions*. The combination of an acid with a base is called a **neutralization reaction,** and the ionic solid formed by combining the spectator ions is called a **salt.**

Some reactions produce gaseous products, and this provides the driving force for the reaction. For example, HCN is a weak electrolyte and a gas that is only slightly soluble in water. If a solution with a large concentration of $CN^-(aq)$ is mixed with one containing a large concentration of $H^+(aq)$, the weak electrolyte HCN forms; when its solubility is exceeded, gas is evolved. Since HCN is a very toxic, odorless gas, $CN^-$ solution should never be acidified.

## TEST 5–2

A.  Indicate the principal species that exist in solution when about 0.01 mole of the following substances are added to a liter of water. (Refer to the solubility rules if necessary.)

   1. $Zn(NO_3)_2$          6. $C_2H_5OH$          11. $H_3BO_3$ (boric acid, an eye wash)

   2. $PbCl_2$              7. $NH_4Cl$            12. $CaF_2$

   3. $Sr(OH)_2$            8. $PbSO_4$            13. $Pb(NO_3)_2$

   4. $CH_3CO_2H$           9. $Na_2CO_3$          14. $Na_2SO_4$

   5. HBr                  10. CsOH               15. $(NH_4)_2SO_4$

B.  The bubbles in soda pop are composed of the slightly soluble gas $CO_2$. When dissolved in water, $CO_2$ reacts to form $H_2CO_3$:

$$H_2O(l) + CO_2(g) \longleftrightarrow H_2CO_3(aq)^*$$

   1.  Predict whether $H_2CO_3$ is a strong or weak acid.

---

*The double arrow is used when significant amounts of both products and reactants exist in solution.

2. Write the equation for the reaction that occurs, if any, when a solution containing $H^+(aq)$ is mixed with one containing $CO_3^{2-}(aq)$.

C. Write the total and net ionic equations for the reaction of excess hydrochloric acid with a solution of $Na_2CO_3$.

D. Indicate whether an aqueous solution can tolerate large concentrations of both of the following ions, and explain your answer:
   1. $Na^+$ and $Cl^-$

   2. $H^+$ and $OH^-$

   3. $CN^-$ and $H^+$

   4. $Ag^+$ and $Cl^-$

5. $H^+$ and $CO_3^{2-}$

# 5-6    PROBLEMS INVOLVING REACTIONS IN SOLUTION

By knowing the concentration of a solution, we can calculate the number of moles contained in a given volume. Thus, we can do the same type of mole-mole, mole-mass, and mass-mass problems for reactions between solutes in solution that we did earlier for the pure materials. A very important relation in this type of problem results from rearranging equation 5–1 to give:

$$\text{moles} = M \times \text{volume (liters)} \tag{5-5}$$

We will now work several sample problems which involve combination of the various problems involving mole relations with those involving molarity.

## Sample Problem 5–15

Given the following equation for a reaction, $NaOH(aq) + H_2SO_4(aq) \rightarrow H_2O(l) + Na_2SO_4(aq)$, what volume of a 0.750 M solution of $H_2SO_4$ is needed to react completely with 15.0 grams of NaOH?

## Solution

First balance the equation if necessary!

$$2\,NaOH + H_2SO_4 \rightarrow 2\,H_2O + Na_2SO_4$$

(a) We need to determine the number of moles in 15.0 g of NaOH.
(b) Then we determine the number of moles of $H_2SO_4$ needed for complete reaction.
(c) Finally, we determine the volume of 0.750 M $H_2SO_4$ needed to provide this number of moles of $H_2SO_4$.

(a)     $? \text{ moles NaOH} = 15.0 \text{ g NaOH} \times \dfrac{1 \text{ mole}}{40.0 \text{ g NaOH}} = 0.375 \text{ mole NaOH}$

(b) From the balanced equation:
$$2 \text{ moles NaOH} \equiv 1 \text{ mole } H_2SO_4$$

This gives us the needed conversion factor.

$$? \text{ moles } H_2SO_4 = 0.375 \text{ mole NaOH} \times \frac{1 \text{ mole } H_2SO_4}{2 \text{ moles NaOH}} = 0.188 \text{ mole } H_2SO_4$$

(c)  $? \text{ liters } H_2SO_4 \text{ solution} = 0.188 \cancel{\text{ mole } H_2SO_4} \times \dfrac{1 \text{ liter}}{0.750 \cancel{\text{ mole}}} = 0.251 \text{ liter}$

---

## Sample Problem 5–16

Given the following equation:

$$Na_2SO_4(aq) + Ba(NO_3)_2(aq) \rightarrow NaNO_3(aq) + BaSO_4(s)$$

how many ml of 0.555 M $Ba(NO_3)_2$ are needed to react completely with 275 ml of 0.322 M $Na_2SO_4$?

## Solution

First, balance the equation if necessary!

$$Na_2SO_4 + Ba(NO_3)_2 \rightarrow 2NaNO_3 + BaSO_4$$

We need to determine the number of moles of $Na_2SO_4$ in 275 ml of 0.322 M $Na_2SO_4$. The same number of moles of $Ba(NO_3)_2$ will be required for complete reaction. We complete the problem by determining the number of ml of 0.555 M $Ba(NO_3)_2$ solution that contain the needed number of moles.

$$? \text{ moles } Na_2SO_4 = 275 \cancel{\text{ ml}} \times \frac{1 \cancel{\text{ liter}}}{1000 \cancel{\text{ ml}}} \times \frac{0.322 \text{ mole } Na_2SO_4}{1 \cancel{\text{ liter}}} = 0.0886 \text{ mole } Na_2SO_4$$

From the balanced equation:

$$1 \text{ mole } Na_2SO_4 \equiv 1 \text{ mole } Ba(NO_3)_2$$

$$\text{so } 0.0886 \text{ mole } Na_2SO_4 \equiv 0.0886 \text{ mole } Ba(NO_3)_2$$

$$? \text{ ml } Ba(NO_3)_2 = 0.0886 \cancel{\text{ mole } Ba(NO_3)_2} \times \frac{1 \cancel{\text{ liter}}}{0.555 \cancel{\text{ mole } Ba(NO_3)_2}} \times \frac{1000 \text{ ml}}{\cancel{\text{ liter}}} = 160 \text{ ml}$$

That is, 160 ml of the 0.555 M $Ba(NO_3)_2$ are needed.

---

Problems of this type can also be solved to calculate the molarity of a solution.

### Sample Problem 5–17

Given the following equation:

$$BaCl_2(aq) + 2\,AgNO_3 \rightarrow Ba(NO_3)_2 + 2\,AgCl(s)$$

What is the molarity of a $AgNO_3$ solution, 85.0 ml of which are required to react completely with 39.5 ml of 0.284 M $BaCl_2$ solution?

### Solution

Given volume and molarity of the $BaCl_2$ solution, we can calculate the number of moles of $BaCl_2$. Twice as many moles of $AgNO_3$ are needed to react completely, and they are contained in 85.0 ml of solution. The molarity can be calculated from this information as follows:

$$? \text{ moles } BaCl_2 = \frac{0.284 \text{ mole}}{1 \text{ liter}} \times 0.0395 \text{ liter} = 0.0112 \text{ mole } BaCl_2$$

From the equation,

$$1 \text{ mole } BaCl_2 \equiv 2 \text{ moles } AgNO_3$$

$$\text{so } 0.0112 \text{ mole } BaCl_2 \equiv 0.0224 \text{ mole } AgNO_3$$

$$? \frac{\text{moles } AgNO_3}{\text{liter}} = \frac{0.0224 \text{ mole } AgNO_3}{85 \text{ ml}} \times \frac{1000 \text{ ml}}{1 \text{ liter}} = \frac{0.264 \text{ moles } AgNO_3}{\text{liter}}$$

In the laboratory, the amount of reactant needed to completely react with another substance is determined by carrying out a **titration.** In this procedure, an acid is slowly added to a solution of the base or vice versa. The exact quantities of solution required for complete reaction can be measured by using burettes. An indicator is used to visually indicate when exact quantities have been added. This **indicator** is a compound that changes color when all of the acid or base in the solution is used up.

## 5–7   EQUIVALENTS, EQUIVALENT WEIGHTS, AND NORMALITY*

If a substance is an acid, we are likely to be concerned with its reactions with bases and vice versa. In particular, the mass of acid that will react exactly with a mole of base is an important quantity. We may not care if the reaction is:

---

*If your instructor omits this topic, this section and the corresponding problems at the end of this chapter can be omitted without any loss in continuity.

$$C_3H_4O_2 + OH^- \rightarrow C_3H_3O_2^- + H_2O \text{ or}$$

$$C_6H_8O_4 + 2OH^- \rightarrow C_6H_6O_4^{2-} + 2H_2O \text{ or even}$$

$$C_9H_{12}O_6 + 3OH^- \rightarrow C_9H_9O_6^{3-} + 3H_2O.$$

Regardless of which reaction is occurring, the same number of grams of acid will react with one mole of $OH^-$ ion. If we did not know the molecular weight of the acid, we could not calculate the mass of a mole or the molarity of solutions. However, we could calculate the mass of acid that will furnish one mole of $H^+$ in a chemical reaction with a base. In the above series of reactions, 72.1 grams of acid will furnish one mole of $H^+$ regardless of whether the formula is $C_3H_4O_2$, $C_6H_8O_4$, or $C_9H_{12}O_6$. A quantity of substance that furnishes one mole of protons or one mole of hydroxide ions in a chemical reaction is called an **equivalent.** If the molecular weight is known, the **equivalent weight** of a substance can be calculated by dividing the molecular weight by the number of moles of $H^+$ or $OH^-$ ions furnished by a mole of material. A **gram equivalent weight** (GEW) is the equivalent weight expressed in grams. With the mass of one equivalent being given by the GEW, we can write:

$$GEW = 1 \text{ equivalent} \qquad \textbf{(5–6)}$$

$$\frac{GEW}{1 \text{ equivalent}} = 1 \qquad \textbf{(5–7)}$$

This factor gives the number of grams per equivalent and can be multiplied by any number of equivalents to give their mass. The reciprocal gives the number of equivalents in a gram and can be multiplied by any number of grams to give the number of equivalents in a given mass of material.

The concentration of a solution can be expressed in terms of equivalents. The term **normality** is defined as

$$\text{normality (N)} = \frac{\text{number of equivalents}}{\text{volume of solution (liters)}} \qquad \textbf{(5–8)}$$

Note the analogy between these definitions and formulas and those involving moles and molarity. We shall now work through a sample problem that illustrates the convenience of these definitions.

## Sample Problem 5–18

It is found that 7.34 grams of an acid react completely with 31.7 ml of 0.618 M NaOH. Calculate the equivalent weight.

## Solution

We can calculate the number of moles of hydroxide ion in 31.7 ml of the sodium hydroxide solution. Since one mole of $OH^-$ combines with one mole of $H^+$, the same number of moles of $H^+$ must be present in the 7.34 grams of acid as in 31.7 ml of 0.618 M NaOH. The mass of acid needed to furnish one mole of protons can be calculated. This is the equivalent weight.

$$\text{? moles NaOH} = 31.7 \cancel{\text{ml}} \times \frac{1 \cancel{\text{liter}}}{1000 \cancel{\text{ml}}} \times \frac{0.618 \text{ mole}}{\cancel{\text{liter}}} = 0.0196 \text{ mole NaOH}$$

$$0.0196 \text{ moles NaOH} \equiv 0.0196 \text{ moles } H^+$$

$$\frac{\text{? g acid}}{\text{mole } H^+} = \frac{\text{? g acid}}{\text{equivalent}} = \frac{7.34 \text{ g acid}}{0.0196 \text{ mole } H^+} = 374 \text{ g/equivalent}$$

$$\text{equivalent weight} = 374 \text{ amu}$$

## Sample Problem 5–19

Given that the molecular formula of the compound described in problem 5–18 is $H_4X_2$ with four reactive protons in the molecule.

(a) what is the molecular weight?
(b) what is the normality of a solution containing 39.9 g in 450 ml of solution?
(c) what is the molarity of a solution containing 39.9 g in 450 ml of solution?

## Solution

(a) From problem 5–18 we know that 374 g provide one mole of protons. Therefore, four protons would be provided by $4 \times 374$ g or 1496 grams. The molecular weight is thus 1,496 amu.

(b)
$$39.9 \cancel{\text{g}} \times \frac{1 \text{ equivalent}}{374 \cancel{\text{g}}} = 0.107 \text{ equivalent}$$

$$\frac{0.107 \text{ equivalent}}{450 \cancel{\text{ml}}} \times \frac{1000 \cancel{\text{ml}}}{1 \text{ liter}} = 0.238 \text{ N}$$

(c)
$$\frac{39.9 \cancel{\text{g}}}{1496 \cancel{\text{g}} \text{ mole}^{-1}} = 0.0267 \text{ mole}$$

$$\frac{0.0267 \text{ mole}}{450 \cancel{\text{ml}}} \times \frac{1000 \cancel{\text{ml}}}{1 \text{ liter}} = 0.0593 \text{ M}$$

# Exercises

### Molarity

1.  Indicate how you would prepare 350. ml of a 0.654 M solution of $Ba(OH)_2$.

2.  How many grams of $Ca(NO_3)_2$ must be added to 684 ml of solution to prepare a 0.166 M solution?

3.  What is the molarity of a solution made by adding 18.5 g of NaOH to 675 ml of solution?

4.  A solution is found to contain 11.2 g of glucose, $C_6H_{12}O_6$, in 515 ml of solution. What is the molarity of this solution?

5.  What must the volume be if 11.5 g of NaOH are dissolved to form a 0.348 M solution?

6.  How many ml of a 1.33 M NaOH solution must be taken to obtain 29.5 g of NaOH?

7.  How many ml of a 1.33 M solution must be taken to obtain 0.750 mole?

8.  How many moles are there in 583 ml of a 0.375 M solution?

9.  A solution is prepared by dissolving 29.4 g of $H_2SO_4$ in 433 ml of solution. Calculate:
    (a) the molarity of the solution;
    (b) the number of moles in 75.0 ml of this solution;
    (c) the volume of solution needed to furnish 0.459 mole of $H_2SO_4$.

10. What is the molarity of the solution obtained by diluting 75.0 ml of 3.00 M $H_2SO_4$ to 125 ml?

11. How would you prepare 325 ml of 0.575 M $H_2SO_4$ from a 2.00 M $H_2SO_4$ solution?

12. One prepares 750 ml of a 0.555 M solution by diluting 36.6 ml of a more concentrated solution. What is the molarity of the more concentrated solution?

13. If 56.3 ml of a 0.666 M solution is diluted to 75.0 ml, what is the molarity of the resulting solution?

14. What is the molarity of a solution if dilution of 83.7 ml of it to 125 ml produces a 0.284 M solution?

**Molality and Other Concentration Units**

15. What is the molality of a solution prepared by dissolving 27.4 g of $C_2H_5OH$ in 536 g of water?

16. How many grams of water should be added to a 0.444 m solution in 69.9 g of water to convert it to a 0.333 m solution?

17. How many grams of glucose ($C_6H_{12}O_6$; MW = 180.2) must be added to 52.5 g of water to form a 0.364 m solution?

18. It is found that 1000. g of an air sample contained $1.0 \times 10^{-4}$ g of $SO_2$. What is the concentration of $SO_2$ in ppm?

19. A solution is made by dissolving 12.3 g of glucose ($C_6H_{12}O_6$) and 15.5 g of $C_2H_5OH$ in 48.5 g of water. Calculate:
    (a) the mole fraction of glucose;
    (b) the mole fraction of $C_2H_5OH$.

20. A fish is reported to contain 3.3 ppm of mercury. How much fish would have to be eaten to ingest $3.9 \times 10^{-3}$ g of mercury?

**Total and Net Ionic Equations**

21. For the following problems, you should write the balanced total ionic equation, the balanced net ionic equation, and the solubility rule which indicates if the substance is soluble. All equations refer to reactions in aqueous solution.
    (a) $ZnCl_2 + H_2S \rightarrow ZnS + HCl$ ($H_2S$ is a weak acid.)
    (b) $AgNO_3 + HBr \rightarrow AgBr + HNO_3$
    (c) $Ba(OH)_2 + HCl \rightarrow H_2O + BaCl_2$
    (d) $NaCH_3CO_2 + HBr \rightarrow NaBr + CH_3CO_2H$
    (e) $HCN + NaOH \rightarrow H_2O + NaCN$
    (f) $Pb(NO_3)_2 + NaCl \rightarrow NaNO_3 + PbCl_2$
    (g) $Cu + AgNO_3 \rightarrow Cu(NO_3)_2 + Ag$
    (h) $Mg(NO_3)_2 + KOH \rightarrow Mg(OH)_2 + KNO_3$
    (i) $Pb(NO_3)_2 + Na_2SO_4 \rightarrow PbSO_4 + NaNO_3$
    (j) $Mg(OH)_2 + HCl \rightarrow MgCl_2 + H_2O$
    (k) $(NH_4)_2CO_3 + Ba(NO_3)_2 \rightarrow BaCO_3 + NH_4NO_3$
    (l) $K_2CO_3 + HCl \rightarrow H_2O + CO_2 + KCl$

22. Give examples of three strong acids and three weak acids for reactions in water. Write equations for the reactions that occur when a strong acid and a weak acid are added to water.

23. Write total ionic equations for the reaction of (a) a strong acid and (b) a weak acid with a strong base in water.

24. Indicate whether an aqueous solution can tolerate large concentrations of both of the following ions, and explain your answer:

(a) $H^+$ and $CH_3CO_2^-$
(b) $Ba^{2+}$ and $SO_4^{2-}$
(c) $Pb^{2+}$ and $NO_3^-$
(d) $Pb^{2+}$ and $Cl^-$
(e) $NH_4^+$ and $SO_4^{2-}$
(f) $H^+$ and $Cl^-$
(g) $Na^+$ and $OH^-$

### Problems Involving Reactions in Solution

25. Given the equation:
$$2\ NaCl(aq)\ +\ Pb(NO_3)_2(aq)\ \rightarrow\ PbCl_2(s)\ +\ 2NaNO_3(aq)$$
    (a) How many ml of 0.444 M NaCl solution are needed to react completely with 0.374 mole of $Pb(NO_3)_2$?
    (b) How many ml of a 0.444 M NaCl solution are needed to react completely with 75.0 ml of a 0.284 M $Pb(NO_3)_2$ solution?

26. It is found that 37.5 ml of a 0.273 M $H_2SO_4$ solution react completely with 78.9 ml of a NaOH solution. What is the molarity of the NaOH solution?

27. Given the following equation:
$$Zn(s)\ +\ 2HCl(aq) \rightarrow ZnCl_2(aq)\ +\ H_2(g)$$
    (a) How many ml of 0.336 M HCl solution are needed to react completely with 6.57 g of zinc?
    (b) If 44.6 ml of an HCl solution react completely with 5.55 g of Zn, what is the molarity of this solution?

28. A 250. ml sample of vinegar (containing $CH_3CO_2H$) requires 75.0 ml of a 0.333 M solution of NaOH to react completely. What is the molarity of acetic acid in the vinegar solution?

29. If 250. ml of 0.112 M $Ba(OH)_2$ solution are added to 250. ml of 0.100 M HCl solution, what will be the resulting concentrations of all the ions in solution?

### Equivalents and Equivalent Weights

30. A 0.511 g sample of a solid acid requires 41.1 ml of a 0.103 M NaOH solution for complete reaction.
    (a) Calculate the equivalent weight of the acid.
    (b) If the acid contained three $H^+$ for each molecule reacted, what would its molecular weight be?
    (c) Calculate the normality of a solution made by dissolving 37.9 g of the acid in 345 ml of solution.

31. If 48.2 ml of 0.612 N HCl solution are required to neutralize 0.859 g of a solid base, what is the equivalent weight of the base?

32. Compare the number of moles of HCl and $H_2SO_4$ that would be needed to prepare 75.0 ml of a solution that is 0.227 N.

33. What is the normality of a $Ba(OH)_2$ solution if 33.6 ml require 71.2 ml of 0.472 M HCl for complete reaction?

34. If the equivalent weight of a basic substance is 258,
    (a) How many ml of 0.351 M $H_2SO_4$ are needed for complete reaction of 25.8 g?
    (b) How many ml of 0.351 N $H_2SO_4$ are needed for complete reaction of 25.8 g?

**Verbalizing General Concepts**
35. Answer each of the following in your own words:
    (a) Distinguish the terms solvent, solute and solution.
    (b) Why is a solution a homogeneous mixture?
    (c) Elaborate on the essential differences between molarity and molality, and describe cases where their magnitudes would be different for the same solution.
    (d) Define the concentration unit parts per million, ppm.
    (e) Define mole fraction.
    (f) Write general statements about what happens when ionic and covalent substances dissolve in water.
    (g) Describe what is meant by the terms strong acid or base and weak acid or base, when applied to substances dissolved in water.
    (h) Define the terms strong and weak (poor) electrolyte, and indicate how they are related to strong and weak acids or bases.
    (i) List some common halides that are expected to be insoluble.
    (j) List eight soluble hydroxides.
    (k) Explain why the molarity of $ClO_3^-$ is twice that of $Ba^{2+}$ in a solution of $Ba(ClO_3)_2$.
    (l) Describe how to write a total ionic equation and a net ionic equation.
    (m) List three driving forces that cause reactions to go nearly to completion.
    (n) What is the similarity between the problems done in the section on Problems Involving Reaction in Solution (5–6) and those done in Chapter 3?
    (o) Indicate one reason for introducing the concept of equivalents.

**Challenging Problems**
36. An aqueous solution contains 25.0 g of glucose, $C_6H_{12}O_6$, in 450. ml of solution. The density of this solution is 1.03 g/ml. Calculate:
    (a) the molarity of the glucose;
    (b) the molality of the glucose;
    (c) the mole fraction of the glucose.

37. An aqueous solution is prepared by mixing 38 g of alcohol ($C_2H_5OH$; density = 0.80 g/ml) with 250. ml of water (density = 1.0 g/ml; assume that volumes are additive). Calculate:

  (a) the molarity of the alcohol;
  (b) the molality of the alcohol;
  (c) the mole fraction of alcohol.

38.  Derive a formula equating moles NaOH and moles $H_2SO_4$ for the reaction of $H_2SO_4$ with NaOH in solution when:
  (a) all concentrations are expressed in molarity units;
  *(b) all concentrations are expressed in normality units.

**Multiple Choice Questions**

39.  How many g of NaOH are required to make 200. ml of 0.40 M NaOH?
  (a) 40 g, (b) 8.0 g, (c) 3.2 g, (d) 32 g, (e) none of these

40.  The laboratory has 6.00 M $H_2SO_4$ solution. How much of this must be used to make 500. ml of 0.750 M solution?
  (a) 250 ml, (b) 125 ml, (c) 62.5 ml, (d) 36.2 ml, (e) none of these

41.  What weight of $Na_2SO_4 \cdot 10H_2O$ is required to prepare 500. ml of 0.40 M $Na_2SO_4$ solution?
  (a) 10 g, (b) 20 g, (c) 56 g, (d) 64 g, (e) none of these

42.  The volume of solution of a given molarity needed to give a specified number of moles of solute is obtained by:
  (a) multiplying moles by molarity, (b) dividing moles by molarity, (c) dividing molarity by moles, (d) converting moles to grams and dividing by density, (e) cannot be determined unless we are given the molality.

43.  If 0.675 moles of solute are present in 500. ml of solution, the molarity is:
  (a) $1.35 \times 10^{-3}$, (b) 1.35, (c) 0.338, (d) 338, (e) none of these

44.  A 375 ml sample of a 0.0125 M solution contains the following number of moles:
  (a) 0.0125, (b) 4.69, (c) 30.0,(d) 2.67, (e) none of these

45.  A 250. ml sample of a 0.111 M $H_2SO_4$ solution is diluted to 375 ml. The final molarity is:
  (a) 0.0740, (b) 0.0278, (c) 27.8, (d) 74.0, (e) none of these

46.  If analysis shows that 50,000 grams of water contain 1.00 gram of DDT, what is the concentration of DDT in ppm?
  (a) 1.00, (b) 50,000, (c) 200, (d) 20.0, (e) the formula of DDT must be given to answer this question.

---

*Optional. Do only if section 5–7 is covered.

47. A solution is made by dissolving 0.127 mole of $C_6H_{12}O_6$ and 0.123 mole of NaCl in 0.500 mole of water. The mole fraction of $C_6H_{12}O_6$ is:
(a) 0.127, (b) 0.508, (c) 0.250, (d) 0.254, (e) none of these to within 0.001

48. Which of the following best answers the question, "What ions cannot exist simultaneously in large concentration in aqueous solution?"
(a) $H^+$ and $Cl^-$, (b) $H^+$ and $CH_3CO_2^-$, (c) $Ag^+$ and $Cl^-$, (d) $Ca^{2+}$ and $Cl^-$, (e) two of the above

49. In writing the total ionic equation, which of the following would not be written as ionic species?
(a) $H_2SO_4$, (b) $Ba(NO_3)_2$, (c) $BaSO_4$, (d) $HNO_3$, (e) two of the above

50. Which of the following is *correct*?
(a) Most nitrates are insoluble. (b) Most chlorides are insoluble. (c) Most sulfides are insoluble. (d) All of the above. (e) None of the above.

51. If a 5.000 g sample of an unknown chloride can be titrated with 70.90 ml of 0.2010 M $AgNO_3$, what is the percentage of chloride in the sample?
(a) 50.52%, (b) 10.10%, (c) 1.425%, (d) 20.20%, (e) none of these within 0.1%

52. How many ml of 0.500 M $Ba(OH)_2$ solution are needed to react completely with 75.0 ml of 0.250 M $HNO_3$ solution?
(a) 75.0 ml, (b) 37.5 ml, (c) 18.8 ml, (d) 9.4 ml, (e) these substances do not react.

53. What is the molarity of an HCl solution if it takes 22.50 ml of a 0.535 M NaOH solution to react completely with 36.30 ml of the acid solution?
(a) 0.866 M, (b) 0.0100 M, (c) 0.332 M, (d) 0.120 M, (e) none of these within 0.01 M.

54. What is the $OH^-$ concentration after 50.00 ml of 0.100 M $HNO_3$ and 50.10 ml of 0.100 M NaOH solution have been mixed?
(a) $1.0 \times 10^{-4}$ M, (b) $2.0 \times 10^{-12}$ M, (c) $1.0 \times 10^{-10}$ M, (d) $5.0 \times 10^{-3}$ M, (e) none of these

55. How many milliliters of a 0.250 M solution of sodium hydroxide are needed to react completely with 50.0 ml of 0.400 M sulfuric acid?
(a) 40.0 ml, (b) 80.0 ml, (c) 160. ml, (d) 240. ml, (e) none of these

56. A 500. ml solution of 6.0 M $H_2SO_4$ will require for complete reaction 200. ml of:

(a) 3.0 M NaOH, (b) 6.0 M NaOH
(c) 12 M NaOH, (d) two of the above, (e) none of the above

57. A laboratory has $6.00M$ $H_2SO_4$ solution. What volume of this solution must be used to make $250.ml$ of a $0.250M$ solution?
(a) 5.20ml, (b) 10.4ml, (c) 20,8ml, (d) 41.7ml, (e) 375ml

58. How many milliliters of a $0.750M$ solution of sodium hydroxide are required to react completely with 50.0ml of $0.500M$ sulfuric acid?
(a) 50.0ml, (b) 66.7ml, (c) 25.0ml, (d) 33.3ml, (e) none of the above

59. For the reaction in aqueous solution

$$(NH_4)_2CO_3 + Ba(NO_3)_2 \rightarrow BaCO_3 + NH_4NO_3$$

the balanced net ionic equation would be:
(a) $2(NH_4)_2CO_3 + 2Ba(NO_3)_2 \rightarrow 2BaCO_3 + 2NH_4NO_3$
(b) $Ba^{2+} + CO_3^{2-} \rightarrow BaCO_3(s)$
(c) $Ba^{2+} + 2NO_3^- \rightarrow Ba(NO_3)_2(s)$
(d) $NH_4^+ + NO_3^- \rightarrow NH_4NO_3(s)$
(e) $(NH_4)_2CO_3 + Ba(NO_3)_2 \rightarrow BaCO_3 + 2NH_4NO_3$

60. Which of the following statements is correct?
(a) Most nitrates are insoluble.
(b) Most chlorides are insoluble.
(c) Most sulfates are soluble.
(d) Most ammonium compounds are insoluble.
(e) None of the above is correct.

61. If 50.0ml of $0.750M$ NaOH is added to a 200. ml solution of $0.200M$ $HNO_3$, what is the $H^+$ concentration of the resulting solution?
(a) $1.25 \times 10^{-2}M$          (d) $5.00 \times 10^{-2}M$
(b) $1.00 \times 10^{-2}M$          (e) $2.50 \times 10^{-3}M$
(c) $2.50 \times 10^{-2}M$

62. A 5.00 g sample of acid requires 15.0 ml of a 0.300 M solution of $Ba(OH)_2$ for complete reaction. What is the equivalent weight of the acid?
(a) 278, (b) 556, (c) $1.01 \times 10^3$, (d) $2.02 \times 10^3$, (e) none of the above

63. A solution that is 0.50 N in acid contains:
(a) 0.50 equivalent/liter, (b) 0.50 moles of $H^+$/liter, (c) 0.50 moles of the acid/liter, (d) all of the preceding, (e) two of the preceding.

# 6

# INTRODUCTORY CONSIDERATIONS OF ENERGY

## Chapter Objectives

### (Begin each of the following with "You should master . . .")

1. the definitions of kinetic and potential energy (memorize equation 6–1).
2. the First Law of Thermodynamics.
3. the definitions of a joule and a calorie.
4. the names of the processes for changes of state.
5. the definitions of exothermic process, endothermic process, enthalpy content, enthalpy change, enthalpy diagram, chemical cycle, enthalpy of formation, and enthalpy of dissociation.
6. the use of equation 6–5 and the construction of enthalpy diagrams to describe processes.
7. Hess' law type problems.

The problems that we shall cover in this chapter involve very simple mathematical operations. The major task is to remember definitions and conventions. The concepts covered here will be extended in Problem Solving in General Chemistry II.

**Energy** exists in a variety of forms, such as heat, light, electrical energy, mechanical energy, kinetic energy, and chemical energy. We shall define these forms as we encounter them. An important underlying principle for all of the problems in this chapter is contained in the **First Law of Thermodynamics** which is a statement of the Law of Conservation of Energy. The law states that although energy can be converted from one form to another and transferred from one body to another, *energy cannot be created or destroyed.* What then do we mean when we say our energy supply is being depleted needlessly by "gas guzzling" automobiles? Gasoline contains a large amount of **potential energy,** that is, energy stored in a body as a consequence of its position or composition. When gasoline is burned completely, it is converted into $CO_2$, $H_2O$ and heat. The energy content of the $CO_2$, water, and heat is equal to the energy content of the gasoline, as required by the First Law of Thermodynamics. However, upon combustion the heat is lost to the surroundings and not easily recovered or concentrated again for use. This is a manifestation of the Second Law, covered in volume II. However, in this way, our supply of fuel is being lost as a usable source of energy.

## 6-1    ENERGY UNITS

The unit traditionally used to describe the change in energy that occurs in a chemical reaction is the calorie. A **calorie** is the amount of energy needed to raise the temperature of one gram of water from 14.5°C to 15.5°C. In the more recent SI (International System) units, the recommended unit of energy is the joule, given the symbol J. A joule can be defined in terms of **kinetic energy,** that is, the energy a body possesses by virtue of its motion. A **joule** is the kinetic energy possessed by a mass of 2 kg moving at a velocity of 1 meter per second. There is a logical basis for this definition which is easy to remember. The kinetic energy of a substance is given by:

$$E_k = (\tfrac{1}{2})\, mv^2 \qquad\qquad\qquad \text{(6–1)}$$

where $E_k$ is the kinetic energy, $m$ the mass of the object, and $v$ the velocity of the object. Now if we substitute the definition of a joule into equation 6–1, we obtain

$$E_k = (\tfrac{1}{2})\,(2\ \text{kg})\,(1\ \text{m}^2/\text{sec}^2) = \frac{1\ \text{kg m}^2}{\text{sec}^2} = 1\ \text{joule}$$

Thus, the definition of a joule is easily recalled by remembering the fundamental equation 6–1. The joule can also be used to describe a quantity of heat because energy can be converted into various forms. One calorie is the same amount of energy as 4.184 joules:

$$1\ \text{calorie} = 4.184\ \text{J} \qquad\qquad\qquad \text{(6–2)}$$

We shall use joules and kilojoules, kJ, as the energy units in this chapter.

The joule is a logical choice for the energy unit in the SI system because it is readily derived from the base units and from the fact that energy is force acting through a distance. Having previously defined a force of one newton as that force necessary to accelerate one kg by one meter per sec², energy (which is force times distance in meters) is given by

energy = force × distance = 1 kg m sec$^{-2}$ × 1 m = 1 kg m² sec$^{-2}$ = 1 joule

## 6-2    ENERGIES ACCOMPANYING CHANGES OF STATE

Matter can exist in the gaseous, liquid, or solid state. Upon heating, many solid substances can be converted into liquids and many liquids can be converted into gases by additional heating. The names of the conversions between the states of matter are indicated in Fig. 6-1. Since condensation is used to describe two different processes, additional descriptive terms such as gas to liquid or gas to solid must be used.

The amount of heat required to bring about the various changes of state depends upon the amount of material. It is usual to select a mole of material, so that the amount of heat required to bring about a change of state for various substances can be compared. For

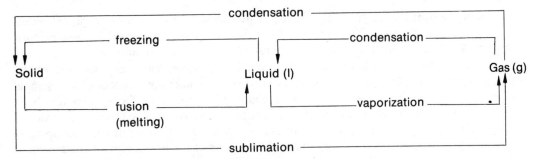

**Figure 6–1**    Definition of terms for various changes of state.

example, the heat of fusion listed in Table 6–1 indicates the heat required to melt a mole of substance. Table 6-1 also contains values for the vaporization process, that is, the heat required to vaporize a mole of substance. When the change of state is carried out at constant pressure, the energy associated with the process is called an **enthalpy change.**

**Table 6-1        Some Representative Enthalpies of Fusion (Melting) and Vaporization**

| Substance | $\Delta H_{fus}$ (kJ mole$^{-1}$) | $\Delta H_{vap}$ (kJ mole$^{-1}$) |
|---|---|---|
| Benzene | 10.7 | 34.6 |
| Mercury | 2.3 | 56.5 |
| Naphthalene | 19.3 | 40.6 |
| Sodium chloride | 28.9 | 255. |
| Water | 6.0 | 43.9 |

Each enthalpy in Table 6-1 correspond to an energy difference between two states, each of which has an **enthalpy content.** We use the symbol $\Delta$ to indicate that the quantity given refers to the *difference* between the enthalpy content of the final, $H_{final}$, and initial, $H_{initial}$, states. That is,

$$\Delta H = H_{final} - H_{initial}$$

The $\Delta H_{fus}$ value refers to the difference between the enthalpy contents, $H$, of the solid and liquid ($\Delta H_{fusion} = H_{liquid} - H_{solid}$), while $\Delta H_{vap}$ indicates the difference between the enthalpy contents of the liquid and gas ($\Delta H_{vap} = H_{gas} - H_{liquid}$). The relationship between $H$ values and $\Delta H$ is shown in Fig. 6–2. The values of the enthalpy content usually are not

Increasing Potential Energy→

$H$ (liquid)

$$\Delta H_{fus} = H_1 - H_s$$

$H$ (solid)

**Figure 6–2**    A potential energy diagram for the fusion process.

known and cannot be measured. However, it is the enthalpy difference, for example, the $\Delta H_{fus}$, that can be measured and will interest us. The value of the enthalpy is independent of temperature over moderately large temperature changes. For accurate work, the value is measured and reported at the temperature of the change and corrected for temperature changes. We shall assume the value is temperature-independent in our work.

Processes that absorb heat (like $\Delta H_{vap}$) are called **endothermic,** and the sign of the enthalpy change for this type of process is positive. The enthalpy content of the sample has been increased by adding heat, and the potential energy of the system has been increased. We would have to add 6.0 kJ of heat to a mole of ice at 0°C to make water at 0°C, so $\Delta H_{fus} = 6.0$ kJ mole$^{-1}$. In order to convert water at 0°C to ice at 0°C, the first law of thermodynamics requires that we remove 6.0 kJ per mole. The enthalpy of condensation (l to s) $\Delta H_{l-s}$ is negative. The freezing process (liquid to solid) gives off heat; that is, heat must be taken out of the system, and this process is **exothermic.**

### TEST 6–1

A.  Write the equation relating mass, $m$, and velocity, $v$, to kinetic energy, $E_k$.

B.  If the velocity of a substance is doubled, what happens to the kinetic energy?

C.  Upon reading an article, you find that the enthalpy of a process is 88.6 kcal mole$^{-1}$. Convert this to the proper SI unit.

D.  We shall next answer a series of questions about the sublimation process.
    1. Describe the process involved in sublimation.

2. Would the gas or solid have the higher potential energy?

3. Would the gas or solid have the higher enthalpy content?

4. What is the sign of $\Delta H$ for the sublimation process, and is this an exothermic or endothermic process?

5. What is the sign of $\Delta H$ for condensation (g to s), and is this endothermic or exothermic?

In addition to the solid, liquid, and gaseous states that exist at the melting and boiling points, many other states exist, each of which is characterized by a certain set of properties. For example, water at 20° and at 80° represents two different states with different enthalpy contents. We describe characteristic properties of a state that depend exclusively on the state and not on the past history of the sample as **state functions.** The enthalpy content and the enthalpy change, $\Delta H$, are state functions. The enthalpy content of water at 80°C, for example, is the same whether the water was obtained at these conditions by condensing water vapor, melting ice, or making the sample from dihydrogen ($H_2$) and dioxygen ($O_2$).

Since $\Delta H$ is a state function, the $\Delta H_{subl}$ of a material is equal to the sum of the heat of fusion plus the heat of vaporization. The enthalpy change is the same whether we go directly from the solid to the gaseous state or whether we first melt the solid to the liquid and then vaporize the liquid to the gas. The enthalpy change is independent of the path. Thus, we can write:

$$\Delta H_{subl} = \Delta H_{fus} + \Delta H_{vap} \qquad \text{(6-3)}$$

The two paths are illustrated in Fig. 6–3a. There, one path is shown with a heavy arrow and the other with light arrows. We shall use diagrams of this type to illustrate two equivalent paths for a process. The enthalpy equivalence of the two paths is shown in Fig. 6-3b with an enthalpy diagram.

We can illustrate these ideas with sample problem 6–1.

## Sample Problem 6–1

Using the data in Table 6–1, calculate the enthalpy of sublimation of solid sodium chloride.

## Solution

The desired process is the enthalpy change for $NaCl(s) \rightarrow NaCl(g)$, and we are given $NaCl(s) \rightarrow NaCl(l)$ and $NaCl(l) \rightarrow NaCl(g)$. We can obtain the desired equation by adding the latter two.

$$\Delta H_{fus} \equiv NaCl(s) \rightarrow NaCl(l); \Delta H = 28.9 \text{ kJ mole}^{-1}$$
$$\Delta H_{vap} \equiv NaCl(l) \rightarrow NaCl(g); \Delta H = 255 \text{ kJ mole}^{-1}$$
$$\overline{\Delta H_{subl} \equiv NaCl(s) \rightarrow NaCl(g); \Delta H = 284 \text{ kJ mole}^{-1}}$$

Upon addition of the equations, $NaCl(l)$ appears on both sides and cancels.

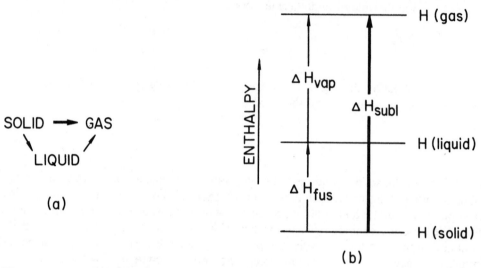

**Figure 6–3**    (a) Two paths for converting a solid to a gas; (b) an enthalpy diagram for two paths for converting a solid to a gas.

## 6–3    ENERGY CHANGES ACCOMPANYING CHEMICAL REACTIONS

Chemical reactions occur with the evolution or absorption of energy. For example, when glucose is burned, heat is evolved:

$$C_6H_{12}O_6(s) + 6O_2(g) \rightarrow 6CO_2(g) + 6H_2O(l); \Delta H = -2.82 \times 10^3 \text{ kJ} \quad \textbf{(6–4)}$$

The quantity of heat evolved refers to a mole interpretation of the equation as written; that is, this equation refers to the combustion of one mole of glucose (the coefficient of glucose in this equation is one) which evolves $2.82 \times 10^3$ kJ of heat. According to the first law of thermodynamics, producing a mole of glucose by the reverse reaction, which is the process of **photosynthesis,** requires that a plant absorb $2.82 \times 10^3$ kJ of energy from the sun. *The enthalpy for a reverse reaction is always equal in magnitude and opposite in sign to that of the forward reaction.*

These processes can be described by an enthalpy diagram by calling the reactants our initial state, and calling the products our final state. Since heat is given off in the combustion of glucose, the enthalpy content (or the potential energy) of glucose must be higher than that of $CO_2$ and $H_2O$. Recalling our convention for $\Delta$, we write

$$\Delta H = \Sigma H \text{ (products)} - \Sigma H \text{ (reactants)} = \Sigma H_p - \Sigma H_r \qquad (6\text{–}5)$$

where $\Sigma$ indicates that the enthalpy content is summed over all the compounds involved; for example, in equation 6-4, $\Sigma H_p = 6H(CO_2) + 6H(H_2O)$. The enthalpy diagram for the combustion of glucose is illustrated in Fig. 6-4. Since the products are at lower potential energy than the reactants, the $\Delta H$ for the combustion of glucose is negative and the reaction is exothermic.

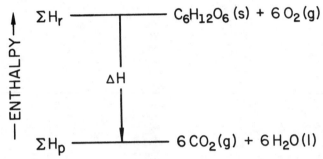

**Figure 6-4**        An enthalpy diagram for the combustion of glucose, $\Sigma H_r$ and $\Sigma H_p$ refer to the sums of the enthalpy content of the reactants and products, respectively.

The formation of glucose from $CO_2$ and water would be described by the same diagram, but the direction in which the arrow points would be reversed. This means that photosynthesis is an endothermic process and energy must be added for the reaction to occur.

It is conventional to refer to systems at lower potential energy as more stable. For example, an apple on a tree has higher potential energy (gravitational) than it does when lying on the ground. On the tree, the apple is unstable because it can fall to the ground. Once on the ground, the apple has lower potential energy. There is no concern about the apple going back up the tree, and the apple is said to be more stable on the ground. In a similar fashion, $CO_2$ and $H_2O$, with lower potential energy than glucose and $O_2$, are said to be more stable.

The heat evolved when a substance is burned is referred to as the **enthalpy of combustion** and is reported in this text in units of kJ mole$^{-1}$ of burned substance. Another commonly reported enthalpy is the **enthalpy of formation** which refers to the heat evolved when a compound is formed from its elements in their standard state. The term "elements in their **standard states**" means the state in which the element exists at room temperature and pressure. By definition, *the heat of formation of any element in its standard state is taken as zero*. The equation for the formation of glucose from the elements—solid carbon (graphite), dihydrogen (g), and dioxygen (g)—is:

$$6C(s) + 6H_2(g) + 6O_2(g) \rightarrow C_6H_{12}O_6(s) \qquad (6\text{–}6)$$

Thus the enthalpy of formation of glucose is the enthalpy of this reaction.

Table 6–2 summarizes the values of some of the known enthalpies of formation of various compounds.

**Table 6–2    Enthalpies of Formation ($\Delta H_f$) in kJ mole$^{-1}$ at 25°C and 1 atm.**

| | | | |
|---|---|---|---|
| $Al_2O_3$ (s) | −1670 | HF (g) | −286.6 |
| $BaCO_3$ (s) | −1217 | HI (g) | 25.9 |
| BaO (s) | −558.6 | HCOOH (l) | −409.2 |
| $CaCO_3$ (s) | −1207 | HgO (s) | −90.71 |
| CaO (s) | −635.1 | $HNO_3$ (aq) | −207 |
| $CH_4$ (g) (methane) | −74.85 | $H_2O$ (g) | −241.8 |
| $CH_3OH$ (l) (methanol) | −238.6 | $H_2O$ (l) | −285.8 |
| $C_2H_2$ (g) (acetylene) | 226.7 | $H_2O_2$ (l) | −187 |
| $C_2H_4$ (g) (ethylene) | 52.30 | $H_2S$ (g) | −20.12 |
| $C_2H_5OH$ (l) (ethanol) | −277.7 | $H_2SO_4$ (aq) | −907.5 |
| $C_2H_6$ (g) (ethane) | −84.68 | NaCl (s) | −410.9 |
| $C_6H_6$ (l) (benzene) | 49.04 | $NH_3$ (g) | −46.19 |
| $C_6H_{12}O_6$ (s) (glucose) | −1260 | NO (g) | 90.37 |
| $C_{12}H_{22}O_{11}$ (s) (sucrose) | −2221 | $NO_2$ (g) | 33.85 |
| CO (g) | −110.5 | $N_2O$ (g) | 81.55 |
| $CO_2$ (g) | −393.5 | $SO_2$ (g) | −296.9 |
| $Fe_2O_3$ (s) | −822.2 | $SO_3$ (g) | −395.2 |
| HBr (g) | −36.23 | ZnO (s) | −83.2 |
| HCl (g) | −92.30 | ZnS (s) | −48.5 |

Chemists are also interested in the strengths of bonds in molecules. The energy needed to break a bond in a gaseous molecule, producing two gaseous fragments each of which has one of the bonding electrons, is the **enthalpy of dissociation.** For example, the bond dissociation energies of HCl and HBr refer to the process:

$$HX(g) \rightarrow H\cdot(g) + X\cdot(g) \qquad \textbf{(6–7)}$$

where X equals Cl or Br and the two dots represent the electrons of the broken bond. Here the gaseous molecule is broken into gaseous atoms. The enthalpies of this reaction for HCl and HBr are +431.0 kJ mole$^{-1}$ of HCl and +364.0 kJ mole$^{-1}$ of HBr respectively. It requires more energy to break the bond in HCl than the bond in HBr. Therefore, the HCl bond is the stronger of the two.

In this text, both the enthalpy of formation and the enthalpy of dissociation are expressed in units of kJ mole$^{-1}$. If we wish to calculate the energy required to dissociate a gram of HCl, we can do this by using the bond dissociation energy (431 kJ mole$^{-1}$) and the mass of a mole of HCl (36.46 g mole$^{-1}$).

## Sample Problem 6-2

The enthalpy of formation of ethanol, $C_2H_5OH$, is $-277.7$ kJ mole$^{-1}$. How much heat would be evolved in the formation of 1.000 g of ethanol from pure elements in their standard states?

### Solution

$$1.000 \text{ g} \times \frac{1 \text{ mole}}{46.06 \text{ g}} = 0.02171 \text{ mole}$$

$$-277.7 \text{ kJ mole}^{-1} \times 0.02171 \text{ mole} = -6.029 \text{ kJ}$$

## Sample Problem 6-3

Using the data in Table 6-2, calculate $\Delta H$ for the reaction

$$CaO(s) + CO_2(g) \rightarrow CaCO_3(s)$$

### Solution

The solution of this problem involves use of equation 6-5 in the form:*

$$\Delta H = \Sigma \Delta H_f \text{ (products)} - \Sigma \Delta H_f \text{ (reactants)} = \Sigma \Delta H_p - \Sigma \Delta H_r$$

$$\Sigma \Delta H_f \text{ (products):}$$
$$\underline{H(CaCO_3(s)) = \Delta H_f \text{ (CaCO}_3) = -1207 \text{ kJ}}$$
$$\Sigma \Delta H_p = -1207 \text{ kJ}$$

$$\Sigma \Delta H_f \text{ (reactants):}$$
$$H(CaO(s)) = \Delta H_f(CaO) = -635.1 \text{ kJ}$$
$$\underline{H(CO_2(g)) = \Delta H_f \text{ (CO}_2) = -393.5 \text{ kJ}}$$
$$\Sigma \Delta H_r = -1028.6 \text{ kJ}$$

$$\Delta H = -1207 \text{ kJ} - (-1028.6 \text{ kJ}) = 178 \text{ kJ}$$

### TEST 6-2

A.  In this test we shall be concerned with the reaction:
$$3NO_2(g) + H_2O(l) \rightarrow 2HNO_3(aq) + NO(g)$$

---

*Since we have arbitrarily set the enthalpy of formation of an element in its standard state equal to zero, we can use the enthalpy of formation (which is a $\Delta H$) as an enthalpy content, $H$; that is, $\Delta H = \Sigma H$(products) $-$ $\Sigma H$ (reactants) $= \Sigma \Delta H_f$(products) $- \Sigma \Delta H_f$ (reactants). Accept this fact for now.

1. Given the data in Table 6–2, which equation in the text would be used?

2. Calculate $\Sigma H$(products).

3. Calculate $\Sigma H$(reactants).

4. Calculate $\Delta H$ for the reaction.

5. Is this reaction endothermic or exothermic?

6. What is the enthalpy change for the reverse reaction?

7. What is the enthalpy change for this reaction in units of kJ mole$^{-1}$ of $HNO_3$?

8. Draw an enthalpy diagram illustrating all the quantities in equation 6–5 and $\Delta H$ for this reaction.

## 6-4    ENTHALPY CYCLES: HESS'S LAW*

Since we can treat the products and reactants of a chemical equation as states, each with a certain enthalpy content, we can combine equations to produce a net equation and also combine the corresponding enthalpies to produce net enthalpies. This statement is

---

*This topic is often postponed until the second semester, and can be omitted for now if this is the case.

referred to as *Hess's Law.* If the equations are added, the enthalpies for each step are added. If equations are subtracted, the enthalpies for the steps are subtracted.

## Sample Problem 6–4

The heat of combustion of $CH_4$ to form $CO_2(g)$ and $H_2O(l)$ is $-890$ kJ mole$^{-1}$ of $CH_4$. Calculate the enthalpy change for the following reaction using the data in Table 6-1:

$$CH_4(g) + 2O_2(g) \rightarrow CO_2(g) + 2H_2O(g)$$

### Solution

To convert the heat of combustion in which liquid water is a product to one in which gaseous water is a product, we must change 2 moles of liquid water to gaseous water; that is,

$$CH_4(g) + 2O_2(g) \rightarrow CO_2(g) + 2H_2O(l) \qquad \Delta H = -890 \text{ kJ}$$

$$\underline{2H_2O(l) \rightarrow 2H_2O(g) \qquad\qquad \Delta H = (2 \text{ moles } H_2O)(44 \frac{\text{kJ}}{\text{mole } H_2O}) = 88 \text{ kJ}}$$

$$CH_4(g) + 2O_2(g) \rightarrow CO_2(g) + 2H_2O(g) \qquad \Delta H = -802 \text{ kJ}$$

The enthalpy of vaporization of water is obtained from Table 6–1. The number given there is multiplied by two to account for the two moles written in this step. In this text, we shall assume that liquid water is the product for any heat of combustion values given, unless otherwise specified.

## Sample Problem 6–5

Given that the enthalpy of formation of $CO_2$ is $-393.5$ kJ mole$^{-1}$ of $CO_2$ and the enthalpy of combustion of CO to $CO_2$ is $-283.0$ kJ mole$^{-1}$ of CO, calculate the enthalpy of formation of CO.

### Solution

First write the equation for the formation of CO from the elements.

$$2C(s) + O_2(g) \rightarrow 2CO(g) \qquad\qquad\qquad \textbf{(6–8)}$$

The enthalpies given correspond to:

$$C(s) + O_2(g) \rightarrow CO_2(g) \qquad\qquad\qquad \textbf{(6–9)}$$

and

$$2CO(g) + O_2(g) \rightarrow 2CO_2(g) \qquad \qquad \textbf{(6-10)}$$

How can we combine equations 6–9 and 6–10 to give the desired one, equation 6–8? We must get rid of $CO_2$ in 6–9 and 6–10, so we first multiply equation 6–9 by two and then subtract 6–10 from 6–9.

Subtracting equation 6–10 from equation 6–9 corresponds to writing 6–10 in the reverse direction, changing the sign of $\Delta H$, and adding it to 6–9. Multiplying equation 6–9 by two and subtracting equation 6–10 is thus done as follows:

$$2C(s) + 2O_2(g) \rightarrow 2CO_2(g) \; \Delta H = (2 \text{ moles } CO_2) \, (-393.5 \text{ kJ mole}^{-1} \text{ of } CO_2) = -787.0 \text{ kJ}$$
$$2CO_2(g) \rightarrow 2CO(g) + 2O_2(g) \; \Delta H = \quad (2 \text{ moles } CO) \, (283.0 \text{ kJ mole}^{-1} \text{ of } CO) \quad = 566.0 \text{ kJ}$$

$$2C(s) + O_2(g) \rightarrow 2CO(g) \; \Delta H = -221.0 \text{ kJ}$$

To the right of the equations written above, the enthalpy for the step is written. The heat of formation of $CO_2$ refers to one mole, but, since we need two moles, we multiply 393.5 kJ mole$^{-1}$ by two. The same is true for the heat of combustion of CO. The total enthalpy of this reaction is calculated from $\Delta H = \Sigma H(CO_2) - \Sigma[H(CO) + H(O_2)]$. The enthalpy for the resulting equation involving 2 moles of CO is $-221.0$ kJ mole$^{-1}$, so the heat of formation of one mole of CO is $-110.5$ kJ mole$^{-1}$.

## Sample Problem 6–6

Draw an enthalpy diagram and a diagram to illustrate the parallel paths described in sample problem 6–5.

## Solution

The enthalpy change for the direct reaction of C(s) and $O_2(g)$ to form two moles of $CO_2(g)$ is $-787.0$ kJ. The other path involves two steps: one to form two moles of CO(g) with an enthalpy change of $-221.0$ kJ and the second to form $CO_2$ from CO with an enthalpy change of $-566.0$ kJ for two moles.

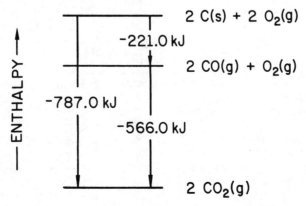

A diagram of two parallel routes to $CO_2$ follows.

$$2 \ C(s) + 2 \ O_2(g) \longrightarrow 2 \ CO_2(g)$$

$$2 \ CO(g) + O_2(g)$$

## Sample Problem 6–7

Using the data in Table 6–2, calculate the enthalpy change for the reaction

$$H_2S(g) + 2O_2(g) \rightarrow SO_3(g) + H_2O(g)$$

## Solution

Since we are given the balanced equation, we need not do this step first. We recognize that the enthalpy contents of the products and reactants can be determined from the data in Table 6–2 and that the enthalpy of the reaction can be determined from equation 6–5 in the form:

$$\Delta H = \Sigma \Delta H_f(\text{products}) - \Sigma \Delta H_f(\text{reactants})$$

We then proceed to sum the enthalpies of the products and reactants.

$\Sigma \Delta H_f(\text{products})$:

$$1 \text{ mole} \times \frac{-395.2 \text{ kJ}}{\text{mole } SO_3(g)} = -395.2 \text{ kJ}$$

$$1 \text{ mole} \times \frac{-241.8 \text{ kJ}}{\text{mole } H_2O(g)} = -241.8 \text{ kJ}$$

$$\overline{\Sigma \Delta H_f(\text{products}) = -637.0 \text{ kJ}}$$

$\Sigma \Delta H_f(\text{reactants})$:

$$1 \text{ mole} \times \frac{-20.12 \text{ kJ}}{\text{mole } H_2S(g)} = -20.12 \text{ kJ}$$

$$2 \text{ moles} \times \frac{0 \text{ kJ}}{\text{mole } O_2(g)} = 0 \text{ kJ}$$

$$\overline{\Sigma \Delta H_f(\text{reactants}) = -20.1 \text{ kJ}}$$

Substituting into equation 6–5, we obtain

$$\Delta H = -637.0 \text{ kJ} - (-20.1 \text{ kJ}) = -616.9 \text{ kJ}$$

## Sample Problem 6–8

Using the enthalpies of formation in Table 6–2, calculate the enthalpy of combustion of glucose to $CO_2(g)$ and $H_2O(1)$.

## Solution

First write the balanced equation for the combustion.

$$C_6H_{12}O_6(s) + 6O_2(g) \rightarrow 6CO_2(g) + 6H_2O(l)$$

To solve this type of problem we use equation 6–5 in the form:
$\Delta H = \Sigma \Delta H_f(\text{products}) - \Sigma \Delta H_f(\text{reactants})$

$\Sigma \Delta H_f(\text{products})$:

$$6 \text{ moles} \times \frac{-393.5 \text{ kJ}}{\text{mole } CO_2(g)} = -2361 \text{ kJ}$$

$$6 \text{ moles} \times \frac{-285.8 \text{ kJ}}{\text{mole } H_2O(l)} = -1715 \text{ kJ}$$

$$\overline{\Sigma \Delta H_f(\text{products}) = -4076 \text{ kJ}}$$

$\Sigma \Delta H_f(\text{reactants})$:

$$1 \text{ mole} \times \frac{-1260 \text{ kJ}}{\text{mole glucose}} = -1260 \text{ kJ}$$

$$6 \text{ moles} \times \frac{0 \text{ kJ}}{\text{mole } O_2(g)} = 0 \text{ kJ}$$

$$\overline{\Sigma \Delta H_f(\text{reactants}) = -1260 \text{ kJ}}$$

Substituting into equation 6–5, we obtain

$$\Delta H = -4076 \text{ kJ} - (-1260 \text{ kJ}) = -2816 \text{ kJ}$$

Note that we would have obtained a different result if gaseous water were produced in the combustion process, since $\Delta H_f(H_2O(g))$ is $-241.8$ kJ mole$^{-1}$.

## Sample Problem 6–8

Given the following equation;

$$Al_2Cl_6(s) + 3H_2O(g) \rightarrow Al_2O_3(s) + HCl(g)$$

All of the heats of formation except that for $Al_2Cl_6$ can be found in Table 6–2. The enthalpy of the above reaction is −350. kJ mole$^{-1}$ of $Al_2Cl_6$ reacted. Calculate the enthalpy of formation of $Al_2Cl_6(s)$.

## Solution

The balanced equation is given. We shall use equation 6–5 for this problem, but this time we will determine the enthalpy content of the reactants and from this the enthalpy of formation of $Al_2Cl_6(s)$. The sum of the enthalpy content of the products is:

$$1 \text{ mole} \times -1670 \text{ kJ mole}^{-1} \ Al_2O_3 = -1670 \text{ kJ}$$
$$6 \text{ moles} \times -92.30 \text{ kJ mole}^{-1} \ HCl(g) = -533.8 \text{ kJ}$$
$$\Sigma\Delta H_f(\text{products}) = -2224 \text{ kJ}$$

Substituting into equation 6–5, we obtain

$$\Delta H = \Sigma\Delta H_f(\text{products}) - \Sigma\Delta_f(\text{reactants})$$
$$-350 \text{ kJ} = -2224 \text{ kJ} - [\Sigma\Delta H_f(\text{reactants}]$$

$$\Sigma\Delta H_f(\text{reactants}) = -1874 \text{ kJ}$$
$$\Sigma\Delta H_f(\text{reactants}) = \Delta H_f(3H_2O + Al_2Cl_6)$$
$$= 3 \text{ moles} \times -241.8 \text{ kJ mole}^{-1} \text{ of } H_2O(g) + \Delta H_f(Al_2Cl_6) = -1874 \text{ kJ}$$

Therefore:

$$\Delta H_f(Al_2Cl_6) = -1874 \text{ kJ} + 725.4 \text{ kJ} = -1149 \text{ kJ}$$

Since the equation is written for 1 mole $Al_2Cl_6$, this enthalpy is −1149 kJ mole$^{-1}$ $Al_2Cl_6$. Should you forget equation 6–5, the equations for the heats of formation of all the substances in the starting equation except $Al_2Cl_6$ could be written and combined with the given equation to produce, via a Hess's Law addition, the equation and enthalpy for the heat of formation of $Al_2Cl_6$.

---

### TEST 6-3

A.  In the commercial production of zinc metal, a valuable byproduct is $SO_2$. The starting material is ZnS. When this substance is heated in air, it reacts with the $O_2$ in air to form $SO_2$.

$$ZnS(s) + O_2(g) \rightarrow ZnO(s) + SO_2(g)$$

The ZnO is then converted to zinc metal. We shall answer some questions relating to the energetics of the above reaction.
   1. Balance the above equation.

2. Write the equation given in this chapter that would be used to calculate the enthalpy change for this reaction from the data in Table 6–2.

3. Sum the enthalpies of the products using the data in Table 6–2.

4. What is the enthalpy of formation of $O_2(g)$?

5. Sum the enthalpy content of the reactants.

6. Calculate the enthalpy change for this reaction.

7. Is this an endothermic or exothermic reaction?

8. What is the enthalpy change for the reaction in units of (a) kJ mole$^{-1}$ of ZnS and (b) kJ mole$^{-1}$ of $SO_2$?

9. Are the products or reactants more stable?

10. $SO_2$ can be oxidized to $SO_3(g)$ by $O_2$. Calculate the enthalpy change for this reaction using the data in Table 6–2.

11. If a process could be found for the direct conversion of ZnS to $SO_3(g)$ by $O_2$, how would the enthalpy of this process be related to the answers to questions 6 and 10 of this test?

12. Draw an enthalpy diagram illustrating the two paths for forming $SO_3$ from ZnS (that is, the direct reaction and the two-step process that is in present use).

13. Draw a diagram for the two parallel paths for converting ZnS to $SO_3$.

# Exercises

**Energy Conventions**

1. Give two examples that illustrate the interconversion of energy.

2. Indicate three substances you might purchase because of the potential energy they contain.

3. Indicate whether each of the following is an example of kinetic or potential energy, or both:
   (a) a swinging baseball bat;
   (b) a moving car;
   (c) a parked car.

4. Is the kinetic energy of a 500. gram object moving at 50 km/hr greater, less than, or the same as that of a 1 kg object moving at 25 km/hr? Explain.

5. Convert 75.0 kJ to kcal.

6. Describe the following:
   (a) sublimation;
   (b) fusion;
   (c) vaporization;
   (d) condensation (g → 1);
   (e) enthalpy of sublimation.

7. Using the data in Table 6-1, calculate the $\Delta H_{subl}$ of naphthalene, a compound used in mothballs.

8. Calculate the enthalpy of vaporization of a compound whose enthalpies of sublimation and fusion are 77.7 kJ mole$^{-1}$ and 35.2 kJ mole$^{-1}$, respectively.

9. The enthalpy of combustion of octane, $C_8H_{18}$, a principal component of gasoline, is about 5440 kJ mole$^{-1}$.
   (a) How much heat would be evolved in the combustion of 100.0 g of octane?
   (b) How many grams of octane must be burned to produce 500. kJ of heat?

10. The heat of formation of $Fe_2O_3(s)$ is −822.2 kJ mole$^{-1}$. How much heat is evolved when 10.0 g of iron is converted to $Fe_2O_3(s)$?

11. Use the data in Table 6-2 to answer the following.
    (a) Indicate the amount of heat associated with the following equation:

$$4Fe(s) + 3O_2(g) \rightarrow 2Fe_2O_3(s)$$

(b) Which is more stable, the products or reactants of the above equation?

(c) Draw an enthalpy diagram for this reaction.

(d) What is the enthalpy associated with the formation of one mole of iron from $Fe_2O_3$?

(e) There are two processes for obtaining iron from $Fe_2O_3$. In one, water is a product and hydrogen a reactant, while in the other carbon is a reactant and CO a product. Would the enthalpy change for converting $Fe_2O_3$ to iron be the same for both? Explain, being sure to distinguish between the enthalpy content difference between $Fe_2O_3$ and iron and the enthalpy difference between the products and reactants for both paths.

**Enthalpy Cycles: Hess' Law**

12. Given the following information:

$$2Cu_2O(s) + O_2(g) \rightarrow 4CuO(s) \quad \Delta H = -288 \text{ kJ}$$
$$CuO(s) + Cu \rightarrow Cu_2O(s) \quad \Delta H = -11.3 \text{ kJ}$$

Calculate the heat of formation of $Cu_2O$.

13. Using the data in Table 6–2, calculate the enthalpy change for the following reaction:

$$SO_3(g) + H_2O(l) \rightarrow H_2SO_4(aq)$$

14. The compound $C_2H_4Cl_2(l)$ can be obtained from the following reaction:

$$C_2H_4(g) + Cl_2(g) \rightarrow C_2H_4Cl_2(l)$$

Using the data in Table 6–2 and the fact that the enthalpy for the above reaction is $-218$ kJ, calculate the enthalpy of formation of $C_2H_4Cl_2$.

15. Using the data in Table 6–2,

(a) Calculate the enthalpy of the following reaction:

$$4NH_3(g) + 5O_2(g) \rightarrow 4NO(g) + 6H_2O(g)$$

(b) Draw an enthalpy diagram for the above reaction.

16. Given the following information:
$$H_2 \rightarrow 2H; \quad \Delta H = 435 \text{ kJ}$$
$$F_2 \rightarrow 2F; \quad \Delta H = 151 \text{ kJ}$$
$$H_2(g) + F_2(g) \rightarrow 2HF(g); \quad \Delta H = -518 \text{ kJ}$$

(a) Write the equation for the bond dissociation enthalpy of H—F.

(b) Combine the information given above to obtain the value of the H—F bond dissociation enthalpy.

(c) Draw an energy diagram and a diagram showing parallel paths for the two ways to dissociate H—F described in this problem.

17.  Using the data in Table 6–2, calculate the enthalpy for the reaction:

$$2CO_2(g) + N_2(g) \rightarrow 2CO(g) + NO(g)$$

18.  The enthalpy of combustion of benzoic acid, $C_6H_5CO_2H$, is $-3.187$ kJ mole$^{-1}$. Calculate the enthalpy of formation of this compound and draw an enthalpy diagram relating the heats of formation and combustion. (Liquid water is a product.)

19.  Calculate the enthalpy change for the following reaction:

$$CaCO_3(s) \rightarrow CaO(s) + CO_2(g)$$

and draw an enthalpy diagram for the reaction.

**Verbalizing General Concepts**

20.  Answer each of the following in your own words:

(a) Reconcile using calories and joules as heat units when one considers the definitions of these two quantities.

(b) Explain the difference between $H$ and $\Delta H$.

(c) State the First Law of Thermodynamics.

(d) What is meant by the statement that mankind is exhausting its energy supply? Does this contradict the First Law of Thermodynamics?

(e) What is the difference between kinetic and potential energy?

(f) Explain how equations 6–3 and 6–5 are manifestations of the First Law of Thermodynamics.

(g) Define the term "bond energy."

(h) Why is it possible for you to write the equation (gaseous or liquid water being specified) for the complete combustion of any compound that consists of carbon and hydrogen, or carbon, hydrogen, and oxygen?

**Multiple Choice Questions**

21.  For a given substance, which would have the largest value?
(a) $\Delta H_{vap}$, (b) $\Delta H_{subl}$, (c) $\Delta H_{fus}$, (d) cannot tell because it would depend on the substance.

22.  Exothermic refers to a process that:
(a) is outside the scope of thermodynamics, (b) does work, (c) gives off heat, (d) absorbs heat, (e) none of the above.

23. Kinetic energy is energy a body possesses:
(a) by virtue of its position, (b) solely by having mass, (c) by being in motion, (d) by virtue of being combustible, (e) by virtue of two of the above descriptions.

24. A joule has units of:
(a) kg m$^2$ sec, (b) m$^2$/sec, (c) m$^2$/sec$^2$, (d) kg m/sec, (e) none of the above.

25. The enthalpy of sublimation is:
(a) $\Delta H_{vap} + \Delta H_{fus}$, (b) $\Delta H_{vap} - \Delta H_{fus}$, (c) $\Delta H_{fus} - \Delta H_{vap}$, (d) $-\Delta H_{cond}$ (gas to solid), (e) two of the above.

26. The enthalpy change of a reaction is given by:
(a) $\Sigma H$(products) $- \Sigma H$(reactants), (b) $\Sigma H$(products) $+ \Sigma H$(reactants), (c) $\Sigma H$(reactants) $- \Sigma H$(products), (d) the sums of all the enthalpies of formation, (e) two of the above.

27. The symbol $\Delta$ refers to:
(a) initial $-$ final states, (b) initial $+$ final states, (c) final $-$ initial states, (d) initial $\div$ final states, (e) none of the above.

28. Referring to the data in Table 6–2, the enthalpy change for the reaction $BaO(s) + CO_2(g) \rightarrow BaCO_3(s)$ is calculated to be:
(a) 265 kJ, (b) $-265$ kJ, (c) $-658$ kJ, (d) $-2169$ kJ, (e) none of these.

29. The enthalpy change for the following reaction is $-92.38$ kJ:
$N_2(g) + 3H_2(g) \rightarrow 2NH_3$ (g). The enthalpy of formation of ammonia is: (a) $-184.76$ kJ mole$^{-1}$, (b) $-92.38$ kJ mole$^{-1}$, (c) 92.38 kJ mole$^{-1}$, (d) $-46.19$ kJ mole$^{-1}$, (e) none of the above within 0.5.

30. Using the information in problem 29, calculate the enthalpy change associated with the conversion of 8.5 g of $NH_3(g)$ into $N_2(g)$ and $H_2(g)$. The answer is:
(a) 46 kJ, (b) 92 kJ, (c) $-46$ kJ, (d) 23 kJ, (e) $-23$ kJ.

31. If one were to draw an enthalpy diagram for the process in problem 30 with increasing enthalpy from botton to top:
(a) the bottom state would be $NH_3(g)$, (b) the bottom state would be $N_2(g) + H_2(g)$, (c) the arrow would point from top to bottom, (d) a and c above are correct, (e) b and c are correct.

32. The enthalpy of formation of any element in its standard state:
(a) is zero based on fundamental principles, (b) is arbitrarily taken as zero, (c) is fundamentally equal to the melting point of the substance, (d) is fundamentally equal to minus the melting point, (e) two of the above.

33.  The enthalpy of combustion of $C_2H_5OH$ to produce water in the gaseous state is calculated from the data in Table 6–2 to be:
     (a) $-357.6$ kJ mole$^{-1}$, (b) $-401.6$ kJ mole$^{-1}$, (c) $-1235$ kJ mole$^{-1}$, (d) $-1367$ kJ mole$^{-1}$, (e) none of the above to within 5 kJ mole$^{-1}$.

# 7

# GASES

## Chapter Objectives

## (Begin each of the following with "You should master . . .")

1. the main assumptions of the kinetic theory and their consequences in terms of the behavior of gases.
2. the meaning and measurement of temperature.
3. the interconversion of the various temperature scales.
4. the measurement of pressure.
5. the ideal gas equation, its interpretation in terms of the kinetic theory, and its use in solving problems involving the behavior of gases.
6. the law of partial pressure and its application in making water vapor corrections.
7. density of gases and the solution of problems that are a consequence of this idea.

Depending on conditions of temperature and pressure, most materials can be obtained in any one of the three states of aggregation. Water, for example, may exist as a solid (ice), a liquid (water), or a gas (steam). Although you easily recognize the various physical states, it is worthwhile to note their characteristic properties. Matter in the solid state has a definite fixed shape and definite fixed volume. In the liquid state, matter has a fixed volume, but it takes the shape of its container. Matter in the gaseous state does not have a fixed volume, but it completely and uniformly fills its container.

Strong intermolecular forces exist in the solid. In most solids the atoms, ions, or molecules move slowly and for many purposes can be thought to occupy definite fixed positions in which they undergo vibrations. In the liquid state, the intermolecular forces are sufficient to prevent the molecules from moving independently but are not strong enough to prevent the molecules from moving about. For this reason, molecules in a liquid can move readily and take the shape of their container but the liquid has a fixed volume. The forces of interaction between gaseous molecules are small and in some instances negligible. In the gaseous state, therefore, the atoms or molecules are relatively free to move about and can occupy any position in the volume of the container.

A gas consists mostly of empty space (e.g., 1 ml of liquid water converted into the gaseous state would have a volume of 1750 ml at room temperature and pressure). As a consequence of this large amount of empty space, gases are compressible. For example, if we had a container fitted with a piston and filled with a gas at atmospheric pressure, it would be relatively easy to push the piston down, decreasing the volume and compressing the gas.

## 7–1    KINETIC THEORY OF GASES

The behavior of gases can be explained on a molecular level by the kinetic theory. The main assumptions of this theory are:

1. All matter is composed of discrete particles: molecules or atoms.
2. These molecules are in constant, chaotic motion and undergo perfectly elastic collisions both with each other and with the walls of the container. (In an elastic collision the molecules rebound without any loss of energy. This occurs in a collision with the wall when the walls are at the same temperature as the gas.)
3. The molecules are very far apart, and consequently possess a volume that is negligibly small compared to the volume of the container.
4. The forces of attraction or repulsion between molecules are insignificant.
5. The average kinetic energy of the molecules is directly proportional to the absolute temperature.

## 7–2    TEMPERATURE AND PRESSURE OF A GAS

The kinetic energy ($E_k$) of a molecule is given by equation 6–1:

$$E_k = \frac{1}{2}mv^2,$$

where $m$ is the mass of the molecule and $v$ its velocity. A finite sample of a gas consists of billions of billions of molecules. Not all the molecules, however, have the same velocity or the same kinetic energy. At any temperature there will be a distribution of molecules with various velocities and kinetic energies as indicated in Figure 7–1, where $f$ is the fraction of molecules with a certain velocity, $v$. The dotted curve represents the distribution at a temperature higher than that of the solid curve. When a thermometer is placed in a sample of a gas, the gas molecules (which are constantly in motion) collide with the thermometer and impart some of their kinetic energy to it. This causes the thermometer to heat up until its temperature is the same as the average temperature of the gas. The mercury in the thermometer expands in direct proportion to the amount of heating, and the temperature is indicated by a scale that measures the expansion of the mercury. *Consequently, the temperature is a measure of the average kinetic energy of all the molecules in the sample.*

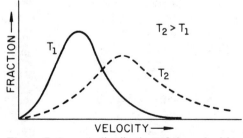

**Figure 7–1**    A distribution of the velocities of the molecules in a sample of a gas.

Several different scales have been used to measure temperature. Only the Fahrenheit, Celsius (or centigrade) and Kelvin (or absolute) scales shall concern us here. Figure 7–2 illustrates the temperatures corresponding to the boiling point and freezing point of water on all three scales.

It is often necessary to convert a temperature measured on one scale to the corresponding temperature on another scale. Our first concern will be with interconversions between the Fahrenheit and Celsius scales. We note that there are 180 Fahrenheit degrees (212 − 32) and 100 Celsius degrees (100 − 0) between the freezing and boiling point of water; that is, over this range there are 1.8 Fahrenheit degrees per 1.0 Centigrade degrees. Furthermore, when we are at 0°C the Fahrenheit temperature is 32°. The following equation satisfies both these requirements and is easily remembered if the above requirements are remembered:

$$T(°F) = 1.8 \left(\frac{°F}{°C}\right) \times T(°C) + 32(°F) \qquad \textbf{(7–1)}$$

This equation reads: the temperature in units of °F equals 1.8 times the temperature in °C plus 32 °F. The parentheses indicate the units on the numbers. Using the operations on an equation discussed in Chapter 1, we subtract 32 from both sides of the equation and divide both sides by 1.8 to obtain an expression for °C:

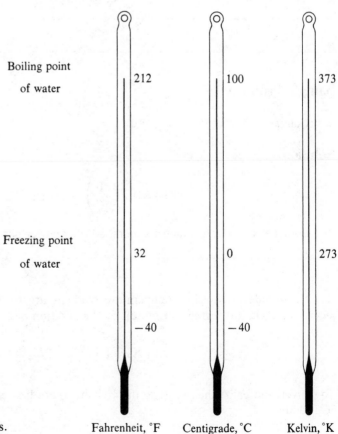

Boiling point
of water

212     100     373

Freezing point
of water

32     0     273

− 40     − 40

**Figure 7–2**    Temperature scales.      Fahrenheit, °F   Centigrade, °C   Kelvin, °K

$$T\,(^\circ\text{C}) = [T\,(^\circ\text{F}) - 32\,(^\circ\text{F})]. \times \frac{^\circ\text{C}}{1.8\,^\circ\text{F}} \qquad\qquad (7\text{--}2)$$

In practice it is necessary only to be able to derive equation 7–1, substitute numbers into it, and solve for the unknown quantity.

## Sample Problem 7–1

Convert 75.0 °F to °C.

## Solution:

$$75.0\,^\circ\text{F} = 1.80\left(\frac{^\circ\text{F}}{^\circ\text{C}}\right) \times T(^\circ\text{C}) + 32.0\,^\circ\text{F}$$

$$1.80\left(\frac{^\circ\text{F}}{^\circ\text{C}}\right) \times T(^\circ\text{C}) = 43\,^\circ\text{F}$$

$$T(^\circ\text{C}) = 23.9\,^\circ\text{C}$$

## Sample Problem 7–2

Convert −23 °C to °F.

## Solution:

$$T(^\circ\text{F}) = 1.8\left(\frac{^\circ\text{F}}{^\circ\text{C}}\right)(-23\,^\circ\text{C}) + 32\,^\circ\text{F} = -9.4\,^\circ\text{F}$$

Both 1.8 and 32 are exact numbers, so the answer has two significant figures.

Centigrade (or Celsius) temperature readings are readily converted into °K, that is, degrees Kelvin (or degrees absolute), by the addition of 273.16 °C.

$$T(^\circ\text{K}) = [\,T(^\circ\text{C}) + 273.16\,(^\circ\text{C})\,]\,\frac{1\,^\circ\text{K}}{1\,^\circ\text{C}}$$

To convert the Fahrenheit scale to the Kelvin, °F are first converted to °C and then 273.16 °C is added.

## Sample Problem 7–3

Convert $-13.0\,°F$ to $°K$.

**Solution:**

$$-13.0\,°F = 1.8\left(\frac{°F}{°C}\right) T(°C) + 32\,°F$$

$$1.8\left(\frac{°F}{°C}\right) T(°C) = -45.0\,°F$$

$$T(°C) = -25.0\,°C$$

$$T(°K) = T(°C) + 273.2(°C) = -25.0 + 273.2 = 248.2\,°K$$

Gases in a container exert pressure on the walls of the container as a result of the gas molecules colliding with the walls. A simple mercury barometer illustrates the basic principles used in several devices to measure pressure. In the barometer, illustrated in Figure 7–3, there is a vacuum in the closed end of the tube above the column of mercury. The mercury surface in the dish is exposed to the atmosphere. The gas molecules of the air strike the surface of the exposed mercury and exert pressure on this surface. Since there is no air over the mercury surface at the top of the tube, no force exists from air molecules striking this surface. Thus the pressure inside the tube is less than that on the

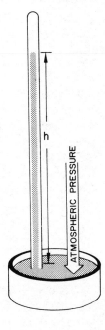

**Figure 7–3**    A simple barometer.

mercury surface in the dish. Consequently, the mercury is pushed up into the tube until the pressure exerted by the height, $h$, of the mercury column equals atmospheric pressure. Pressure is often expressed in units of millimeters of mercury, i.e., the height of the mercury column in millimeters (mm). The word torr is currently used instead of mm, in honor of the discoverer of the barometer, Torricelli (1608-1674).

The temperature unit °K is one of the base units of the SI system. Pressure is not a base unit, but it can be derived from them. Pressure is force per unit area, and the unit for area is meter². Force exerted on a body will cause it to accelerate, so force can be defined as mass (kg) times acceleration (m/sec²). Thus, force is given by kg m sec⁻², and the amount of force required to accelerate one kg by one meter per second² is called a Newton, N. Pressure (force per unit area) is given by (N) (m⁻²) = (kg m sec⁻²) (m⁻²) = kg sec⁻² m⁻¹.

The unit of pressure corresponding to one kg per sec² per meter is called a Pascal, Pa. One torr equals 133.3 Pa and one atm equals exactly 101,325 Pa. Again we see that the SI unit indicates the fundamental relationship of the quantity to the base units.

## 7–3    PRESSURE, VOLUME, AND TEMPERATURE RELATIONSHIPS FOR IDEAL GASES

Since gases are compressible and expand on heating, the volume occupied by a given number of moles of gas will depend upon the temperature and pressure. In order to compare the volumes of different samples of gas, a set of conditions called standard temperature and pressure, STP (or sometimes standard conditions) is defined. The standard temperature is 0 °C (273 °K), and the standard pressure is 1 atm or 760 torr.

An interesting relationship, called the ideal gas equation, describes the conditions that influence a gas sample:

$$PV = nRT \qquad\qquad (7\text{–}3)$$

where $P$ is the pressure, $V$ is the volume, $T$ is the absolute temperature, $n$ is the number of moles, and $R$ is the ideal gas law constant. The constant $R$ has the value 82.05 ml atmosphere mole⁻¹ °K⁻¹ or 0.08205 liter atmosphere mole⁻¹ °K⁻¹. These units for $R$ require that the volume be expressed in ml or liters, respectively; the pressure must be expressed in atmospheres (atm) (1 atm = 760 torr), $n$ is expressed in moles, and $T$ is expressed in °K. Given any four of these quantities, we can solve the equation for the fifth one. Since $R$ is a known constant, we can see that specifying any three of the remaining four quantities uniquely determines the fourth.

In the SI system R has the value:

$$0.08205 \text{ liter atm °K}^{-1} \text{ mole}^{-1} \times \frac{1 \text{ dm}^3}{1 \text{ liter}} \times \frac{101,325 \text{ Pa}}{1 \text{ atm}} =$$

$$8{,}314 \text{ decimeter}^3 \text{ Pascal mole}^{-1} \text{ °K}^{-1}$$

These units require that you use the Pascal as the pressure unit; volume is expressed in cubic decimeters (liters), T in °K and $n$ in moles. An R value of $8.314 \times 10^6$ would be need for volume in cubic centimeters (ml).

An ideal gas is one that obeys the postulates of the kinetic theory. We shall assume this behavior in all of the problems we do in this text.

---

## Sample Problem 7-4

If 2.00 moles of a gas are present in a 50.0 liter container at 100. °C, what is the pressure of the gas?

### Solution

Any particular sample of gas must obey the equation $PV = nRT$. First we check all given information to be sure that it has the units appropriate for $R$. In this problem, 100. °C must be converted to 373 °K. Substituting the given information into the ideal gas equation, we obtain:

$$P(50.0 \text{ liter}) = (2.00 \text{ moles}) (0.08205 \text{ liter atm mole}^{-1} \text{ °K}^{-1}) (373 \text{ °K})$$

$$P = \frac{61.2 \text{ liter atm}}{50.0 \text{ liter}} = 1.22 \text{ atm}$$

---

Suppose we were comparing two different gas samples under two sets of conditions. We can rearrange Eq. 7-3 to read:

$$\frac{P\,V}{n\,T} = R$$

Now using the subscripts 1 and 2 to label the different sets, we can write:

$$\frac{P_1 V_1}{n_1 T_1} = \frac{P_2 V_2}{n_2 T_2} \qquad (7\text{-}4)$$

Equation 7-4 is a form of the ideal gas equation that is useful for comparing two different samples of gases, or the same sample ($n_1 = n_2$) under two different sets of conditions. *If, in reading the problem, you note that only a single set of conditions is described, equation 7-3 will be required. If two different samples or two different sets of conditions are involved, equation 7-4 should be used.* If, in the comparison of two samples, certain quantities are the same, these quantities can be omitted from the expression. For example, when $P_1$ and $P_2$ are the same and $T_1$ and $T_2$ are the same but $n_1$ and $n_2$ are different, we can write:

$$P_1 = P_2 = P \text{ and } T_1 = T_2 = T \text{ so } \frac{PV_1}{n_1 T} = \frac{PV_2}{n_2 T}$$

Eliminating $P$ and $1/T$ from both sides.

$$\frac{V_1}{n_1} = \frac{V_2}{n_2}$$

## Sample Problem 7–5

A sample of gas in a container at 30 °C has a pressure of 700. torr. What is the pressure of this gas if the temperature of the system is raised to 200. °C?

### Solution

Since we are comparing a sample of gas under two sets of conditions, equation 7–4 is signalled. With no change in $n$ or $V$ mentioned, we assume they are constant and write

$$\frac{P_1}{T_1} = \frac{P_2}{T_2}$$

(Remember: Temperature is expressed in °K.)
$P_1 = 700$ torr
$T_1 = 30$ °C = 303 °K
$P_2 = x$
$T_2 = 200$ °C = 473 °K

$$\frac{700 \text{ torr}}{303 \text{ °K}} = \frac{x}{473 \text{ °K}}$$

$$x = \frac{(700)(473)}{(303)}$$

$$x = P_2 = 1.09 \times 10^3 \text{ torr}$$

As a check, we know that the final pressure $x$ must be larger because the temperature is higher, and this is indeed the case. Since we do not use the gas law constant in this equation, *we can use any units for P as long as they are the same for the two sets of conditions.*

## Sample Problem 7–6

If a sample of gas in a container at 30 °C has a pressure of 250. torr, at what temperature would the sample have a pressure of 1000. torr?

## Solution

$P_1 = 250.$ torr
$T_1 = 30\ °C = 303\ °K$
$P_2 = 1000.$ torr
$T_2 = x$

$$\frac{250\ \text{torr}}{303\ °K} = \frac{1000\ \text{torr}}{x}$$

$$x = \frac{(1000)(303)}{(250)}$$

$$x = T_2 = 1.21 \times 10^3\ °K$$

It is easy to explain why pressure increases with temperature. As the temperature increases, the average kinetic energy of the molecules increases. Consequently, in a given time, the gas molecules collide with the walls of the container more frequently and with more force. This causes the gas to exert a greater pressure.

## Sample Problem 7–7

A gas sample of 1.50 moles at 25 °C exerts a pressure of 400. torr. Some gas is added to the container and the temperature is also increased to 50. °C. If the pressure is now 800. torr, how many moles of gas were added to the container?

## Solution

Again we note that two different samples are being compared. With $V$ assumed constant, we write:

$$\frac{P_1}{n_1 T_1} = \frac{P_2}{n_2 T_2}$$

$P_1 = 400.$ torr
$T_1 = 25\ °C = 298\ °K$
$n_1 = 1.50$ mole
$V_1 = V_2$
$P_2 = 800.$ torr
$T_2 = 50\ °C = 323\ °K$
$n_2 = x$

$$\frac{400\ \text{torr}}{(1.50\ \text{moles})(298\ °K)} = \frac{800\ \text{torr}}{(x\ \text{moles})\ (323\ °K)}$$

$$x = \left(\frac{800}{400}\right)\left(\frac{298}{323}\right)(1.50 \text{ moles})$$

$$x = n_2 = 2.77 \text{ moles}$$

If there were 1.50 moles initially and 2.77 moles finally, then 1.27 moles (2.77 − 1.50) were added.

---

**TEST 7–1**

A.  The law

$$\frac{P_1V_1}{n_1T_1} = \frac{P_2V_2}{n_2T_2}$$

followed from studies by Charles and Boyle. Boyle studied the effect of changes in volume on the pressure of the gas at constant $n$ and $T$.

1.  The law rewritten for this case is $P_1V_1 = ?$

2.  $P_1V_1 = P_2V_2$ shows that if the pressure of a gas increases (i.e., if $P_2$ is greater than $P_1$), then the volume of the gas _____ ; i.e., $V_2$ is _____ than $V_1$.

3.  To formulate this finding into words, we would state that at constant $n$ and $T$ the volume of a gas is _____(inversely or directly) proportional to the pressure.

4.  If the volume of a container holding a gas is increased, the molecules have to travel _____ distances before striking the container walls.

5. In a given time, there are _____(fewer or more) collisions per unit area with the wall in the larger volume container than in the smaller one, resulting in a _____ pressure.

6. If a gas in a 2.5-liter container has a pressure of 350 torr, what would the pressure be if the volume were reduced to 1.25 liters, while the temperature was held constant?

B.  Charles' Law deals with a volume-temperature relationship.
    1. Write the ideal gas equation for comparing two samples at constant $n$ and $P$.

    2. Rearrange the previous equation and complete:
       $V_1/V_2 =$

    3. If the temperature of a sample is increased (constant $n$ and $P$), the volume must _____ .

4. If the temperature of a 50.0 ml sample is increased from 27 to 54 °C, what is the final volume?

5. Answer using *increase, decrease,* or *remain the same:* If the temperature of the gas increases, the speed of the molecules _____. The only way the pressure can remain constant (for constant $n$) is for the volume to_____. This change in volume causes a _____in the number of wall collisions to compensate for the_____that would result from increased temperature if the volume remained constant.

C.    1. A sample of 2.0 moles of gas is placed in a 50 ml container at 100 °C. If 1.0 mole is added and the temperature is raised to 150 °C, what must be the volume for the pressure to remain constant?

2. If $V$ and $T$ are constant, then as $n$ increases, $P$ must _____.

3. If $V$ and $P$ are constant, as $n$ increases $T$ must _____.

D. A sample of gas has a pressure of 700. torr at 30 °C in a 500. ml container.

1. How many sets of conditions are involved and which equation is signalled?

2. How many and which quantities in the above equation are not given in this problem?

3. Rearrange the above equation into the form $n = ?$

4. Substitute the appropriate numbers for this problem into the equation in 3 ($n = $ _____) and solve.

# 7–4   LAW OF PARTIAL PRESSURE

The **Law of Partial Pressure** applies to mixtures of gases, and states that *the total pressure of a mixture is the sum of the partial pressures of all the gases composing the mixture.* This statement can be understood in terms of the postulates of the kinetic theory. In a mixture, all gases are at the same average temperature and occupy the same volume. Under these conditions the identity of the gas molecules is irrelevant, and only their number is important. The total number of moles of gas is given by

$$n_{total} = \Sigma n_i$$

where $n_i$ is the number of moles of a given kind of gas in the mixture. With $R$, $T$, and $V$ being independent of the number of molecules, we can write

$$P_iV = n_iRT \text{ and}$$
$$\Sigma P_iV = \Sigma n_iRT$$

where $\Sigma P_i = P_{total}$. Each $P_i$ corresponds to the pressure of that $n_i$ quantity of gas $i$ in a volume $V$ at the specified temperature. For example, consider a container of $N_2$, $O_2$, and water vapor. If the pressure in this container due to $N_2$ alone was 50 torr, that due to $O_2$ alone was 40 torr, and that due to water vapor alone was 15 torr, then the total pressure would be the sum of all these partial pressures or 105 torr.

The Law of Partial Pressure is important for gases collected over water, because water has a significant vapor pressure (see below). Collection of a gas over water is illustrated in Figure 7–4.

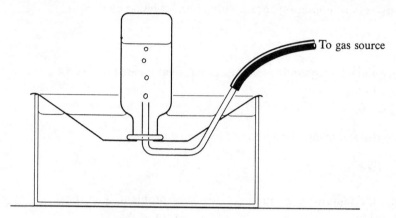

**Figure 7–4.**   Collection of gas over water.

The gas is collected in the bottle and the water is displaced as the bottle is filled with gas. The gas in the bottle is **saturated** with water vapor. The amount of water vapor in the saturated gas will depend upon the vapor pressure of the water, i.e., the pressure of the water vapor over the water. As is indicated in Table 7–1, the vapor pressure of water is a function of temperature.

**Table 7-1**    **Vapor Pressure of Water at Various Temperatures**

| °C | $P_{torr}$ | $P_{Pa}$ | °C | $P_{torr}$ | $P_{Pa}$ | °C | $P_{torr}$ | $P_{Pa}$ |
|---|---|---|---|---|---|---|---|---|
| 0 | 4.6 | 613 | 23 | 21.1 | 2813 | 60 | 149 | $1.986 \times 10^4$ |
| 5 | 6.5 | 866 | 25 | 23.8 | 3172 | 70 | 234 | $3.119 \times 10^4$ |
| 10 | 9.2 | 1226 | 27 | 26.7 | 3559 | 80 | 355 | $4.732 \times 10^4$ |
| 15 | 12.8 | 1706 | 30 | 31.8 | 4239 | 90 | 526 | $7.012 \times 10^4$ |
| 18 | 15.5 | 2066 | 40 | 55.3 | 7371 | 100 | 760 | $1.013 \times 10^5$ |
| 20 | 17.5 | 2333 | 50 | 92.5 | $1.233 \times 10^4$ | | | |

The use of this table is illustrated in sample problem 7–8.

## Sample Problem 7–8

A sample of oxygen gas collected over water at 27 °C has a total pressure of 750 torr. What is the partial pressure of oxygen?

## Solution

The total pressure, consisting of $O_2$ and water, is 750 torr. From Table 7–1, we find that the vapor pressure of water at 27 °C is 26.7 torr. Thus, by difference the pressure of $O_2$ is:

$$P_{O_2} = P_{total} - P_{H_2O}$$

$$P_{O_2} = 750. \text{ torr} - 26.7 \text{ torr} = 723 \text{ torr}$$

Sample problem 7–9 indicates how we handle problems involving a combination of the Law of Partial Pressures and the Gas Law. Standard pressure is 760 torr, 1 atm, or 101,325 Pa, and standard temperature is 0 °C (273 °K).

## Sample Problem 7–9

A 750. ml sample of $H_2$ is collected over water at 30 °C. The total pressure is 740. torr. What is the volume of hydrogen at STP? (Recall that STP is 760 torr and 273 °K.)

## Solution

$P_{total} = 740.$ torr, and from Table 7-1 the partial pressure of $H_2O$ at 30 °C is 31.8 torr. Therefore, the partial pressure of hydrogen in the sample is 708 torr.

$P_{H_2} = P_{total} - P_{H_2O} = 740 - 32 = 708$ torr
$P_1 = 708$ torr
$T_1 = 30$ °C $= 303$ °K
$V_1 = 750.$ ml
$P_2 = 760$ torr (standard pressure)
$T_2 = 273$ °K (standard temperature)
$V_2 = x$

Inserting these values into equation 7–4 produces

$$\frac{(708 \text{ torr})(750. \text{ ml})}{303 \text{ °K}} = \frac{(760. \text{ torr})(x \text{ ml})}{273 \text{ °K}}$$

$$x = \frac{(708)(750)(273)}{(303)(760)}$$

$$x = V_2 = 630. \text{ ml of } H_2$$

## 7-5    OTHER CONSEQUENCES OF THE IDEAL GAS EQUATION; MOLECULAR WEIGHTS AND DENSITIES OF GASES

There are several important problems that can be solved by rewriting the ideal gas equation in terms of the mass (in grams) of the gas. Substituting for $n$ with

$$\text{number of moles } (n) = \frac{\text{grams (g)}}{\text{Gram Molecular Weight (GMW)}}$$

into the ideal gas equation leads to

$$PV = nRT = \frac{g}{GMW}RT \tag{7-5}$$

You need not remember this equation if you remember the above derivation of it from $PV = nRT$.

Recalling the definition of density as mass per unit volume,

$$d = g/V$$

and rearranging the above equation by solving for $g/V$ we can write

$$d = \frac{g}{V} = \frac{P(GMW)}{RT} \tag{7-6}$$

With the ideal gas equation in this form, we are in a position to calculate the density, $d$, of any gas under any conditions. Remember that any change in $P$ or $T$ that affects volume will also change the density.

---

### Sample Problem 7-10

Calculate the density of methane gas ($CH_4$) at standard conditions.

### Solution

The molecular weight of $CH_4$ is 16.0. Therefore, the density is given by:

$$d = \frac{(1 \text{ atm})(16.0 \text{ g mole}^{-1})}{(0.08205 \text{ liter atm } °K^{-1} \text{ mole}^{-1})(273 \text{ °K})} = 0.714 \text{ g/liter}$$

Note the unit cancellation.

---

## Sample Problem 7–11

Calculate the density of methane gas at 30 °C and 500. torr pressure.

### Solution

$$d = \frac{\frac{500}{760} \text{ atm* } (16.0 \text{ g mole}^{-1})}{(0.08205 \text{ liter atm °K}^{-1} \text{ mole}^{-1})(303 \text{ °K})} = 0.423 \text{ g/liter}$$

It is also possible to solve the equation

$$PV = \frac{\text{g}}{\text{GMW}} RT$$

for the gram molecular weight. Rearranging gives

$$\text{GMW} = \text{g}\,\frac{RT}{PV}$$

## Sample Problem 7–12

It is found that 250. ml of gas, measured at standard conditions, weighs 0.400 g. What is the molecular weight?

### Solution

$$\text{GMW} = \frac{(0.400 \text{ g})(0.08205 \text{ liter atm °K}^{-1} \text{ mole}^{-1})(273 \text{ °K})}{(1 \text{ atm})(0.250 \text{ liter})}$$

$$\text{GMW} = 35.8 \text{ g mole}^{-1}$$

$$\text{MW} = 35.8 \text{ amu}$$

### TEST 7–2

A.  A gas with empirical formula $UF_6$ was used in the separation of the $^{235}U$ isotope used in the original atomic bomb production. In order to establish the molecular formula, the molecular weight must be deter-

---

*This results from combining $\frac{500 \text{ torr}}{760 \text{ torr atm}^{-1}} = \frac{500}{760}$ atm.

mined. It is found that the density of this material at 100 °C and 1.00 atm is 11.5 g/liter. Answer the following questions, which will lead to the calculation of the molecular weight.

1. Rearrange and substitute into the equation $PV = nRT$ to produce an expression for GMW.

2. What mass and volume should be substituted into the expression in part 1?

3. What are the value and units to be used for $R$?

4. Substitute into the expression for GMW and solve.

5. What is the molecular weight?

B. At 98 °C and 754 torr, a 127 ml sample of a gas weighs 0.495 g. Proceed as in part A to calculate the molecular weight.

C.  Given $PV = nRT$ and $n = g/GMW$, derive an expression for the density.

# 7–6   MASS-VOLUME AND MOLE-VOLUME RELATIONS IN CHEMICAL REACTIONS

In Chapter 3 we used the balanced chemical equation to solve problems involving mass and mole relations in a chemical reaction. The volume relationships of gases undergoing chemical reactions at constant temperature and pressure are indicated for several reactions, below each of the following equations:

$$H_2 + Cl_2 \rightarrow 2HCl$$
1 liter + 1 liter → 2 liters

$$2H_2 \rightarrow O_2 \rightarrow 2H_2O$$
2 liters + 1 liter → 2 liters

$$3H_2 + N_2 \rightarrow 2NH_3$$
3 liters + 1 liter → 2 liters

We can see that the volume relationships between gaseous products and reactants are the same as the mole relationships. Consequently, 1 liter of any of the above gases at the same conditions of temperature and pressure must contain the same number of moles as 1 liter of any of the other gases. Furthermore, samples containing the same number of moles of any gas must all occupy the same volume at the same set of conditions. Therefore, the chemical equation provides information about mole-volume and mass-volume relationships in a chemical reaction. We can calculate the mole-mole or mass-mole relations of gaseous materials as was done in Chapter 3. We can then substitute the number of moles and the other conditions into $PV = nRT$ to calculate the volume of material produced or used. Given the mass, temperature, pressure, and volume of a sample of gas, we can calculate the molecular weight.

## Sample Problem 7–13

What volume of $H_2$ at 28 °C and 755 torr would be produced by the reaction of 5.00 g of Zn with excess HCl in accordance with the following equation?

$$Zn + 2HCl \rightarrow ZnCl_2 + H_2$$

## Solution

First we determine the number of moles of $H_2$ by doing a mass-mole problem.

$$? \text{ moles } H_2 = 5.00 \text{ g Zn} \times \frac{1.00 \text{ mole}}{65.4 \text{ g Zn}} \times \frac{1 \text{ mole } H_2}{1 \text{ mole Zn}} = 0.0765 \text{ mole } H_2$$

Substituting into $PV = nRT$ we obtain

$$V = \frac{(0.0765 \text{ mole})(0.08205 \text{ liter atm mole}^{-1}\,°K^{-1})(301\ °K)}{\dfrac{755}{760} \text{ atm}}$$

$$= 1.90 \text{ liters}$$

## Exercises

### Temperature Conversions

1.  a. 26.6 °F to °C.
    b. 66.9 °C to °F.
    c. 44.0 °F to °K.
    d. −19.2 °F to °K.
    e. 44 °K to °F.
    f. −21.1 °C to °F.

### Ideal Gas Law Problems

2. A gas occupies 450. ml at 650. mm pressure and 30 °C. What will its volume be at STP?

3. A 200. ml sample of gas contains 3.00 moles at 30 °C. If 2.00 moles of gas are added, what will the volume be at STP?

4. Calculate the weight of 500. ml of $Cl_2$ at STP.

5. A driver puts 30.0 lb/in² into the automobile's tires at 22 °C. After the car has been driven for a while, the pressure has increased to 45.0 lb/in². Assuming no volume change, what is the temperature of the gas in the tires?

6. A 100. liter sample of gas was compressed to 10.0 ml, where its pressure is 350. torr. What was the original pressure of the 100. liter sample?

7. A gas sample in a 17.5 liter container is heated from $-33.0\ ^\circ C$ to 33.0 $^\circ C$. In order for the pressure to remain constant, what would the volume of the container have to be at 33.0 $^\circ C$?

8. Calculate the weight of 1 liter of $N_2$ at 25 $^\circ C$ and 700. mm pressure.

9. Gas in a hot air balloon has a volume of 5500. liters at 40.0 $^\circ C$. To what temperature must the gas be heated to increase the volume to 7500. liters?

10. How many moles are contained in a sample of gas that has a pressure of 11.0 torr at 75 $^\circ F$ in a 5.00 liter container?

11. Butane gas is stored in a tank at a pressure of 10.0 atmospheres at 22 $^\circ C$. The tank can hold a pressure of 50.0 atm before bursting. During a fire the gas is heated to 500. $^\circ C$. What is the gas pressure, and will the tank contain the gas without bursting?

12. If 200. ml of gas have a pressure of 444 torr at 85 $^\circ F$, what will be the volume at standard conditions?

13. Calculate the number of moles of gas contained in the sample described in problem 12.

**Law of Partial Pressure**
**(Use the data in Table 7–1 when needed.)**
14. If a 450. ml sample of $O_2$ collected over water at 23 $^\circ C$ has a total pressure of 750. torr, what is the $O_2$ partial pressure?

15. A 50.0 ml sample of dry $N_2$ at 15 $^\circ C$ and 750. torr will occupy what volume over water at this temperature and total pressure?

16. A 300. ml quantity of $H_2$ is collected over water at 25 $^\circ C$. The total pressure is 755 torr. What is the volume of $H_2$ at STP?

17. If the volume of a container were doubled at constant temperature, the number of moles of gas would have to be doubled in order for the pressure to remain constant. If this statement is true, explain.

**Other Consequences of the Ideal Gas Equation**
18. Calculate the volume of 38.8 g of $CO_2$ at 725 torr and 25 $^\circ C$.

19. A 150. ml sample of gas at STP weighs 0.973 g. What is the molecular weight of the gas?

20. A 250. ml sample of a gas collected at 30.°C and 752 mm pressure weighs 1.95 g. What is the molecular weight?

21. Calculate the density of $SO_2$ at STP.

22. A 650. ml sample of a gas weighs 1.71 g at 100. °C and 750. mm pressure. Calculate the molecular weight.

23. A 75 g sample of sulfur is burned in air. What volume of $SO_2$ at STP will be formed? $S + O_2 \rightarrow SO_2$.

24. Given the equation:

$$Ni(s) + 4CO(g) \rightarrow Ni(CO)_4 \ (g)$$

how many liters of CO at STP are needed to react with 15 g of nickel?

25. A 40.0 g sample of Zn is allowed to react with 15.5 g of HCl. How many liters of $H_2$ at STP are produced?

$$Zn(s) + 2HCl(aq) \rightarrow ZnCl_2(aq) + H_2(g)$$

26. On reacting with HCl, how many grams of Zn are needed to produce 5.00 liters of $H_2$ at STP?

27. Calculate the density of $SO_2(g)$ at 1.00 atm and 23 °C.

28. A vapor has a volume of 250. ml at 85 °C and 740. torr. The mass of the vapor is 0.750 g. Calculate the molecular weight.

29. Calculate the molecular weight of a gas whose density is 1.2505 g/liter at STP.

30. How many liters of $O_2$ at 25 °C and 1.00 atm pressure are needed to burn 15.0 grams of $CH_4$ to $CO_2$ and $H_2O$?

**Verbalizing General Concepts**
31. Answer each of the following in your own words:
    (a) How does a simple barometer work?
    (b) Using the kinetic theory, explain why the pressure of a gas increases when the temperature increases.
    (c) Using kinetic theory, explain why the pressure of a gas decreases when the volume is increased.
    (d) State the Law of Partial Pressure.
    (e) How is it possible that 3 liters of dihydrogen and one liter of dinitrogen react to form 2 liters of ammonia?
    (f) How can the molecular weight of a gas be calculated from its density?

**Challenging Problems**

32. If a 125 ml sample of $H_2(g)$ collected over water at 23 °C has a total pressure of 725 torr, what would the volume of this gas sample be over water at 40. °C and a total pressure of 744 torr?

33. In reaction with HCl, 1.00 mole of Al yields 1.50 moles of $H_2$, while 1.00 mole of Zn yields 1.00 mole of $H_2$. A 0.150 g sample of an Al-Zn mixture evolves 145 ml of $H_2$ (dry) at 27 °C and 1.00 atm pressure. Calculate the percent Al in the sample.

34. The combustion of 0.125 g of a sample to $CO_2(g)$ and $H_2O(l)$ produced 136.4 ml of $CO_2$ at STP. What is the percent carbon in the sample?

**Multiple Choice Questions**

35. A gas is compressed to half its volume without changing the temperature. The average kinetic energy of the molecules:
    (a) increases, (b) is doubled, (c) decreases, (d) does not change, (e) two of the above.

36. The temperature of a gas is raised from 20 °C to 40 °C. The pressure will:
    (a) increase, (b) double, (c) decrease, (d) not change, (e) two of the above.

37. A gas sample is heated from −20.0 °C to 57.0 °C and the volume is increased from 2.00 liters to 4.50 liters. If the initial pressure is 0.850 atm, what is the final pressure?
    (a) 0.377 atm, (b) 1.11 atm, (c) 1.41 atm, (d) 0.493 atm, (e) none of these.

38. The total pressure of a mixture of gases is:
    (a) the sum of the partial pressures of the components.
    (b) obtained by multiplying the individual pressures by the number of moles and averaging.
    (c) obtained by multiplying the individual pressures by the number of moles without averaging.
    (d) dependent only upon the pressure of the gas which is present to the greatest extent.
    (e) none of these.

39. What volume will 16.0 g of dioxygen occupy at STP?
    (a) 5.60 liters, (b) 11.2 liters,(c) 22.4 liters, (d) not enough information is given to calculate the volume.

40. A gas sample is heated from −10 °C to 87 °C, and the volume is increased from 1.00 liter to 3.30 liters. If the initial pressure is 0.750 atm, what is the final pressure?
    (a) 0.165 atm, (b) 0.311 atm, (c) 1.81 atm, (d) 3.38 atm.

41.   Benzene, $C_6H_6$, can be burned in oxygen according to the equation:

$$2C_6H_6 + 15O_2 \rightarrow 12CO_2 + 6H_2O$$

If 5.0 liters of dioxygen measured at STP were required to burn a given amount of benzene, the STP volume of $CO_2$ formed would be:

(a)
$$\frac{15}{12} \times 5.0 \text{ liters,}$$

(b)
$$\frac{12}{15} \times 5.0 \text{ liters,}$$

(c)
$$2.78 \text{ g benzene} \times \frac{12 \text{ liters } CO_2}{1.0 \text{ g benzene}},$$

(d)
$$\frac{44 \times 12}{15 \times 32} \times 5.0 \text{ liters,}$$

(e) none of the above.

42.   At STP, a 1-liter vessel is filled with hydrogen and a vessel of equal size filled with oxygen (also at STP). If $X$ is the number of hydrogen molecules in one container, then:
(a) $X = 6.02 \times 10^{23}$,
(b) the number of oxygen molecules is $X/16$,
(c) the number of oxygen molecules is $16\,X$,
(d) the number of oxygen molecules is equal to $X$,
(e) none of the above.

43.   What volume of pure $N_2O$ at STP could be prepared by the controlled decomposition of 8.00 g of ammonium nitrate?

$$NH_4NO_3 \text{ (s)} \rightarrow N_2O(g) + 2H_2O(l)$$

(a) 1.12 liters, (b) 2.24 liters, (c) 3.36 liters, (d) 4.48 liters, (e) none of the above.

44.   Which of the following is a correct statement?
(a) At STP, $NH_3$ is more dense than $CO_2$.
(b) At STP, $CO_2$ is more dense than $H_2S$.
(c) At STP, HCl is more dense than $CO_2$.
(d) Density is independent of STP.
(e) The density cannot be determined for any of the above
     combinations because the volume is not given.

45. What volume will 14 g of $N_2$ occupy at STP?
    (a) 5.6 liters, (b) 11.2 liters, (c) 22.4 liters, (d) 44.8 liters, (e) none of these.

46. It is found that 250. ml of a gas at STP weighs 2.00 g. What is the molecular weight of the material?
    (a) 179 g/mole, (b) 56.0 g/mole, (c) 28.0 g/mole, (d) 44.8 g/mole, (e) none of these.

47. $C_2H_4$ reacts with $O_2$ according to the following equation:

$$C_2H_4(g) + 3O_2(g) \rightarrow 2CO_2(g) + 2H_2O(g)$$

    How many liters of dioxygen at STP are needed to react with 1.00 mole of $C_2H_4$?
    (a) 3.00 liters, (b) 22.4 liters, (c) 44.8 liters, (d) 67.2 liters, (e) not enough information given.

Questions 48 through 50 refer to an experiment. A plastic bag is weighed and then filled successively with two gases, X and Y. The following data are gathered:

Temperature: 0.0 °C (273 °K)
Pressure: 1.00 atmosphere
Weight of empty bag, stopper, etc.: 20.77 g
Weight of bag filled with gas X: 24.97 g
Weight of 1.12 liters of air at conditions given: 1.30 g
Volume of bag: 1.12 liters
Molar volume at STP: 22.4 liters

48. The actual weight of 1.12 liters of gas Y is found to be 6.23 g. The density of gas Y is:
    (a) 10.56 g/l, (b) 5.56 g/l, (c) 15.6 g/l, (d) 0.200 g/l, (e) 0.180 g/l.

49. The molecular weight of gas Y in grams per mole is:
    (a) 56.0, (b) 89.0, (c) 125, (d) 140, (e) 157.

50. The bag is emptied and refilled, successively, with gases X and Y, this time at one atmosphere pressure and a temperature 30 °C *higher*. Assume that the volume of the bag is the same as before. Which one of the following statements is WRONG?
    (a) The full bag contains fewer molecules of each gas than it did at 0.0 °C.
    (b) The *ratio* of the density of gas Y to the density of gas X is the same as at 0.0 °C.
    (c) The molecular weights of the two gases are the same as they were at 0.0 °C.

(d) The weight of each gas filling the bag is now $\frac{303}{273}$ times the weight held at 0.0 °C.

(e) The average velocity of the molecules of gas $X$ at 30 °C is higher than it was at 0.0 °C.

51. A 1.168 g sample of an oxide, $XO_2$, reacts completely with exactly 500. ml of $H_2$ gas measured at STP. What is the molecular weight of $XO_2$?

$$XO_2(s) + 2H_2(g) \rightarrow X(s) + 2H_2O(g)$$

(a) 52.0 g/mole, (b) 93.0 g/mole, (c) 105 g/mole, (d) 210 g/mole,

52. Propane ($C_3H_8$) can be burned in oxygen according to the equation:

$$C_3H_8 + 5O_2 \rightarrow 3CO_2 + 4H_2O$$

If 7.0 liters of $O_2$ measured at STP were required to burn a given amount of propane, the STP volume of $CO_2$ formed would be
(a) $\frac{5}{3}$ times 7.0 liters
(b) $\frac{5}{3}$ times 22.4 liters
(c) $\frac{3}{5}$ times 7.0 liters
(d) $\frac{3}{5}$ times 32 times 7.0 liters
(e) none of these expressions

53. At STP, a 2-liter vessel is filled with $CO_2$. A vessel of equal size is filled with $O_2$ at STP. If X is the number of $CO_2$ molecules in the first vessel, then
(a) X = 6.023 times $10^{23}$ divided by 2.
(b) the number of $O_2$ molecules is $\frac{X}{32}$.
(c) the number of $O_2$ molecules is $\frac{32}{44}$ X.
(d) the number of $O_2$ molecules is $\frac{2}{3}$ X.
(e) the number of $O_2$ molecules is equal to X.

54. Which of the following statements is correct?
(a) At STP, $H_2S$ is more dense than $C_3H_8$.
(b) At STP, $CO_2$ is more dense than $SO_2$.
(c) At STP, NO is more dense than $Cl_2$.
(d) All gases have the same density at STP, 1 mole/22.4$l$.
(e) none of the above.

55. When the pressure of a gas is halved without changing the temperature or the number of moles of the system, which of the following statements is/are true of this system?
(a) The volume is halved also.
(b) The volume is doubled.
(c) The average kinetic energy of the particles in the system doubles.
(d) Both (a) and (c) are correct.
(e) Both (b) and (c) are correct.

# 8

# ATOMIC STRUCTURE, PERIODICITY, AND LEWIS STRUCTURES

## Chapter Objectives

### (Begin each of the following with "You should master . . .")

1. memorization of the Aufbau order and use of it to write the electron configurations of the first 88 elements.
2. the rules for writing the electronic configurations of ions.
3. the relationship of atomic structure to the location of an atom in the periodic table.
4. the use of box diagrams to represent the electronic structures of atoms and ions.
5. the definitions of electronegativity, polar covalent bonds, pure covalent bonds, and resonance.
6. the trends in electronegativities of the atoms in the periodic table.
7. the application of the rules for writing Lewis structures.
8. the recognition of resonance forms and the determination of the bond order in the resonance hybrid.

In this chapter, we will be concerned with the distribution and energies of the electrons within the atom. These properties govern the form of the periodic table and the structures of the molecules that the atoms form. In this treatment, we shall briefly summarize those aspects of this topic that are essential for the solution of typical problems relating to this subject. You are referred to your textbook for a more complete explanation of the ideas summarized here.

## 8-1  ELECTRON CONFIGURATION OF ATOMS

Electrons have observable properties that can be accounted for by assuming that the electron is spinning in either a clockwise or a counterclockwise direction. The electrons in the atom are assigned to **orbitals**, each of which can accommodate two electrons that must have opposite spins. Thus, in an atom with 58 electrons, for instance, there must be a lot of orbitals to contain the electrons. The orbitals in an atom can be divided into groups that are equal in energy. These groups are called **subshells.** All of the subshells of roughly similar size and energy are grouped together into a **shell.** Each orbital is labelled; for example, we have *1s, 2s, 2p_x, 2p_y, 2p_z, 3s* orbitals, and so forth. All of the orbitals beginning with the same number belong to the same shell, and they have roughly similar size and energy. This number is referred to as the **principal quantum number** and is given the general symbol $n$. For any given principal quantum number, $n$, there is one orbital that we label $s$. Thus there are a series of different $s$ orbitals that we distinguish by their $n$ values; for example, $1s$, $2s$, $3s$, etc. for $n$ values of 1, 2, 3, etc., respectively. When the principal quantum number is 2 or more, there are three equal-energy $p$ orbitals (a subshell) for each $n$ value. The individual orbitals of the $p$ subshell are distinguished by the subscripts $x$, $y$, and $z$. The letters $s$, $p$, and so forth indicate the orbital's shape. The shapes of the $s$ and $p$ orbitals are illustrated in Figure 8–1.

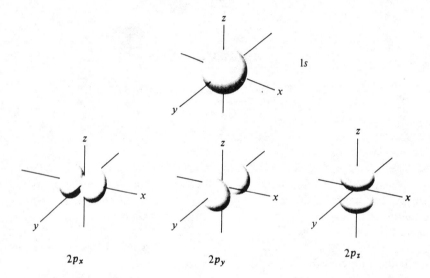

**Figure 8–1**    The shapes of $s$ and $p$ orbitals.

The subscripts $x$, $y$, and $z$ on the $p$ orbitals indicate that the orbitals lie along the $x$, $y$, and $z$ axes, respectively. For $n = 2$, we have $2p_x$, $2p_y$, and $2p_z$ orbitals, while for $n = 3$ we have $3p_x$, $3p_y$, and $3p_z$ orbitals, and so forth for larger $n$ values.

When we come to principal quantum number $n = 3$, we have $d$ orbitals in addition to the $s$ and $p$ orbitals. There are five equal-energy $d$ orbitals, which we label $d_{xy}$, $d_{yz}$, $d_{xz}$, $d_{z^2}$, and $d_{x^2-y^2}$. We shall not be concerned with the shapes of these orbitals or the meaning of the subscripts. All $n$ values greater than three also have five $d$ orbitals. This discussion is summarized in Table 8–1, where the number of electrons that a given shell ($n$ value) can accommodate are also listed.

The $n=1$ shell holds two electrons, $n=2$ holds eight, $n=3$ holds eighteen, and so forth. The capacity of any shell is given by $2n^2$, where $n$ is the principal quantum number of the shell.

The electronic configuration of an atom is a listing of the orbitals occupied by the electrons of an atom. The configuration is important to the understanding of the reactivity of the various elements. It is so important and basic to chemistry that every student of chemistry should be able to write electronic configurations. In order to write an electronic configuration we need to:

**Table 8-1    A Summary of Orbital Types**

| $n$ value | Subshells | Orbitals | Electron capacity for this $n$ |
|---|---|---|---|
| 1 | $s$ | $s$ | 2 |
| 2 | $s, p$ | $s, p_x, p_y, p_z$ | 8 |
| 3 | $s, p, d,$ | $s, p_x, p_y, p_z, d_{xy},$ $d_{xz},\ \ d_{yz},\ \ d_{z^2},$ $d_{x^2-y^2}$ | 18 |
| 4 | $s, p, d, f$ | $s, p_x, p_y, p_z, d_{xz},$ $d_{yz},\ \ d_{xy},\ \ d_{z^2},$ $d_{x^2-y^2}, f^*$ | 32 |

*There are seven different $f$ orbitals, whose shapes or individual labels need not concern us.

1. know the relative energies of the orbitals,
2. count the total number of electrons in the atom,
3. add the electrons to the lowest energy orbitals first and continue until all the electrons have been placed in orbitals.

The energy order to be used in filling is called the **Aufbau order** (aufbau is German for "to build up"). The order is:

$1s < 2s < 2p$ (3 orbitals) $< 3s < 3p$ (3 orbitals) $4s < 3d$ (5 orbitals) $< 4p$ (3 orbitals) $< 5s < 4d$ (5 orbitals) $< 5p$ (3 orbitals) $< 6s < 4f$ (7 orbitals) $< 5d$ (5 orbitals) $< 6p$ (3 orbitals) $< 7s$ . . .

In listing this order, we group all three $p$ orbitals together because they are equal in energy. The same is true for the five $d$ and seven $f$ orbitals. We must remember that each $p$ subshell can hold six electrons, each $d$ subshell ten and each $f$ subshell fourteen. The electronic configuration is written by listing the occupied orbitals of the atom, placing the number of electrons in each orbital as a superscript to the label for that orbital.

---

## Sample Problem 8–1

Write the electronic configuration of the sulfur atom.

## Solution

Sulfur has an atomic number of 16, and therefore there are 16 electrons in the neutral atom. Using the Aufbau order we obtain

$$1s^2\, 2s^2\, 2p^6\, 3s^2\, 3p^4$$

---

## Sample Problem 8–2

Write the electron configuration of Kr.

## Solution

The Kr atom has 36 electrons.

$$1s^2\ 2s^2\ 2p^6\ 3s^2\ 3p^6\ 4s^2\ 3d^{10}\ 4p^6$$

We note in doing problems of this type that knowledge of the Aufbau order is essential. There is an easy way to remember this order and at the same time see how this order produces the form of the periodic table. The ideas are illustrated in Figure 8–2. The periodic table in Fig. 8–2 has been divided into blocks which correspond to the type of orbital ($s, p, d$, or $f$) into which the last Aufbau electron was added. (Helium was moved over to the left for this reason.) If we follow the solid arrow, and return via the dashed arrow, the table reads like a book, giving us $1s^2, 2s^2, 2p^6, 3s^2, 3p^6, 4s^2, 3d^{10}, 4p^6$, and so forth. This is the Aufbau order. If an atom is in the middle of any block, it has only the number of electrons corresponding to the number of elements to its left in the block plus one. For example, arsenic (As) is in row 4 and is the third element in the $p$ block, so its electronic configuration ends with $\cdots 4p^3$. On the other hand, nickel (Ni) is also in the fourth row and is the eighth element in the $d$ block, so its electron configuration ends with $\cdots 3d^8$.

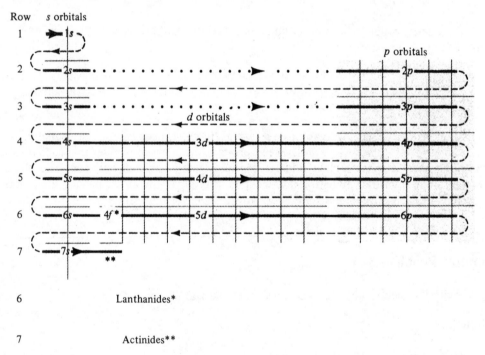

**Figure 8–2**    Relation of the Aufbau order to the periodic table.

### TEST 8–1

A.    How many electrons are there in:
   1. Rb

2. Te

3. Co

B.  List the eight lowest energy subshells in order of increasing energy.

C.  Using the Aufbau order, write the electronic configuration of:
1. P

2. As

3. Fe

4. Ca

5. Se

D.  Referring to Fig. 8–2 and the periodic table, list all the atoms for
    which the last Aufbau electron would give a
    1. $p^2$ configuration

    2. $s^1$ configuration.

    3. $p^6$ configuration.

E.  Referring to a periodic table, write the electron configuration for:
    1. Nb

    2. Re

    3. Nd

    (If you have trouble finding the element in the periodic table, look up
    its atomic number in the alphabetical listing.)

F.   Draw the $p_y$ orbital on the coordinate system:

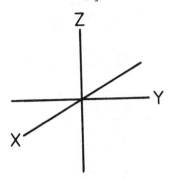

The electron configurations of all the atoms from H to Lw are summarized in Table 8–2. The symbols (He) or (Ar) and so forth are abbreviations that signify all the electrons and orbitals of that atom. The atoms in parentheses are called noble gases. You will note that some of the configurations, for example Cu, are exceptions to the general rules for using the Aufbau order. You will not be responsible for remembering these exceptions in this book.

The elements in which the last Aufbau electron goes into an $s$ or $p$ orbital are called **main group elements.** Those in which the $d$ orbitals are being filled are called **transition elements,** and those in which the $4f$ orbitals are being filled are called *lanthanide elements*. The fourteen elements with atomic numbers 89 to 103 are called **actinide elements.**

## 8–2    BOX DIAGRAMS

Most atoms contain many electrons, but only a few of these electrons are involved in chemical reactions. Those electrons that govern the chemistry of an element are called **valence electrons.** For any given atom, all of the electrons that the atom has in orbitals that are filled in the preceding noble gas are called **core electrons.** In Table 8–2 the core electrons are indicated by (noble gas). Any additional electrons are valence electrons. An exception to this statement is that electrons in a completed $d$-shell ($nd^{10}$) are not considered to be valence electrons. Thus, the elements Ga or Sb have three and five valence electrons, respectively, and not 13 and 15. For these elements, the preceding $d$ shell is not considered to contain valence electrons.

A common way to represent the atomic structure of an element involves indication of only the valence electrons with a box diagram. In the **box diagram** representation, each valence orbital is represented by a box and the valence electrons are added to these boxes. A single box is used to represent an $s$ orbital, three connected boxes for a degenerate (equal-energy) set of three $p$ orbitals, five connected boxes for a degenerate set of $d$ orbitals, and so on. The electrons are represented by arrows that point in different directions for the two different spins. By convention, the first electron added to the box (orbital) has the arrow pointing up. Using this convention, we represent the atomic structure of Li, Be, and B as follows:*

---

*In some texts, all of the electrons in the atom are added to boxes. The inner orbitals are represented by boxes in the same way as described above for the valence electrons.

### Table 8-2 Electronic Configurations of Atoms

| Atom | Orbital Electronic Configuration | Atom | Orbital Electronic Configuration |
|------|----------------------------------|------|----------------------------------|
| H | $1s^1$ | I | $(Kr)5s^24d^{10}5p^5$ |
| He | $1s^2$ | Xe | $(Kr)5s^24d^{10}5p^6$ |
| Li | $(He)2s^1$ | Cs | $(Xe)6s^1$ |
| Be | $(He)2s^2$ | Ba | $(Xe)6s^2$ |
| B | $(He)2s^22p^1$ | La | $(Xe)6s^25d^1$ |
| C | $(He)2s^22p^2$ | Ce | $(xe)6s^24f^15d^1$ |
| N | $(He)2s^22p^3$ | Pr | $(Xe)6s^24f^3$ |
| O | $(He)2s^22p^4$ | Nd | $(Xe)6s^24f^4$ |
| F | $(He)2s^22p^5$ | Pm | $(Xe)6s^24f^5$ |
| Ne | $(He)2s^22p^6$ | Sm | $(Xe)6s^24f^6$ |
| Na | $(Ne)3s^1$ | Eu | $(Xe)6s^24f^7$ |
| Mg | $(Ne)3s^2$ | Gd | $(Xe)6s^24f^75d^1$ |
| Al | $(Ne)3s^23p^1$ | Tb | $(Xe)6s^24f^9?$ |
| Si | $(ne)3s^23p^2$ | Dy | $(Xe)6s^24f^{10}$ |
| P | $(Ne)3s^23p^3$ | Ho | $(Xe)6s^24f^{11}$ |
| S | $(Ne)3s^23p^4$ | Er | $(Xe)6s^24f^{12}$ |
| Cl | $(Ne)3s^23p^5$ | Tm | $(Xe)6s^24f^{13}$ |
| Ar | $(Ne)3s^23p^6$ | Yb | $(Xe)6s^24f^{14}$ |
| K | $(Ar)4s^1$ | Lu | $(Xe)6s^24f^{14}5d^1$ |
| Ca | $(Ar)4s^2$ | Hf | $(Xe)6s^24f^{14}5d^2$ |
| Sc | $(Ar)4s^23d^1$ | Ta | $(Xe)6s^24f^{14}5d^3$ |
| Ti | $(Ar)4s^23d^2$ | W | $(Xe)6s^24f^{14}5d^4$ |
| V | $(Ar)4s^23d^3$ | Re | $(Xe)6s^24f^{14}5d^5$ |
| Cr | $(Ar)4s^13d^5$ | Os | $(Xe)6s^24f^{14}5d^6$ |
| Mn | $(Ar)4s^23d^5$ | Ir | $(Xe)6s^24f^{14}5d^7$ |
| Fe | $(Ar)4s^23d^6$ | Pt | $(Xe)6s^14f^{14}5d^9$ |
| Co | $(Ar)4s^23d^7$ | Au | $(Xe)6s^14f^{14}5d^{10}$ |
| Ni | $(Ar)4s^23d^8$ | Hg | $(Xe)6s^24f^{14}5d^{10}$ |
| Cu | $(Ar)4s^13d^{10}$ | Tl | $(Xe)6s^24f^{14}5d^{10}6p^1$ |
| Zn | $(Ar)4s^23d^{10}$ | Pb | $(Xe)6s^24f^{14}5d^{10}6p^2$ |
| Ga | $(Ar)4s^23d^{10}4p^1$ | Bi | $(Xe)6s^24f^{14}5d^{10}6p^3$ |
| Ge | $(Ar)4s^23d^{10}4p^2$ | Po | $(Xe)6s^24f^{14}5d^{10}6p^4$ |
| As | $(Ar)4s^23d^{10}4p^3$ | At | $(Xe)6s^24f^{14}5d^{10}6p^5$ |
| Se | $(Ar)4s^23d^{10}4p^4$ | Rn | $(Xe)6s^24f^{14}5d^{10}6p^6$ |
| Br | $(Ar)4s^23d^{10}4p^5$ | Fr | $(Rn)7s^1$ |
| Kr | $(Ar)4s^23d^{10}4p^6$ | Ra | $(Rn)7s^2$ |
| Rb | $(Kr)5s^1$ | Ac | $(Rn)7s^26d^1$ |
| Sr | $(Kr)5s^2$ | Th | $(Rn)7s^26d^2$ |
| Y | $(Kr)5s^24d^1$ | Pa | $(Rn)7s^25f^26d^1$ |
| Zr | $(Kr)5s^24d^2$ | U | $(Rn)7s^25f^36d^1$ |
| Nb | $(Kr)5s^14d^4$ | Np | $(Rn)7s^25f^46d^1$ |
| Mo | $(Kr)5s^14d^5$ | Pu | $(Rn)7s^25f^6$ |
| Tc | $(Kr)5s^24d^5$ | Am | $(Rn)7s^25f^7$ |
| Ru | $(Kr)5s^14d^7$ | Cm | $(Rn)7s^25f^76d^1$ |
| Rh | $(Kr)5s^14d^8$ | Bk | $(Rn)7s^25f^9$ |
| Pd | $(Kr)4d^{10}$ | Cf | $(Rn)7s^25f^{10}$ |
| Ag | $(Kr)5s^14d^{10}$ | Es | $(Rn)7s^25f^{11}$ |
| Cd | $(Kr)5s^24d^{10}$ | Fm | $(Rn)7s^25f^{12}$ |
| In | $(Kr)5s^24d^{10}5p^1$ | Md | $(Rn)7s^25f^{13}$ |
| Sn | $(Kr)5s^24d^{10}5p^2$ | No | $(Rn)7s^25f^{14}$ |
| Sb | $(Kr)5s^24d^{10}5p^3$ | Lr | $(Rn)7s^25f^{14}6d^1$ |
| Te | $(Kr)5s^24d^{10}5p^4$ | | |

*The noble gas symbol in parentheses is an abbreviation that simplifies writing the configuration. It signifies all the electrons and orbitals of that atom. For example, (Ne) signifies $1s^2, 2s^2, 2p^6$. Substituting this for the electronic configuration given for sodium in the table gives $1s^2, 2s^2, 2p^6, 3s^1$.

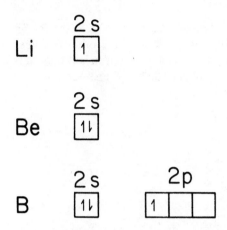

Before we can write the box diagram for carbon, we have to know another fact. We have mentioned that the three $p$ orbitals with the same $n$ value are all equal in energy. The term degenerate is used to mean equal in energy. The $d$ orbitals of a given $n$ value are also degenerate. Now, when electrons are added to degenerate orbitals, they fill up these orbitals with one electron at a time and all the electrons have the same spin. The electrons do not pair up in a given box (orbital) until they have to. This is called **Hund's rule** or the **law of maximum multiplicity.** The idea is demonstrated in the box diagram representations of C, N, O, F, and Ne that follow:

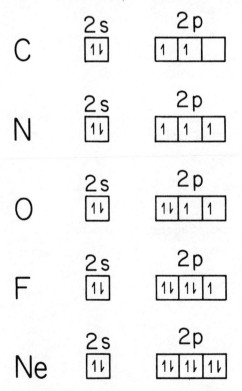

Since all the elements in the carbon family (the vertical column in the periodic table headed by carbon) have the same valence electron configuration, they all have the same box diagram representation as carbon except for the labels over the box; for example, Sn has $5s$ and $5p$ labels where C has $2s$ and $2p$ labels. The same is true of the other families.

In the box diagrams of the transition elements, the $d$ orbitals with a principal quantum number one less than that of the valence $s$ electrons are being filled. For example,

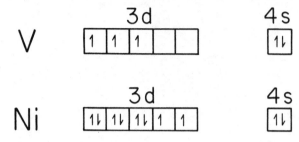

The box diagram is also used to represent the electronic configurations of ions. The cation of a main group atom is represented by removing the last electrons added in the Aufbau procedure. However, when the configuration of a transition metal ion is represented, the first and second electrons of the neutral atom configuration to be removed are from the $4s$ orbital (recall that in the Aufbau order, the last electron added went into the $d$ orbital). The box diagram for $Ni^{2+}$ is:

For this reason the $4s$ is often placed after the $3d$ box even in neutral atoms.

In summary, to write a box diagram we:

1. Determine the number of valence electrons.
2. Add the valence electrons to boxes that represent $s$, $p$, $d$ orbitals and so forth.
3. Do not pair up electrons in degenerate orbitals until we have to; that is, obey Hund's rule.

**TEST 8–2**

A.  Using the box diagram representation, indicate the electronic structure of:
   1. Br

2. Ba

3. Cr

4. $Fe^{3+}$

5. $Sn^{2+}$

6. Zr

## 8–3 LEWIS STRUCTURES

When atoms combine to form molecules with covalent type bonds, the electrons in the bond are shared by both atoms. In the molecules formed, the electrons usually fill all of the available valence orbitals on both of the atoms involved in the bond. For example, in the H-F molecule, we could represent the valence electrons in this molecule with the following formula:

$$\mathrm{H} \overset{\cdot}{\times} \underset{\cdot\cdot}{\overset{\cdot\cdot}{\mathrm{F}}}:$$

where the dots represent the seven electrons that the fluorine originally had and × represents hydrogen's original electron. We use different symbols for these electrons only for bookkeeping purposes. In the HF molecule all the electrons are indistinguishable. The dot and the × in between the two atoms constitute a pair of bonding electrons. The pair is being shared by both atoms. This shared pair in effect fills the 1*s* orbital of hydrogen and also gives fluorine eight electrons to fill all its valence orbitals. In fact, we count the shared pair twice. This is what we mean when we say the pair is shared. The two electrons involved in this pair have opposite spins. The atoms have combined so as to fill all valence shell orbitals on the two atoms. Structures that indicate all the valence electrons, as in the HF example above, are called **Lewis structures.** The electrons in a Lewis structure that are not involved in bonding are called **non-bonding** or **lone pair** electrons.

The bond in the HF molecule is a covalent bond. However, the pair of electrons is not shared equally between the two atoms, because the fluorine atom attracts the shared electron density more strongly than does hydrogen. The tendency of an atom to attract bonding electron density is called **electronegativity.** Fluorine is more electronegative than hydrogen. The electronegativities of atoms are indicated in Figure 8–3. In general, one

EN increases →

EN decreases ↓

| | | | | | | | | | | | | | | | | |
|---|---|---|---|---|---|---|---|---|---|---|---|---|---|---|---|---|
| 1<br>H<br>2.1 | | | | | | | | | | | | | | | | |
| 3<br>Li<br>1.0 | 4<br>Be<br>1.5 | | | | | | | | | | | 5<br>B<br>2.0 | 6<br>C<br>2.5 | 7<br>N<br>3.0 | 8<br>O<br>3.5 | 9<br>F<br>4.0 |
| 11<br>Na<br>0.9 | 12<br>Mg<br>1.2 | | | | | | | | | | | 13<br>Al<br>1.5 | 14<br>Si<br>1.8 | 15<br>P<br>2.1 | 16<br>S<br>2.5 | 17<br>Cl<br>3.0 |
| 19<br>K<br>0.8 | 20<br>Ca<br>1.0 | 21<br>Sc<br>1.3 | 22<br>Ti<br>1.5 | 23<br>V<br>1.6 | 24<br>Cr<br>1.6 | 25<br>Mn<br>1.5 | 26<br>Fe<br>1.8 | 27<br>Co<br>1.8 | 28<br>Ni<br>1.8 | 29<br>Cu<br>1.9 | 30<br>Zn<br>1.6 | 31<br>Ga<br>1.6 | 32<br>Ge<br>1.8 | 33<br>As<br>2.0 | 34<br>Se<br>2.4 | 35<br>Br<br>2.8 |
| 37<br>Rb<br>0.8 | 38<br>Sr<br>1.0 | 39<br>Y<br>1.2 | 40<br>Zr<br>1.4 | 41<br>Nb<br>1.6 | 42<br>Mo<br>1.8 | 43<br>Tc<br>1.9 | 44<br>Ru<br>2.2 | 45<br>Rh<br>2.2 | 46<br>Pd<br>2.2 | 47<br>Ag<br>1.9 | 48<br>Cd<br>1.7 | 49<br>In<br>1.7 | 50<br>Sn<br>1.8 | 51<br>Sb<br>1.9 | 52<br>Te<br>2.1 | 53<br>I<br>2.5 |
| 55<br>Cs<br>0.7 | 56<br>Ba<br>0.9 | 57–71<br>La–Lu<br>1.1–1.2 | 72<br>Hf<br>1.3 | 73<br>Ta<br>1.5 | 74<br>W<br>1.7 | 75<br>Re<br>1.9 | 76<br>Os<br>2.2 | 77<br>Ir<br>2.2 | 78<br>Pt<br>2.2 | 79<br>Au<br>2.4 | 80<br>Hg<br>1.9 | 81<br>Tl<br>1.8 | 82<br>Pb<br>1.8 | 83<br>Bi<br>1.9 | 84<br>Po<br>2.0 | 85<br>At<br>2.2 |
| 87<br>Fr<br>0.7 | 88<br>Ra<br>0.9 | 89–<br>Ac–<br>1.1–1.7 | | | | | | | | | | | | | | |

**Figure 8–3** Electronegativities of the elements. The electronegativity is seen to decrease as we proceed down the column for a family of main group elements, and increase for main group elements as we proceed from left to right in a given row.

notes that the electronegativity of the atoms of the main group elements increases as one moves from left to right and from the bottom to the top of the periodic table. Though the bond in H-F is of the covalent type, it is referred to as a **polar covalent** bond because the pair is not equally shared. In the H-H molecule, where the pair is equally shared by both atoms, the bond is called a **non-polar** or **pure covalent** bond. If the electronegativity difference between the two bonded atoms is 2.0 or greater, there will be nearly complete transfer of the electron to the more electronegative atom and the bonding will be called **ionic**. The Lewis structure of an ionic compound would be written as shown below for sodium fluoride:

$$[Na]^+[:\overset{..}{\underset{..}{F}}:]^- \text{ or as } [Na]^+ [\,|\overline{F}|\,]^-$$

In the latter case the line represents a pair of electrons and the superscript shows the minus charge.

Using lines to represent the formula of HF, we would write:

$$H - \overline{F}|$$

with the horizontal line joining the two atoms representing the bonding pair of electrons. The differences in the charge distribution of the electrons involved in bonding are illustrated in Figure 8· 4 for molecules containing pure covalent ($H_2$), polar covalent (HF), and ionic (LiF) bonds. Note the different ways in which the electron density is attracted by the two atoms.

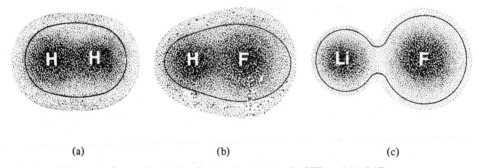

(a)                    (b)                    (c)

**Figure 8–4**    Electron charge cloud distribution in (a) $H_2$, (b) HF, and (c) LiF. The solid line indicates the overall molecular shape.

In order to write the Lewis structure of a polyatomic molecule (one containing several atoms), you must know which atoms are bonded to each other. The chemist has several tools for determining this information, but this topic is beyond the scope of this chapter. You will be provided this information in the form of a skeleton formula. This type of formula indicates which atoms are directly bonded by joining them with a line. In writing a Lewis structure, the following steps should be followed:

1. Begin by writing the skeleton structure if it is not given.
2. Total the valence electrons of all the atoms that make up the molecule. For positive ions, subtract one electron for each positive charge; for negative ions, add one electron for each negative charge.
3. Subtract two electrons from the total in (2) for each bond contained in the skeleton formula in (1).
4. Take the remaining total from part (3), and distribute these electrons over the

skeleton formula so as to give hydrogen a share of two (which it will have from the bond to it), and atoms from the second or higher rows of the periodic table a share of eight. Use single bonds and lone pairs to do this. If there are electrons remaining after all atoms have eight, there will be third or higher row atoms in the molecule. These atoms can be given ten or twelve electrons if necessary.

5. If upon carrying out the operations in (4) you find that there are too few electrons to satisfy all the atoms, make double or triple bonds. One double bond will take care of a deficiency of two electrons because it takes a lone pair assigned to one atom and shares it between two atoms. Two double bonds or one triple bond will take care of a deficiency of four electrons.

We shall illustrate these rules with some sample problems before discussing some additional complicating factors.

## Sample Problem 8–3

Write the Lewis structure of $NH_3$.

### Solution

Step 1, write the skeleton formula. Since we know hydrogen can only be bound covalently to one other atom, we write

$$N \begin{matrix} \diagup H \\ {-} H \\ \diagdown H \end{matrix}$$

Step 2, we total eight valence electrons (three hydrogens have 3 and nitrogen has 5.)
Step 3, $8 - 6 = 2$ (The six corresponds to the three bonds.) A pair of electrons.
Step 4,

$$|N \begin{matrix} \diagup H \\ {-} H \\ \diagdown H \end{matrix}$$

## Sample Problem 8–4

Write the Lewis structure of $SO_4^{2-}$, given the skeletal formula

$$\begin{matrix} & O & {}^{2-} \\ & | & \\ O & {-} S {-} & O \\ & | & \\ & O & \end{matrix}$$

## Solution

Step 2, we total 32 valence electrons (four oxygens have 24, one S has 6, plus 2 for the $-2$ charge).

Step 3, $32 - 8 = 24$ (Eight for the bonds) Add 12 lone pairs, three each to four oxygens.

Step 4,

$$
\begin{array}{c}
|\overline{O}|\ ^{2-} \\
| \\
|\overline{O}-S-\overline{O}| \\
| \\
|\underline{O}|
\end{array}
$$

## Sample Problem 8–5

Write the Lewis structure for $ClF_3$, given the skeleton formula

$$
\begin{array}{c}
F-Cl-F \\
| \\
F
\end{array}
$$

## Solution

Step 2, we total 28 valence electrons (three fluorines have 21 and chlorine has 7).
Step 3, $28 - 6 = 22$
Step 4,

$$
\begin{array}{c}
|\overline{F}-\overset{\wedge}{Cl}-\overline{F}| \\
| \\
|\underline{F}|
\end{array}
$$

Chlorine is a third row element and can have more than eight electrons.

## Sample Problem 8–6

Write the Lewis structure for CO.

## Solution

Step 1, C—O
Step 2, we total 10 valence electrons (C has 4 and O has 6).
Step 3, 10 − 2 = 8

Step 4, $|\overline{C}\!-\!\overline{O}|$

Step 5, we are four electrons short, so there must be a triple bond:

$$|C \equiv O|$$

---

### TEST 8–3

A. The hydrogen peroxide molecule has the formula $H_2O_2$. There is an O—O bond in the molecule, and one hydrogen is attached to each oxygen. We shall answer some questions illustrating the logic to be used in drawing the Lewis structure.
   1. Complete step 1.

   2. Total up the valence electrons in the molecule.

   3. Complete step 3.

   4. Complete step 4.

   5. Is step 5 relevant?

B. The molecule acetylene has the following skeleton formula: H—C—C—H. We shall answer some questions pertinent to writing its Lewis structure.

1. Complete the second step.

2. Subtract the number of electrons in the skeleton formula from the total.

3. Distribute the electron total in step 2 over the skeleton.

4. Using single bonds, how many more electrons are needed to give all atoms eight?

5. Carry out step 5 and write a Lewis structure.

C. Some of the Group III elements form stable chloride, bromide, and iodide compounds that are exceptions to these rules because they have only six electrons around the central atom. $BCl_3$, with three B-Cl bonds, is an example. Draw its Lewis structure using the steps outlined above.

D.  By virtue of the fact that $BCl_3$ has only six electrons around boron, $BCl_3$ has a tendency to form compounds by reacting with substances that have a lone pair to furnish to boron. The reaction with $Cl^-$ leads to $BCl_4^-$ with four B-Cl bonds. Draw the Lewis structure of $BCl_4^-$.

---

Now for some added complications.

6.  Sometimes it is possible to write two or more plausible Lewis structures. The actual molecule is then said to be a **resonance hybrid** of these two Lewis structures. To describe the molecule, the two Lewis structures are written and connected with a double-headed arrow.

The resonance concept is a very important one and we shall devote the next section to a further discussion of its meaning. Here we are just interested in recognizing when it can exist. If you can write two or more plausible Lewis structures for a molecule *in which the arrangement of the atoms is the same* both should be written and connected with a double-headed arrow. Sample problem 8–7 illustrates this idea.

---

## Sample Problem 8–7

Write the Lewis structure of O—S—O.

## Solution

Step 2, we total 18 electrons (two oxygens have 12 and sulfur 6).
Step 3, $\underline{18 - 4} = 14$
Step 4, $|\overline{O}\!-\!\overline{S}\!-\!\overline{O}|$
Step 5, we are two electrons short, so we should make a double bond.
$$|\overline{O}\!-\!S\!=\!\overline{O}|$$
Step 6, we could just as well have written
$$|\overline{O}\!=\!\overline{S}\!-\!\overline{O}|$$
Therefore, we have resonance:
$$|\overline{O}\!=\!\overline{S}\!-\!\overline{O}| \leftrightarrow |\underline{\overline{O}}\!-\!\overline{S}\!=\!\overline{O}|$$

---

## 8–4    RESONANCE

As mentioned above, whenever two or more plausible Lewis structures can be written for a molecule, the actual molecule is described as a resonance hybrid of these Lewis structures. The actual molecular structure will not correspond to any of the resonance structures, but is a *hybrid* of them in the same way that a mongrel dog is a hybrid of pure breeds. For example, the $SO_2$ molecule does not contain one single S—O bond and one double S=O bond as the structures written in sample Problem 8–8 imply. Instead, both bonds are identical and are an average of a double and single bond; that is, one and one half bonds. (This can be experimentally verified.) The concept of resonance is introduced to account for the fact that the actual structure cannot be adequately described with a conventional Lewis structure. The different Lewis structures that can be written for a molecule in which resonance occurs are called **resonance forms,** to distinguish them from a true structure, which is a description of the electronic structure of the molecule. It should be emphasized that resonance does *not* imply that the molecule rapidly oscillates between the resonance forms. Instead it is a single molecule with an electron distribution given by the average of the forms.

One further example of resonance is illustrated by the carbonate ion, for which the following three resonance forms can be drawn:

Again the actual ion is a hybrid of these three forms.

The term **bond order** is used to indicate the amount of bonding between any two atoms in a molecule. A single bond has a bond order of one, and a double bond has a bond order of two. In $CO_3{}^{2-}$, each bond is an average of one double bond and two single bonds, leading to an average of one and one-third bonds joining the carbon to each oxygen. The C—O bond order is 1⅓. Using similar reasoning, the S—O bond order in the $SO_2$ molecule is 1½.

Some molecules contain an odd number of electrons, so it is not possible to assign each of the atoms in the molecule eight electrons in a Lewis structure. An even number of electrons is required to write a conventional Lewis structure. In molecules containing an odd number of electrons, resonance often exists, spreading the odd electron over all the atoms in the molecule. The N—O molecule illustrates this behavior. The two resonance forms are:

$$|N=\underline{O}| \quad \leftrightarrow \quad |\underline{N}=\overline{O}$$

The two forms are not equal in energy because the more electronegative oxygen will be less satisfied with seven electrons than nitrogen would be if it had seven electrons. Thus, the form on the left is more stable and is said to contribute more to the actual structure. Experiments can be carried out to indicate quantitatively the relative importance of the two forms, but they are beyond the scope of our treatment. In any molecule containing an odd number of electrons, resonance forms can be written that distribute the odd electron over all the atoms in the molecule.

## TEST 8-4

A.  The nitrite ion has the formula $NO_2^-$ and has two N—O bonds.
    1. Write the skeleton formulas.

    2. Count the total number of electrons in the ion.

    3. Perform the next step in writing the Lewis structure.

    4. Distribute the electrons over the structure using single bonds.

    5. Is step 5 necessary? If so, do it.

    6. Are there resonance forms? If so, write them.

    7. What is the N—O bond order?

B.   The molecule $ClO_2$ has two Cl—O bonds.
   1. Write the skeleton formula.

   2. Carry out the next step in writing the Lewis structure.

   3. Carry out the third step.

   4. Distribute the electrons over the structure using single bonds.

   5. Are multiple bonds needed? If so, draw them.

   6. Do resonance forms exist? If so, draw them.

C.   Using the systematic approach described for writing Lewis structures, write one for $N_2$.

D.   Draw the Lewis structure for

$$\begin{array}{c} H \\ \diagdown \\ H \diagup \end{array} C - \underset{\underset{H}{|}}{\overset{\overset{H}{|}}{C}} - \underset{}{\overset{\overset{H}{|}}{C}} - O$$

E.   Draw the Lewis structure for

$$O - \underset{\underset{O}{|}}{S} - O$$

Most texts adequately cover and provide a lot of examples of the rules for predicting the geometry of these molecules. Accordingly, we refer you to one of them for problems of this type. The same is true of the topics of hybridization and molecular orbital theory. We mention this so that you will be aware that they are important topics, even though we do not discuss them.

# Exercises

**Electronic Configurations of Atoms and Ions**

1.  Write the electronic configurations (using $s$, $p$, etc. notation) of the following atoms:
    (a) Mn, (b) Br, (c) Na, (d) Se, (e) Fe, (f) Kr, (g) Ir, (h) Cr

2.  Using $s$, $p$, etc. notation, write the electron configuration of the following ions:
    (a) $Rb^+$, (b) $Mg^{2+}$, (c) $Cr^{2+}$, (d) $Cr^{3+}$, (e) $Sn^{2+}$, (f) $Bi^{3+}$, (g) $Co^{3+}$

3.  Using the box diagram representation, indicate the electronic configuration of the valence electrons in:
    (a) Al, (b) Te, (c) Ni, (d) Ba, (e) Fe, (f) Ce, (g) Tc, (h) W, (i) V

4.  Using the box diagram representation, indicate the atomic structure of:
    (a) Ge, (b) $Co^{3+}$, (c) $Ni^{2+}$, (d) $Fe^{3+}$, (e) $Sn^{2+}$, (f) $Cr^{3+}$, (g) $Ti^{3+}$

5.  Arrange the following orbitals in order of increasing energy: $2s$, $4s$, $5p$, $3d$, $6s$, $2p$, $4f$, $3p$

6.  Which of the following orbitals cannot exist in an atom? $7p$, $5f$, $2d$, $4d$, $3f$, $5p$

7.  How many electrons can be accommodated in:
    (a) all of the $4d$ orbitals?
    (b) all of the $5f$ orbitals?
    (c) all of the $6p$ orbitals?

8.  What elements are represented by the following box diagram?

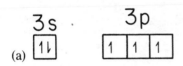

(a)

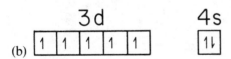

(b)

(c)

9.  What elements are represented by the following electron configurations?

(a) $1s^2, 2s^2, 2p^6, 3s^2, 3p^6, 4s^2$
(b) $1s^2, 2s^2, 2p^4$
(c) $1s^2, 2s^2, 2p^6, 3s^2, 3p^6, 4s^2, 3d^3$

10. Identify the first element in the periodic table that has:
    (a) three $4p$ electrons.
    (b) three electrons in a $d$ orbital set.
    (c) two electrons in the $4d$ orbitals.
    (d) one electron in a $5s$ orbital.

## Lewis Structures

11. Draw Lewis structures and indicate whether the bonds are ionic, polar covalent, or pure covalent for the following molecules.
    (a)

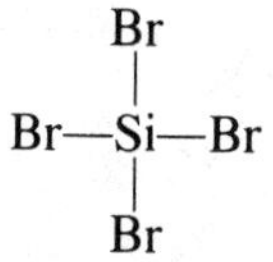

$$\begin{array}{c} Br \\ | \\ Br-Si-Br \\ | \\ Br \end{array}$$

    (b) $SiH_4$
    (c) $N-O^+$
    (d) $N-O^-$
    (e) $F-N-N-F$
    (f)

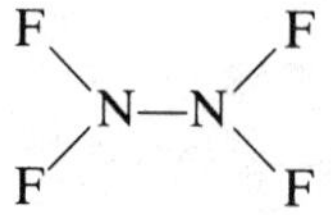

$$\begin{array}{cc} F & F \\ \diagdown & \diagup \\ N-N & \\ \diagup & \diagdown \\ F & F \end{array}$$

    (g) $H-C-C-H$
    (h)

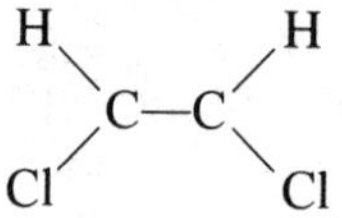

$$\begin{array}{cc} H & H \\ \diagdown & \diagup \\ C-C & \\ \diagup & \diagdown \\ Cl & Cl \end{array}$$

    (i)

$$\begin{array}{cc} H & H \\ \diagdown & \diagup \\ Cl-C-C-Cl \\ \diagup & \diagdown \\ H & H \end{array}$$

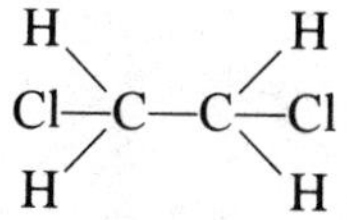

(j)

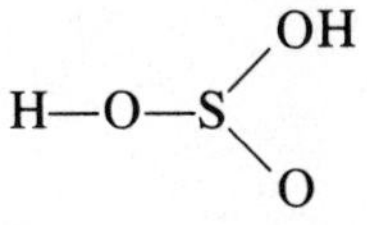

$$H-O-S\begin{matrix} \diagup OH \\ \diagdown O \end{matrix}$$

(k) $Rb_2O$

12. Draw Lewis structures for the following, being sure to indicate resonance forms where they exist:

(a)

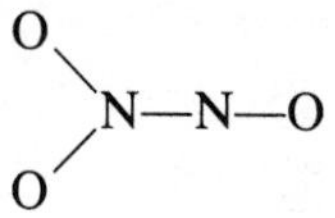

$$\begin{matrix} O \diagdown \\ O \diagup \end{matrix} N-N-O$$

(b) $O-Cl-O^-$

(c)

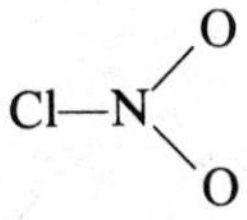

$$Cl-N\begin{matrix} \diagup O \\ \diagdown O \end{matrix}$$

(d) $O-C-O$

(e) $O-C$

(f) $O-O-O$

(g)

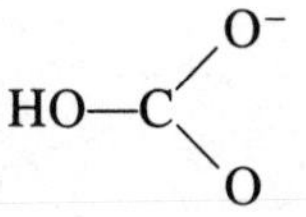

$$HO-C\begin{matrix} \diagup O^- \\ \diagdown O \end{matrix}$$

(h)

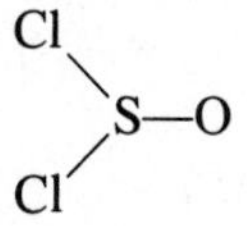

$$\begin{matrix} Cl \diagdown \\ Cl \diagup \end{matrix} S-O$$

(i)

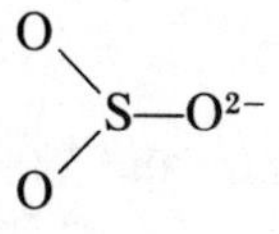

$$\begin{matrix} O \diagdown \\ O \diagup \end{matrix} S-O^{2-}$$

(j)

$$\begin{matrix} F & F \\ & \diagup \\ F-S-F \\ \diagup & \\ F & F \end{matrix}$$

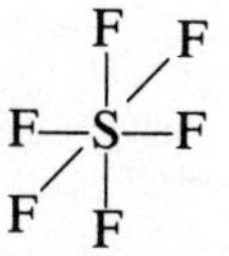

(k)

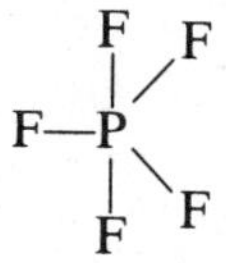

$$\begin{array}{ccc} & F & F \\ & | & \diagup \\ F\!-\!\!\!\!&P& \\ & | & \diagdown \\ & F & F \end{array}$$

(l) O—N—O

13. Draw Lewis structures for the following, being sure to indicate resonance forms where they exist:
   (a) F—Xe—F
   (b)

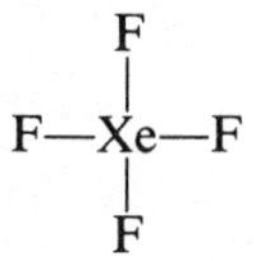

$$\begin{array}{c} F \\ | \\ F\!-\!Xe\!-\!F \\ | \\ F \end{array}$$

   (c) $XeF_6$
   (d) $ClO^-$
   (e) $OClO^-$
   (f)

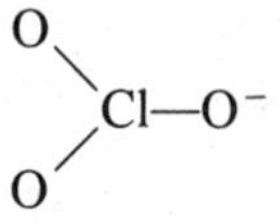

$$\begin{array}{c} O \diagdown \\ \quad\ \ Cl\!-\!O^- \\ O \diagup \end{array}$$

   (g) $ClO_4^-$
   (h) NaCl
   (i)

$$\begin{array}{c} H \diagdown \\ \quad\ \ C\!-\!O \\ H \diagup \end{array}$$

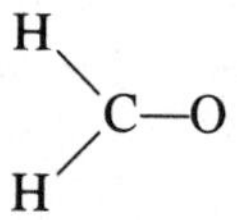

   (j) H—C—N

14. Indicate the bond order of each of the different bonds in the molecules in problems 11c and d, and 12a, f, g, and k.

15. Draw Lewis structures and indicate bond orders for the following:
   (a)

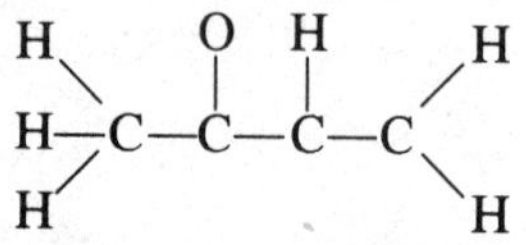

$$\begin{array}{ccccccc} H & & O & H & & H \\ \diagdown & & \| & | & & \diagup \\ H\!-\!C&-&C&-&C&-&C \\ \diagup & & & | & & \diagdown \\ H & & & H & & H \end{array}$$

(b)

$$
\begin{array}{c}
\text{H} \\
\text{H}-\text{C}-\text{N} \\
\text{H}
\end{array}
\begin{array}{c}
\text{O} \\
\text{O}
\end{array}
$$

(c)

$$
\begin{array}{c}
\text{O} \\
\text{H}-\text{C}-\text{N} \\
\end{array}
\begin{array}{c}
\text{H} \\
\text{H}
\end{array}
$$

(d) O—Cl—O

**Verbalizing General Concepts**

16. Answer each of the following in your own words:
    (a) Describe what is indicated by the principal quantum number, $n$.
    (b) What do the subscripts on the $p$ orbitals indicate?
    (c) Indicate the labels of all the orbitals that exist for $n=4$ (do not worry about distinguishing labels for $d$ and $f$ orbitals, but only indicate how many there are).
    (d) What is meant by the term Aufbau order?
    (e) What is indicated in a box diagram that is not indicated with an Aufbau representation?
    (f) What is the difference between a core electron and a valence electron?
    (g) Define the term degeneracy and indicate its meaning in terms of Hund's rule.
    (h) Define the term electronegativity and indicate some general trends in its values relative to the ordering of elements in the periodic table.
    (i) What does the term resonance indicate?
    (j) Describe the meaning of the term bond order.
    (k) Explain why the following are not resonance forms:

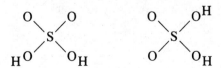

**Multiple Choice Questions**

17. Which of the following electronic configurations would correspond to a halogen?

(a) $1s^22s^22p^63s^23p^3$, (b) $1s^22s^22p^5$, (c) $1s^22s^22p^63s^1$, (d) $1s^22s^22p^63s^23p^1$, (e) none of these.

18.   Which of the following is the configuration of a neutral transition element atom?
(a) $1s^22s^22p^63s^23p^4$, (b) $1s^22s^22p^63s^23p^63d^3$, (c) $1s^22s^22p^63s^23p^64s^23d^3$, (d) $1s^22s^22p^63s^23p^64s^23d^{10}4p^1$ (e) more than one of the above.

19.   Which of the following would be a Group IV element?
(a) $1s^22s^22p^6$, (b) $1s^22s^22p^4$, (c) $1s^22p^4$, (d) $1s^22s^22p^63s^2$, (e) none of these.

20.   Which box diagram represents the ground state electron configuration for the oxygen atom?

(a)  2s [1]  2p [1][1][1]

(b)  2s [1↓]  2p [1↓][1↓][ ]

(c)  2s [1↓]  2p [1↓][1↓][1↓]

(d)  2s [1↓]  2p [1↓][1][↓]

(e)  2s [1↓]  2p [1↓][1][1]

21.   How many different orbitals can have principal quantum number $n = 3$?
(a) 4, (b) 9, (c) 6, (d) 5, (e) 18

22.   Identify the element which, as a single positively charged ion, $X^+$, has an electronic configuration of $1s^2,2s^2,2p^6$.
(a) F, (b) Ne, (c) Na, (d) K, (e) none of these.

Indicate the answers to questions 23 through 25 by using the following.
    (a) one electron
    (b) two electrons
    (c) three electrons
    (d) four electrons
    (e) none of these

23.   Germanium has _____ electrons in the $4p$ orbitals.

24.   Ti has _____ in its $d$-orbitals.

25.  Fe has _____ that are unpaired in its $d$-orbitals.

26.  The $Fe^{3+}$ ion is represented by the box diagram

(a)  | 1↓ | 1 | 1 | 1 | 1 |    | 1↓ |

(b)  | 1 | 1 | 1 |   |   |    | 1↓ |

(c)  | 1↓ | 1 | 1 | 1 | 1 |    |   |

(d)  | 1 | 1 | 1 | 1 | 1 |    |   |

(e) none of these have the right number of electrons.

27.  Which of the following has a $p^3$ configuration?
     (a) Ba, (b) Ga, (c) V, (d) Bi, (e) none of these.

28.  In which pair do *both* compounds exhibit predominantly ionic bonding?
     (a) $SO_2$, HCl; (b) $KNO_3$, $CH_4$; (c) NaF, MgO; (d) KCl, $CO_2$; (e) $CH_4$, $SO_2$

.29.  Which atom has the highest electronegativity?
     (a) F, (b) Cl, (c) Br, (d) I, (e) N

30.  The most reasonable Lewis structure for HOCl is

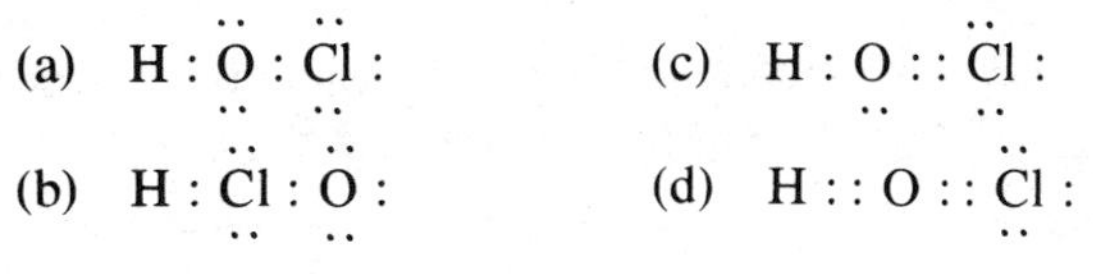

     (a)  H : Ö : Cl̈ :          (c)  H : O :: Cl̈ :

     (b)  H : C̈l : Ö :          (d)  H :: O :: Cl̈ :

                                  (e)  none of these

31.  Which of the following is the most correct Lewis structure for $XeF_2$?

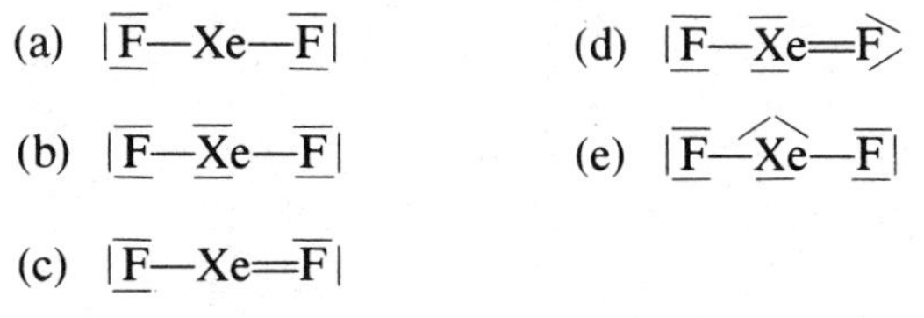

     (a)  |F̄—Xe—F̄|          (d)  |F̄—X̄e=F⌢

     (b)  |F̄—X̄e—F̄|          (e)  |F̄—⌢Xe—F̄|

     (c)  |F̄—Xe=F̄|

32.  Which of the following is the most correct Lewis structure for $SCl_2$?

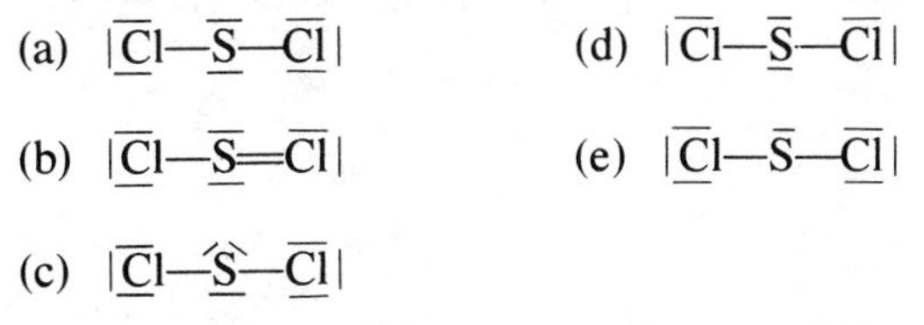

     (a)  |C̄l—S̄—C̄l|          (d)  |C̄l—S̲—C̄l|

     (b)  |C̄l—S̄=C̄l|          (e)  |C̄l—S—C̄l|

     (c)  |C̄l—⌢S̲—C̄l|

33. Indicate which of the following is a valid Lewis structure for $O_3$.

 (a) 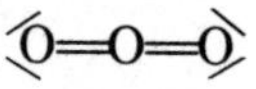 $\overset{\cdot\cdot}{O}{=}O{=}\overset{\cdot\cdot}{O}$

 (b) 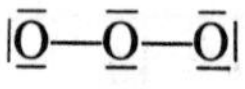 $|\overline{O}{-}\overline{O}{-}\overline{O}|$

 (c) 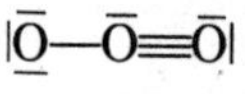 $|\overline{O}{-}\overline{O}{=}\overline{O}|$

 (d) 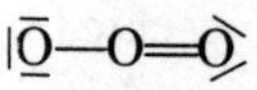 $|\overline{O}{-}O{=}\overset{\cdot\cdot}{O}$

 (e) none of these

34. Indicate which of the following is a valid Lewis structure for $I_3^-$.

 (a) 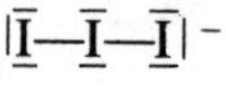 $|\overline{I}{-}\overline{I}{-}\overline{I}|^-$

 (b) 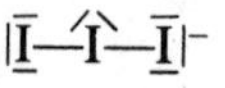 $|\overline{I}{-}\overset{\cdot}{I}{-}\overline{I}|^-$

 (c) 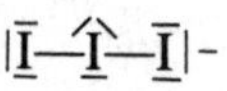 $|\overline{I}{-}\overset{\cdot}{I}{-}\overline{I}|^-$

 (d) 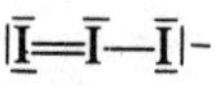 $|\overline{I}{=}\overline{I}{-}\overline{I}|^-$

 (e) none of these

35. Which one of the following molecules exhibits resonance?

 (a) $H_2S$

 (b) $NH_3$

 (c) $SO_2$

 (d) $SO_2Cl_2$

 (e) $O_2$

36. Which one of the following molecules does *not* exhibit resonance?
 (a), $SO_2$, (b) $NO_2^-$, (c) $H_2S$, (d) $O_3$, (e) two of these.

# 9

# OXIDATION STATE, REDOX REACTIONS AND NOMENCLATURE

## Chapter Objectives

### (Begin each of the following with "You should master . . .")

1. the assignment of oxidation state numbers to atoms in molecules or ions.
2. the prediction of formulas and the naming of compounds using oxidation state considerations.
3. balancing redox equations in acidic or basic solution by the method of half reactions.
4. the definition of oxidation, reduction, oxidizing agent, and reducing agent.

The oxidation state is a number assigned to an element that enables us to keep track of the electrons in a molecule. The concept is of use in balancing complicated equations. If we know the most common oxidation states of elements, we shall be able to predict the formulas of many polar covalent compounds directly. The concept of oxidation state also is needed to be able to name compounds by the systematic procedures employed by chemists. These ideas will be developed in this chapter.

## 9–1    OXIDATION STATE CONVENTIONS

The assignment of oxidation state involves the following set of rules, which must be memorized and consistently employed:

1. *The oxidation state of every atom in the pure element is defined as zero.* For example, the oxidation state of H in $H_2$ is zero, and that of O in $O_2$ is also zero.
2. *For any ion consisting of only one element, the oxidation state of that element is the same as the charge of the ion.* For example, the oxidation state of Cu in $Cu^{++}$ is +2 and that of Cl in $Cl^-$ is −1.
3. *In a polar covalent molecule, the atoms are assigned oxidation states that are equal to the charges the atoms would have if the shared electrons were assigned*

*arbitrarily to the more electronegative atom.* In a pure covalent bond, the bonding electrons are divided equally between the atoms. According to this rule, the four bonding electrons in $H_2O$ are assigned to oxygen, giving it a $-2$ oxidation state. That is, it would be a $-2$ ion if it had all four bonding electrons. Each hydrogen is then left with no electrons assigned, so each hydrogen has an oxidation state of $+1$.

4. *The sum of the positive oxidation states must equal the sum of the negative oxidation states in a neutral molecule.* For any ion, *the sum of the oxidation states of the various elements must equal the charge on the ion.* For example, in the neutral water molecule the sum of the oxidation states of the two hydrogens is $+2$ and that of the oxygen is $-2$. In sample problem 9–1, we shall see how this rule applies to ions.

## Sample Problem 9–1

Determine the oxidation states of all the atoms in $NH_4^+$.

### Solution

If all the electrons in the bonds are assigned to nitrogen, its oxidation state becomes $-3$. The hydrogens then each have an oxidation state of $+1$. The positive oxidation states total $+4$. The sum of the positive and negative oxidation states equals $+1$, the charge on the ammonium ion.

$$N = -3$$
$$(4)(H) = +4$$
$$\overline{\phantom{(4)(H) = +4}}$$
$$+1 \text{ is the charge on the ion, } NH_4^+$$

This problem illustrates rules 3 and 4.

## Sample Problem 9–2

Determine the oxidation state of all the atoms in $Cl_2$.

### Solution

Using rules 1 or 3, we conclude that the oxidation state is zero.

Often the Lewis structure of a molecule is not known, or it is too much trouble to write it. The following generalizations, which are a consequence of the rules described above, make it possible to determine the oxidation state without writing the Lewis structure or employing rule 3. (Note, application of rule 3 requires that we know the Lewis structure.)

1. The oxidation state of O in most oxygen-containing compounds is $-2$. Exceptions to this rule include the peroxides. You will be told when you are dealing with a peroxide. In peroxide compounds the oxidation state of oxygen is $-1$. Other exceptions exist, but they are rare.
2. The oxidation state of H in most hydrogen-containing compounds is $+1$. The hydrides of the alkali and alkaline earth metals, where H has an oxidation state of $-1$, are the only exceptions to this rule.
3. The oxidation state of the alkali metals in most compounds is $+1$ and for the alkaline earth metals it is $+2$.
4. The oxidation state of the halogens in the halides ($F^-$, $Cl^-$, $Br^-$, and $I^-$) is $-1$.
5. The oxidation state of S in sulfide is $-2$.
6. The maximum oxidation state for an atom is the positive number equal to the number of electrons an atom has in the valence shell $s$ or $p$ orbitals (transition elements do not obey this rule); e.g., Al is $+3$, P is $+5$, Cl is $+7$, etc. For Groups IV, V, VI, and VII, the minimum oxidation state is given by the negative number corresponding to the number of electrons needed to fill the valence shell $s$ and $p$ orbitals; e.g., Cl is $-1$, S is $-2$, P is $-3$.

We shall illustrate the use of these generalizations in determining the oxidation states of elements in a compound in sample problem 9–3.

## Sample Problem 9–3

Determine the oxidation states of the elements in $SO_3^{2-}$.

## Solution

The oxidation state of oxygen is $-2$, so three oxygens total up to $-6$. The charge on the ion is $-2$, so the oxidation state of sulfur must be $+4$;

$$3(-2) + S(\text{ox. st.}) = -2 \text{ (charge on ion)}$$
$$S(\text{ox. st.}) = +4$$

Note that this ion is not a sulfide because the oxidation state of sulfur is not $-2$.

## Sample Problem 9–4

Determine the oxidation state of all the atoms in $KMnO_4$.

## Solution

Beginning with those elements with a single common oxidation state, we write:

$$4\,O = 4\,(-2) = -8$$
$$K = +1 = +1$$
$$\overline{\text{difference} = -7}$$

To have a neutral compound, the Mn oxidation state must equal $+7$; that is, $+1+7-8 = 0$.

---

### TEST 9–1

    A.   Consider the compound $Na_2Cr_2O_7$.
        1. For which atoms can the oxidation state be written directly?

        2. Sum the oxidation states of the oxygen atoms and sodium atoms.

        3. What must the sum of the oxidation states of the two chromium atoms equal?

        4. What is the oxidation state of each Cr atom?

    B.   Consider the ion $CrO_2^{-}$.
        1. What is the total oxidation state of the oxygen atoms?

2. What is the charge on the ion?

3. According to rule 4, the oxidation state of the chromium is _____.
C. The oxidation state of Cu in copper metal is _____.
D. The oxidation state of carbon in $CH_3Cl$ is _____.
E. Consider the compound potassium peroxide, $K_2O_2$.
   1. What is the sum of the oxidation states of the two potassium ions?

2. What is the sum of the oxidation states of the two oxygens atoms?

3. What is the oxidation state of each oxygen?

# 9-2    FORMULA PREDICTION AND NOMENCLATURE

Oxidation state considerations can be used to predict the formulas of compounds. For example, we know that the maximum oxidation state for sulfur is +6 and that the oxidation state of oxygen in an oxide is −2. We would predict that the highest oxidation state oxide of sulfur has the formula $SO_3$. Similarly, the highest oxidation state of nitrogen is +5, so the oxide has the formula $N_2O_5$. The highest oxidation state halide of antimony is predicted to be $SbCl_5$. All of these predicted compounds exist. Although we might have predicted the compound $NCl_5$ to exist by using the above considerations, it apparently does not. A nitrogen atom is small enough that there is not enough space about the nitrogen for five chlorines (or fluorines, for that matter).

While the maximum oxidation state oxide is predicted as described above, many of these elements form other compounds as well. Nitrogen, for example, forms the following oxides: $N_2O$, $NO$, $NO_2$ and $N_2O_5$. The official nomenclature of these compounds distinguishes them by the use of the oxidation state in the name. They are named as follows:

$N_2O$ is nitrogen (I) oxide
$NO$ is nitrogen (II) oxide
$NO_2$ is nitrogen (IV) oxide
$N_2O_5$ is nitrogen (V) oxide

Whenever binary compounds exist in two or more oxidation states, they are named by indicating the oxidation states, as in the above examples. The chloride compounds formed by copper are named copper (I) chloride for CuCl and copper (II) chloride for $CuCl_2$. In the past these compounds were called cuprous chloride and cupric chloride. In general, the *ous* suffix is employed for the lower oxidation state, and the *ic* suffix is employed for the higher oxidation state compound. This nomenclature is not recommended, but we mention it because you may encounter it in your reading. Almost all transition metal ions exist in more than one oxidation state, so when we name compounds of these elements, we must always indicate the oxidation state. Many of the atoms in Groups III, IV, V, VI, and VII also have more than one oxidation state. The alkali metals and alkaline earths usually have oxidation states of +1 and +2, respectively, so the oxidation state is not indicated in the names of these compounds.

Compounds containing the OH group attached to a nonmetallic atom are acids; an example is $HNO_3$, which has the structure

$$H\!-\!\overline{\underline{O}}\!-\!N\!\!\underset{\diagdown \underline{O}}{\overset{\diagup \overline{O}}{ }}$$

When placed in water, the hydroxy compounds of non-metals ionize to produce $H_3O^+$ and an anion: e.g.,

$$HNO_3 + H_2O \rightarrow H_3O^+ + NO_3^-$$

The following rules for naming these acids and anions apply to all groups in the periodic table, but there are some exceptions in Group VII. The highest oxidation-state acid is generally most common and has a suffix *ic*; e.g., $HNO_3$ (oxidation state of N is +5) is called nit*ric* acid. If the acid contains one O atom less than found in the maximum oxidation state, the suffix changes from *ic* to *ous*; e.g., $HNO_2$ is nitrous acid.

If the acid contains two O atoms less than that in the highest oxidation state, the prefix *hypo-* and the suffix *-ous* are used; e.g., $(HNO)_2$ is called hyponitrous acid.

These rules apply to Group VII acids except that, using the chlorine compounds as examples, $HClO_3$ is called chloric acid instead of the maximum oxidation state acid $HClO_4$, which is called perchloric acid. In accord with the above rules, $HClO_2$ is called chlorous acid and HClO is called hypochlorous acid. Let me emphasize that though we write formulas for acids as $HNO_3$, $HClO_4$, HClO, etc., many are hydroxyl compounds with structures such as

The anions that are formed when these acids are dissolved in water are very stable and occur as an entity in many compounds; e.g., $NO_3^-$ occurs in $NaNO_3$, $Ca(NO_3)_2$, $Cu(NO_3)_2$, etc. The anion from an acid with an *ic* ending has the suffix *ate*; e.g., $NO_3^-$ from nitric acid is called nitrate. The compound $NaNO_3$ is called sodium nitrate and $Cu(NO_3)_2$ is named copper (II) nitrate.

The anion from an acid with an *ous* ending has the suffix ite; e.g., $NO_2^-$ from nitrous acid is called nitrite.

The anion from a hypo...ous acid is called a hypo...ite; e.g., the $OCl^-$ anion from hypochlorous acid is called hypochlorite. The anion from a per...ic acid is called a per...ate; e.g., $ClO_4^-$ is called perchlorate.

Sometimes we encounter compounds that have more than one kind of ion with a positive oxidation state, one of which is hydrogen, e.g., $NaH_2PO_4$ or $Na_2HPO_4$, which are called monosodium dihydrogen phosphate and disodium monohydrogen phosphate, respectively.

## TEST 9–2

A.   Name the following compounds.
   1. $FeCl_3$

   2. $FeCl_2$

   3. $P_4O_{10}$

   4. $P_4O_6$

   5. $Cl_2O_7$

   6. $Cu_2O$

B.   The maximum positive oxidation state for phosphorus is _____ .

2. The oxidation state of phosphorus in $H_3PO_4$ is _____.

3. $H_3PO_4$ is called _____ acid.

4. The oxidation state of phosphorus in $H_3PO_3$ is _____ and the name of this acid is _____ .

5. The anion $PO_4^{3-}$ is called _____ .

C.  Name $H_2SO_3$ and $SO_3^{2-}$.

## 9–3   BALANCING REDOX REACTIONS

In many chemical reactions, the oxidation states of some atoms in the reactants change upon formation of products. For example, when a strip of copper metal is placed into a colorless solution of silver nitrate, a reaction occurs in which the solution becomes blue, and silver metal is deposited on the copper. The following equation describes the reaction:

$$Cu(s) + 2AgNO_3(aq) \rightarrow 2Ag(s) + Cu(NO_3)_2(aq)$$

The copper metal is oxidized in this reaction to the +2 oxidation state in copper (II) nitrate. Silver, in the +1 oxidation state in $AgNO_3$, is reduced to a zero oxidation state in silver metal. **Oxidation** *results in an increase in the oxidation state of the reactant.* **Reduction** *causes a decrease in the oxidation state of the reactant.* Since copper is the agent which reduces silver, copper is called the **reducing agent.** Note!! that copper is oxidized and behaves as the reducing agent. On the other hand, $Ag^+$ is reduced and behaves as the **oxidizing agent.** Maybe it will help to remember that an oxidizing agent causes something to be oxidized just as an insurance agent causes someone to be insured. Reactions of this sort that involve oxidation and reduction are abbreviated as **redox reactions.** Whenever oxidation occurs, something else must be reduced, so the two processes always occur together.

Redox reactions are often difficult to balance by using the procedures discussed so far. Try to balance the equation:

$$MnO_4^-(aq) + Cl^-(aq) + H^+(aq) \rightarrow Cl_2(g) + Mn^{2+}(aq) + H_2O(l)$$

There is a procedure to use for balancing equations of this sort, called the **method of half reactions.** There are other methods, but we shall discuss only this one because it almost invariably works and because you will need to know it later when you study electrochemistry. The steps involved in the method of half reactions will be presented below, and at the same time the equation given above will be balanced to illustrate these steps.

Step 1: If you are not given a net ionic equation, convert the given equation into a net ionic equation.

The equation given above is a net ionic equation.

Step 2: Convert the net ionic equation into two **half reactions.** In one, indicate only the reactants being oxidized and the corresponding products; in the other, do the same for the reactants being reduced.

$$MnO_4^- \rightarrow Mn^{2+} \text{ (reduction half reaction)}$$
$$Cl^- \rightarrow Cl_2 \text{ (oxidation half reaction)}$$

Step 3: Balance each of these equations in terms of the atoms involved. The atoms besides hydrogen and oxygen are balanced first. Before balancing the hydrogen and oxygen, determine if the reaction is occurring in acidic or basic solution. If the solution is basic, use the procedure we shall discuss in the next example. If the reaction occurs in acidic solution, we balance the oxygen atoms by adding $H_2O$ to the oxygen-poor side of the equation; and balance the hydrogen atoms by adding $H^+$ as needed to the other side of the equation:

$$8H^+ + MnO_4^- \rightarrow Mn^{2+} + 4H_2O$$
$$2Cl^- \rightarrow Cl_2$$

The atoms are balanced in these equations. We shall refer to this step as **chemical balancing.**

Step 4: The total charge on the two sides of the equation for each half reaction is balanced by adding electrons to the appropriate side. We shall refer to this step as **charge balancing.**

To charge balance the $MnO_4^-$ half reaction written above, we note that the left-hand side totals up to 7 positive charges, while the right side totals 2 positive charges. We add 5 electrons to the left side to charge balance the equation.

$$5e^- + 8H^+ + MnO_4^- \rightarrow Mn^{2+} + 4H_2O$$

The other half reaction is simply charge balanced by adding two electrons to the right-hand side:

$$2Cl^- \rightarrow Cl_2 + 2e^-$$

We need only be concerned with the total charge on the ions when we charge balance.

Step 5: Find the smallest common factor of the numbers of electrons in the two half reactions. Multiply the individual half reactions by the appropriate factors required to make the electrons cancel when the half reactions are added.

$$2[5e^- + 8H^+ + MnO_4^- \rightarrow Mn^{2+} + 4H_2O]$$
$$5[2Cl^- \rightarrow Cl_2 + 2e^-]$$

$$\overline{10e^- + 16H^+ + 2MnO_4^- + 10Cl^- \rightarrow 2Mn^{2+} + 8H_2O + 5Cl_2 + 10e^-}$$

Step 6: Check to be sure the coefficients correspond to the simplest whole numbers. If a molecular equation was given initially, convert the net ionic equation to the molecular equation by adding the ions that were dropped when the net ionic equation was written. The same number of ions of a given kind must be added to both sides of the equation.

Since, in this example, we began with a net ionic equation and since the coefficients above are the simplest whole number set, the problem is completed and the equation is balanced.

$$16H^+(aq) + 2MnO_4^-(aq) + 10Cl^-(aq) \rightarrow 2Mn^{2+}(aq) + 8H_2O(l) + 5Cl_2(g)$$

We shall illustrate the other parts of step 3 in the next equation, which we will balance in basic solution.

Step 7, for basic solution: If a reaction occurs in basic solution, the procedure is identical except for step 3. If the solution is basic, balance the equation chemically using $H^+$ and $H_2O$ just as you did in step 3 for an acid solution. Then add enough $OH^-$ to the side containing $H^+$ to convert all the $H^+$ to water; that is, let $H^+ + OH^- \rightarrow H_2O$. The same number of $OH^-$ ions must be added to the other side of the equation. Cancel water from both sides if necessary. We illustrate this procedure by balancing the half reaction for the reduction of $NO_3^-$ to $NH_3$ in basic solution.

$$NO_3^- \rightarrow NH_3$$

For an acid balance we would write:

$$9H^+ + NO_3^- \rightarrow NH_3 + 3H_2O$$

For basic solution we then change this to:

$$9H_2O + NO_3^- \rightarrow NH_3 + 3H_2O + 9OH^-$$

Cancelling water we obtain:

$$6H_2O + NO_3^- \rightarrow NH_3 + 9OH^-$$

This is the chemically balanced half reaction for basic solution. Charge balance leads to the half reaction:

$$8e^- + 6H_2O + NO_3^- \rightarrow NH_3 + 9OH^-$$

---

## Sample Problem 9–5

Balance the following equation for a reaction occurring in basic solution:

$$Zn(s) + KNO_3(aq) \rightarrow NH_3(aq) + K_2Zn(OH)_4(aq)$$

## Solution

Step 1, Net ionic equation:

$$Zn + NO_3^- \rightarrow NH_3 + Zn(OH)_4^{2-}$$

Step 2, Half reactions:

$$Zn \rightarrow Zn(OH)_4^{2-}$$
$$NO_3^- \rightarrow NH_3$$

Steps 3 and 7, chemical balance:

$$4OH^- + Zn \rightarrow Zn(OH)_4^{2-}$$
$$9H^+ + NO_3^- \rightarrow NH_3 + 3H_2O$$

In basic solution:

$$9H_2O + NO_3^- \rightarrow NH_3 + 3H_2O + 9OH^-$$
$$\text{or } 6H_2O + NO_3^- \rightarrow NH_3 + 9OH^-$$

Step 4, Charge balance:

$$4OH^- + Zn \rightarrow Zn(OH)_4^{2-} + 2e^-$$
$$8e^- + 6H_2O + NO_3^- \rightarrow NH_3 + 9OH^-$$

Step 5, Cancel electrons and total:

$$4[4OH^- + Zn \rightarrow Zn(OH)_4^{2-} + 2e^-]$$
$$8e^- + 6H_2O + NO_3^- \rightarrow NH_3 + 9OH^-$$

$$8e^- + 16OH^- + 4Zn + 6H_2O + NO_3^- \rightarrow 4Zn(OH)_4^{2-} + NH_3 + 9OH^- + 8e^-$$
$$7OH^- + 4Zn + 6H_2O + NO_3^- \rightarrow 4Zn(OH)_4^{2-} + NH_3$$

Step 6,

We have the lowest common denominator of coefficients. To convert to a molecular equation we need $8K^+$ on each side:

$$7KOH + 4Zn + 6H_2O + KNO_3 \rightarrow 4K_2Zn(OH)_4 + NH_3$$

---

## TEST 9–3

A. In this test we shall go through the steps to balance the following equation describing a reaction in acidic solution:

$$K_2Cr_2O_7(aq) + HCl(aq) \rightarrow CrCl_3(aq) + Cl_2(g)$$

1. Briefly state step 1 and carry it out.

2. Briefly state step 2 and carry it out.

3. Briefly state step 3 and carry it out.

4. Briefly state step 4 and carry it out.

5. Briefly state step 5 and carry it out.

6. Briefly state step 6 and carry it out.

B.  Referring to the equation in part A,
    1. which substance is the reducing agent?

    2. which substance is the oxidizing agent?

# Exercises

### Oxidation State Determination
1.  Indicate the oxidation state of each atom in the following molecules:
    (a) $N_2H_4$
    (b) $NH_2Cl$
    (c) $NCl_3$
    (d) $NO_2$
    (e) $HNO_3$
    (f) $MoO_3$
    (g) $Cr_2O_7^{2-}$
    (h) $SO_4^{2-}$
    (i) $K_2MnO_4$
    (j) $H_4P_2O_7$

2.  Given the following reaction:

    $$3Cu(s) + 8H^+(aq) + 2NO_3^-(aq) \rightarrow 3Cu^{2+}(aq) + 2NO(g) + 4H_2O(l)$$

    (a) Indicate the substance oxidized.
    (b) Indicate the substance reduced.
    (c) Indicate the reducing agent.
    (d) Indicate the oxidizing agent.

3.  Given the following reaction:

    $$H_2O(l) + 2MnO_4^-(aq) + 3SO_3^{2-}(aq) \rightarrow 2MnO_2(s) + 3SO_4^{2-}(aq) + 2OH^-(aq)$$

    (a) Indicate the substance reduced.
    (b) Indicate the substance oxidized.
    (c) Indicate the oxidizing agent.
    (d) Indicate the reducing agent.

**Nomenclature**
4.  Name the following compounds:
    (a) $SO_3$
    (b) $Cr_2O_3$
    (c) $SeO_2$
    (d) $TiCl_3$
    (e) $CuCl_2$
    (f) $AgO$
    (g) $PbO_2$
    (h) $NCl_3$
    (i) $H_3PO_4$
    (j) $Na_2PO_4$
    (k) $H_3PO_3$
    (l) $H_2SO_4$
    (m) $H_2SO_3$
    (n) $Na_2SO_4$
    (o) $NaHSO_4$
    (p) $K_2SO_3$

5.  Write out the following equation in words:

    $$H_2S + 2HNO_3 \rightarrow 3S + 2NO + 4H_2O$$

**Formula Prediction from Oxidation State Considerations**
6.  Indicate the maximum positive oxidation state of the following elements:
    (a) Cl
    (b) P
    (c) S
    (d) V
    (e) Ti
    (f) Pb
    (g) Ba
    (h) N
    (i) Ga

7.  Indicate the most negative oxidation state of the following elements:
    (a) Br
    (b) N

(c) S

(d) C

(e) Si

(f) Se

8.  From maximum and minimum oxidation state considerations, predict the formula of the compound formed from
    (a) Si and O
    (b) Ti and S
    (c) Cl and O
    (d) Ba and C
    (e) Ga and S
    (f) As and S

## Balancing Redox Equations

9.  Using the method of half reactions, balance the following equations:
    (a) $H_2S(aq) + HNO_3(aq) \rightarrow S(s) + NO(g)$
    (b) $Pb(s) + PbO_2(s) + H_2SO_4 \rightarrow PbSO_4(s)$
    (c) $FeSO_4(aq) + KClO_3(aq) \rightarrow Fe_2(SO_4)_3(aq) + KCl(aq) + H_2O$
    (d) $MnO_4^-(aq) + CN^-(aq) \rightarrow MnO_2(s) + CNO^-(aq)$ (basic soln.)
    (e) $Se(s) + NO_3^-(aq) \rightarrow SeO_2(s) + NO(g)$
    (f) $S_2O_3^{2-}(aq) + MnO_4^-(aq) \rightarrow MnO_2(s) + S_4O_6^{2-}(aq)$ (basic soln.)
    (g) $SO_2 + H^+ + Cr_2O_7^{2-} \rightarrow SO_4^{2-} + Cr^{3+}$
    (h) $C_2O_4^{2-} + MnO_4^{2-} \rightarrow CO_3^{2-} + MnO_2$ (basic soln.)
    (i) $KOH(aq) + Cl_2(g) \rightarrow KClO(aq) + KCl(aq)$
    (j) $PbO_2(s) + MnSO_4(aq) + H_2SO_4 \rightarrow PbSO_4(s) + HMnO_4(aq)$
    (k) $CrO_2^-(aq) + ClO^-(aq) + OH^- \rightarrow CrO_4^{2-}(aq) + Cl^-(aq) + H_2O$
    (l) $H_3AsO_4(aq) + Zn(s) + HNO_3(aq) \rightarrow AsH_3(g) + Zn(NO_3)_2(aq)$
    (m) $HCl(aq) + K_2Cr_2O_7(aq) \rightarrow KCl(aq) + Cl_2(g) + CrCl_3(aq)$
    (n) $CH_3OH(aq) + MnO_4^-(aq) \rightarrow CO_2(g) + MnO_2(s) + OH^-(aq)$
    (o) $P_4(s) + OH^-(aq) \rightarrow PH_3(aq) + H_2PO_2^-(aq)$
    (p) $Fe(OH)_2(s) + O_2(g) \rightarrow Fe(OH)_3(s)$ (basic soln.)

## Verbalizing General Concepts

10.  Answer each of the following in your own words:
     (a) Briefly state the four rules for oxidation state determination.
     (b) Define the terms oxidation and reduction.
     (c) Define the terms oxidizing agent and reducing agent, and explain their relation to the terms oxidation and reduction.

## Multiple Choice Questions

11.  Which of following compounds contains an element with an oxidation state of +5?
     (a) $HClO$, (b) $HNO_2$, (c) $HClO_2$, (d) $HClO_3$, (e) two of these.

12.  The sum of the oxidation states in the $SO_4^{2-}$ ion is
     (a) zero, (b) 2, (c) $-2$, (d) 6, (e) none of these.

13. The oxidation state of nitrogen in $NO_2^-$ is
    (a) +4, (b) −4, (c) +3, (d) −3, (e) none of these.

14. The oxidation state of each nitrogen in $N_2O_4$ is
    (a) +8, (b) −8, (c) +4, (d) −4, (e) none of these.

15. Which pair of name and formula is most consistent with currently preferred systematic nomenclature and correct formulation?
    (a) ferric sulfate, $Fe_2(SO_4)_3$
    (b) manganese (VI) fluoride, $MnF_6$
    (c) nitric oxide, NO
    (d) chromic chloride, $CrCl_3$
    (e) all of the above

16. The anion of an acid that ends in -*ous* will end in
    (a) -*ic*, (b) -*ite*, (c) -*ate*, (d) -*en*, (e) none of the above.

17. The maximum oxidation state of Sb is
    (a) +2, (b) +3, (c) −3, (d) +5, (e) none of these.

18. The formula of the oxide of Sb in its maximum oxidation state is
    (a) $SbO_3$, (b) $Sb_2O_5$, (c) $SbO_2$, (d) $SbO$, (e) none of these.

19. The compound $SO_3$ is the maximum oxidation state oxide of sulfur. $SO_3$ cannot behave as
    (a) an oxidizing agent, (b) a reducing agent, (c) a compound that can be reduced, (d) two of the above, (e) none of the above.

20. The following unbalanced reaction occurs in acidic solutions:

$$MnO_4^- + C_2O_4^{2-} \rightarrow Mn^{2+} + CO_2$$

How many moles of $MnO_4^-$ are required to react with one mole of $C_2O_4^{2-}$?
(a) 0.1, (b) 0.2, (c) 0.3, (d) 0.4, (e) none of these.

21. The following unbalanced reaction occurs in basic solution:

$$IO_4^- + I^- \rightarrow IO_3^- + I_2$$

How many moles of $IO_4^-$ are required to react with one mole of $I^-$?
(a) 0.5, (b) 1.0, (c) 1.5, (d) 2.0, (e) none of these.

In questions 22 to 27, given the following unbalanced equation,

$$Zn(s) + NO_3^-(aq) \rightarrow Zn^{2+}(aq) + NH_4^+(aq)$$

consider the reaction occurring in acidic solution. In order to answer the following questions, balance this equation by the method of half reactions in this space.

22. The reducing agent is
    (a) $Zn(s)$
    (b) $NO_3^-(aq)$
    (c) $Zn^{2+}(aq)$
    (d) $NH_4^+(aq)$
    (e) the acid

23. The oxidation number of nitrogen in $NO_3^-$ is
    (a) +6, (b) +5, (c) −6, (d) −5, (e) none of these.

24. The oxidation state of zinc in $Zn(s)$ is
    (a) 0, (b) +1, (c) +2, (d) −2, (e) none of these.

25. In the balanced half reaction for $NO_3^-$, how many electrons are added to the $NO_3^-$ side?
    (a) zero (they are added to the $NH_4^+$ side), (b) four, (c) six, (d) eight, (e) none of these.

26. In the balanced chemical equation, water has a coefficient of:
    (a) 0, (b) 1, (c) 2, (d) 3, (e) none of these.

27. In the balanced chemical equation, $Zn^{2+}$ has a coefficient of
    (a) 1, (b) 2, (c) 3, (d) 4, (e) none of these.

The following equation applies to problems 28 to 31.

$$4NH_3 + 5O_2 \rightarrow 4NO + 6H_2O$$

28. What compound was oxidized?
    (a) $NH_3$, (b) $O_2$, (c) $NO$, (d) $H_2O$, (e) none of these.

29. What compound is the reducing agent?
    (a) $NH_3$, (b) $O_2$, (c) NO, (d) $H_2O$, (e) none of these.

30. The oxidation number of nitrogen in NO is
    (a) 0, (b) +1, (c) +2, (d) +3, (e) +4.

31. The oxidation number of oxygen in $O_2$ is
    (a) 0, (b) −1, (c) −2, (d) −3, (e) −4.

The following unbalanced equation in aqueous acid solution occurs spontaneously and applies to questions 32 and 33:

$$NO_3^- + I^- \rightarrow IO_3^- + NO_2$$

32. In the balanced equation, the coefficient in front of $NO_3^-$ is
    (a) 2, (b) 3, (c) 4, (d) 5, (e) 6.

33. In the balanced equation, the coefficient in front of water is
    (a) 1, (b) 2, (c) 3, (d) 4, (e) 5.

34. Which of the following compounds contains an element with an oxidation state of +3?
    (a) $NH_2Cl$, (b) $HClO_3$, (c) $HNO_3$, (d) $HNO_2$, (e) $NH_3$

35. The maximum and minimum oxidation states of Sb are, respectively
    (a) +3 and −3          (d) +15 and −3
    (b) +5 and −3          (e) none of these
    (c) +5 and −5

36. HClO and $OCl^-$ are, respectively
    (a) perchloric acid and perchlorate
    (b) hyperchloric acid and hyperchlorate
    (c) chlorous acid and chlorite
    (d) chloric acid and chlorite
    (e) Hypochlorous acid and Hypochlorite

37. The following unbalanced reaction occurs in basic solution:

$$Mn(CN)_6^{4-}(aq) + O_2(g) \rightarrow Mn(CN)_6^{3-}(aq)$$

How many moles of $O_2$ are required to react with one mole of $Mn(CN)_6^{4-}$?
    (a) 0.25, (b) 0.5, (c) 1, (d) 2, (e) 4

38. Balance the following equation (in aqueous acid solution) by the method of half-reactions:

$$Pb(s) + PbO_2(s) + H_2SO_4 \rightarrow PbSO_4(s)$$

In the above reaction, the reducing agent is
    (a) Pb, (b) $PbO_2$, (c) $H_2SO_4$, (d) $PbSO_4$, (e) $H^+$

# 10

# COLLIGATIVE PROPERTIES

## Chapter Objectives

## (Begin each of the following with "You should master . . .")

1. the factors responsible for the determination of the freezing point lowering and boiling point elevation of a solvent.
2. solving problems in which two of the three quantities influencing freezing point lowering or boiling point elevation are given.
3. determination of the molecular weight of a substance from the freezing point depression or boiling point elevation.

There are several properties of a solution that depend upon only the number of solute particles dissolved in the solvent. These properties are called **colligative properties** and include the depression of the freezing point of a solvent and the elevation of the boiling point. The reasons for this behavior are presented in most textbooks along with other properties of solutions that depend upon colligative behavior. Here we shall present a short chapter that describes how to solve freezing point depression and boiling point elevation problems. Since the molality concentration unit is used in these problems, problem A in Test 5–1 and the molality problems at the end of Chapter 5 should be reviewed if necessary.

## 10–1  SOLUTIONS OF NONELECTROLYTES

The boiling points of solutions are higher than the boiling points of the corresponding pure solvents. The extent of the increase, $\Delta T_{bp}$, depends upon the molality of the solute, $m$, and the solvent as described by the following relation:

$$\Delta T_{bp} = k_{bp} \times m \qquad \text{(10–1)}$$

where $k_{bp}$ is a constant whose numerical value depends upon the particular solvent. Since $\Delta T_{bp}$ has units of °C, $k_{bp}$ must have units of °C molal$^{-1}$ ( °C $m^{-1}$). Some typical values of $k_{bp}$ are given in Table 10–1. According to equation 10–1, solutions of the same concentration of any *nonelectrolyte* in a given solvent will have the same boiling point.

**Table 10–1    Freezing Points, $k_{fp}$ Values, Boiling Points, and $k_{bp}$ Values for Various Solvents**

| Solvent | Freezing Point, °C* | $k_{fp}$ °C molal$^{-1}$ | Boiling Point, °C* | $k_{bp}$ °C molal$^{-1}$ |
|---|---|---|---|---|
| Acetic acid | 17 | − 3.90 | 118 | 2.93 |
| Benzene | 5.48 | − 5.12 | 80.1 | 2.53 |
| Camphor | 178.4 | −37.7 | 208 | 5.95 |
| Carbon tetra-chloride | − 22.3 | −29.8 | 76.8 | 5.02 |
| Chloroform | −63.5 | − 4.68 | 61.26 | 3.63 |
| Cyclohexane | 6.5 | −20.2 | 81 | 2.79 |
| Naphthalene | 80.2 | − 6.90 | — | — |
| Nitrobenzene | 5.67 | − 8.10 | 210.9 | 5.24 |
| Water | 0.0 | − 1.86 | 100.0 | 0.512 |

*The normal boiling and freezing points at 1.00 atmosphere pressure.

Similar behavior is observed for the freezing point depression of a solution by a nonelectrolyte. The extent of lowering is given by

$$\Delta T_{fp} = k_{fp} \times m \qquad (10\text{–}2)$$

where the subscript fp refers to freezing point. Since the freezing point decreases, both $\Delta T_{fp}$ and $k_{fp}$ will be negative numbers. For a given solvent, different constants describe the freezing point lowering and the boiling point elevation. Some typical values of freezing point depression constants are also given in Table 10–1.

To further illustrate the meaning of these numbers, consider acetic acid as an example of a solvent. Since $k_{fp}$ is −3.90 °C molal$^{-1}$, one mole of any nonelectrolyte in 1 kg of this solvent will lower the freezing point of the acetic solution by 3.90 °C, from 17.0 °C to +13.1 °C.

The concept contained in equations 10–1 and 10–2, simply stated is: any nonelectrolyte lowers the freezing point or raises the boiling point of a given solvent in direct proportion to the molality. Different constants govern the freezing and boiling processes. As we have shown in the past, we can solve a whole set of problems based on an equation like 10–1 or 10–2. When any two of the three quantities in the equation are given, the third can be solved for. When necessary in working problems, Table 10–1 should be referred to for needed information.

## Sample Problem 10–1

A solution is prepared by dissolving 3.86 g of $C_2H_5OH$ in 325 g of nitrobenzene. What is the freezing point of this solution?

## Solution

? $\Delta T_{fp}$; so $m$ must be given in the problem and $k_{fp}$ is obtained from Table 10–1. The molality is calculated as in Chapter 5.

$$3.86 \text{ g} \times \frac{1 \text{ mole}}{46.1 \text{ g}} = 0.0837 \text{ mole}$$

$$\frac{0.0837 \text{ mole}}{325 \text{ g}} \times \frac{1000 \text{ g}}{1 \text{ kg}} = 0.258 \; m$$

$$\Delta T_{\text{fp}} = -8.10 \text{ °C } m^{-1} \times 0.258 \; m = -2.09 \text{ °C}$$

Since the solvent freezes at 5.67 °C and the freezing point is lowered 2.09 °C by the solute, the solution freezes at:

$$5.67 \text{ °C} - 2.09 \text{ °C} = 3.58 \text{ °C}$$

## Sample Problem 10–2

A solution of nitrobenzene freezes at 5.11 °C. What is the molality of solute in this solvent?

### Solution

? molality, so $\Delta T_{\text{fp}}$ and $k_{\text{fp}}$ must be given.

$$\Delta T_{\text{fp}} = 5.11 \text{ °C} - 5.67 \text{ °C} = -0.56 \text{ °C } (\Delta \text{ is final} - \text{initial})$$

$$-0.56 \text{ °C} = -8.10 \text{ °C } m^{-1} \times m$$

$$m = 0.069$$

The next problem is a slight but very important variation on sample problem 10–2. If we are given the number of grams of an unknown material dissolved in the nitrobenzene solution described in problem 10–2, we can calculate its molecular weight.

## Sample Problem 10–3

A solution made by dissolving 2.58 grams of an unknown material in 250. g of nitrobenzene freezes at 5.01 °C. What is the molecular weight of the unknown?

### Solution

The molality of this solution can be determined as in problem 10–2.

$$\Delta T_{fp} = 5.01 \text{ °C} - 5.67 \text{ °C} = -0.66 \text{ °C}$$

$$-0.66 \text{ °C} = -8.10 \text{ °C } m^{-1} \times m$$

$$m = 0.082$$

The 2.58 g in 250 g of solvent corresponds to

$$\frac{2.58 \text{ g}}{250 \text{ g}} \times \frac{1000 \text{ g}}{1 \text{ kg}} = 10.32 \text{ g/kg solvent}$$

Therefore,

$$\frac{10.32 \text{ g solute}}{1 \text{ kg solvent}} = \frac{0.082 \text{ mole solute}}{1 \text{ kg solvent}}$$

$$\frac{10.32 \text{ g/kg}}{0.082 \text{ moles/kg}} = 1.3 \times 10^2 \text{ g/mole } = \text{MW}$$

## Sample Problem 10–4

A solution containing 5.00 g of ethanol ($C_2H_5OH$) in 455 g of solvent boils at 93.33 °C, while the boiling point of pure solvent is 90.00 °C. Calculate the boiling point elevation constant of the solvent.

## Solution

? $k_{bp}$, so the molality and $\Delta T_{bp}$ must be given.

$$\Delta T_{bp} = 93.33 \text{ °C} - 90.00 \text{ °C} = 3.33 \text{ °C}$$

$$\text{No. of moles} = \frac{5.00 \text{ g}}{46.1 \text{ g/mole}} = 0.108 \text{ mole } C_2H_5OH$$

$$m = \frac{0.108 \text{ mole}}{455 \text{ g solvent}} \times \frac{1000 \text{ g}}{1 \text{ kg}} = 0.238 \text{ mole/kg}$$

$$3.33 \text{ °C} = k_{bp} \times 0.238 \, m$$

$$k_{bp} = 14.0 \text{ °C } m^{-1}$$

## 10–2    SOLUTIONS OF ELECTROLYTES

So far we have restricted our attention to solutions of nonelectrolytes. For this type of solute, one mole of substance provides one mole of particles in solution. When a mole of the *electrolyte* sodium chloride dissolves, however, two moles of particles are formed (one mole of $Na^+$ and one mole of $Cl^-$) if the ions dissociate completely in solution. Complete dissociation occurs only in very dilute solutions. In more concentrated solutions aggregates exist, of the form $(Na^+ Cl^-)_x$, called ion pairs. Thus, the number of independent particles is some value less than two moles per mole of NaCl, and deviation from this value varies with concentration. This behavior makes it difficult to do exact colligative property types of calculations on solutions of electrolytes. The simplifying assumption that complete dissociation occurs will be made in this text for any solutions of electrolytes. You must remember that, as a result of such an assumption, observed behavior in the laboratory will deviate from results we calculate.

---

### Sample Problem 10–5

Calculate the boiling point of an aqueous solution containing 0.736 mole of $MgCl_2$ in 4.25 kg of water. (Assume complete dissociation of the ions.)

### Solution

? $\Delta T_{bp}$, so the molality and $k_{bp}$ must be given.
The molality of $MgCl_2$ is:

$$\frac{0.736 \text{ mole}}{4.25 \text{ kg}} = \frac{0.173 \text{ mole}}{\text{kg}} = m$$

If $MgCl_2$ were to ionize completely, a solution 0.520 molal in particles would form (if you do not carry a fourth significant figure from the initial calculation, you would calculate 0.519 molal).

$$\Delta T_{bp} = 0.512 \text{ °C } m^{-1} \times 0.520 \, m \text{ (in particles)} = 0.266 \text{ °C}$$

Since the normal boiling point is 100. °C, this elevation would result in a solution that boils at 100.266 °C.

---

### TEST 10–1

A.    In this test we shall answer questions to demonstrate the approach to solving the following problem: If 3.66 g of a nonelectrolyte dissolved in 86.7 g of $CCl_4$ lowered the freezing point to $-25.0\ °C$, what is its molecular weight?

1. Of the three quantities $\Delta T_{fp}$, $k_{fp}$, and $m$, which is unknown if the molecular weight is unknown?

2. Calculate $\Delta T_{fp}$.

3. Look up $k_{fp}$ and record it here.

4. Substitute into equation 10–2 and solve for the unknown.

5. What is the mass of nonelectrolyte in 1 kg of $CCl_4$?

6. To how many moles does the mass in part 5 correspond?

7. Calculate the molecular weight.

## Exercises

1. Calculate the freezing point of a solution that contains 6.50 g of ethylene glycol ($C_2H_6O_2$) (a common automotive antifreeze) in 175 g of water.

2. A 6.60 g sample of a compound dissolved in 250. g of benzene gives a solution that freezes at 4.45 °C. Calculate the molecular weight of the compound.

3. Calculate the boiling point of a solution prepared by dissolving 255. g of DDT ($C_{14}H_9Cl_5$) in 877 g of benzene.

4. A solution of 15.9 g of a nonelectrolyte in 250. g of water freezes at −0.744 °C. Calculate the molecular weight.

5. List the following aqueous solutions in order of decreasing freezing point: 0.05 $m$ $CaBr_2$, 0.10 $m$ NaCl, 0.10 $m$ ethylene glycol (a nonelectrolyte), 0.07 $m$ NaCl.

6. A solution of 0.750 g of a nonelectrolyte in 40.0 g of $CCl_4$ boils at 78.6 °C. Calculate the molecular weight.

7. Calculate the freezing point of a solution containing 0.166 moles of a nonelectrolyte in 250. g of $CHCl_3$ (chloroform).

8. Calculate the boiling point of a solution that contains 0.178 moles of a nonelectrolyte in 58.0 g of cyclohexane.

9. Calculate the boiling point and freezing point of a solution made by dissolving 10.0 g of ethylene glycol ($C_2H_6O_2$) in 85.5 g of water.

10. The Great Salt Lake in Utah contains about 13.6 g of NaCl per 100. g of water. Assuming complete ionization, calculate the freezing point of the lake.

11. A solution of 0.325 mole of solute in 500. g of solvent results in a freezing point lowering of 0.386 °C. Calculate the freezing point depression constant for this solvent.

**Verbalizing General Concepts**
12. State the factors that determine the freezing point of a solution.

13. How can you calculate the molecular weight of a substance from the freezing point depression of a solution of the substance?

14. How would you go about determining the freezing point depression constant of a solvent whose value has not been reported?

**Challenging Problems**
15. The acid HF partially ionizes in water. A solution of 0.100 mole of HF in 100.0 g of water freezes at −1.91 °C. Calculate the number of moles of ionized and unionized HF in the solution.

16. How many grams of ethylene glycol, $C_2H_6O_2$, must be added to a 16.0 liter automobile radiator to protect against freezing at −20.0 °C? The density of ethylene glycol is 1.12 g/cm³, and you should assume that the volumes of water and ethylene glycol are additive to produce the 16.0 liters.

**Multiple Choice Questions**
17. The molality of a solution containing 39.4 g of $C_2H_5OH$ in 100. g of water is
(a) 2.54 $m$, (b) 394 $m$, (c) 0.855 $m$, (d) 8.55 $m$, (e) none of these.

18. The freezing point of benzene is 5.48 °C and the freezing point depression constant is 5.12 °C/$m$. A solution of 10.0 g of a nonelectrolyte in 100. g of benzene freezes at 4.20 °C. The molecular weight is
(a) 40.0 g/mole
(b) 400 g/mole
(c) 131 g/mole
(d) 122 g/mole
(e) none of these

19. Which of the following, dissolved in 1 liter of water, will result in the greatest freezing point lowering of the water?
    (a) 10 g of $C_2H_5OH$
    (b) 10 g of NaCl
    (c) 10 g of $CaCl_2$
    (d) 10 g of $CH_3CO_2H$
    (e) all of the above will raise the freezing point of water.

20. Which of the following solutions would have the lowest freezing point?
    (a) 1.00 $m$ $AlCl_3$, (b) 1.00 $m$ $CaCl_2$, (c) 1.00 $m$ NaCl, (d) 1.00 $m$ $Mg(OH)_2$, (e) 1.00 $m$ ethylene glycol.

21. Addition of a nonvolatile solute to a solvent:
    (a) lowers the freezing point and boiling point,
    (b) raises the freezing point and boiling point,
    (c) raises the freezing point and lowers the boiling point,
    (d) lowers the freezing point and raises the boiling point,
    (e) affects only the freezing point.

22. It is found that 3.90 g of benzene dissolved in 100 g of a solvent lowers the freezing point to 10.0 °C. The pure solvent freezes at 25.0 °C. The molal freezing point depression constant in °C $m^{-1}$ of the solvent is
    (a) 60.0, (b) 20.0, (c) 3.0, (d) 2.0, (e) none of these within 0.1.

23. In order to calculate the freezing point of a solution, one needs to know
    (a) the molality; (b) the molality and freezing point depression constant; (c) the freezing point of pure solvent, molality, and freezing point depression constant; (d) all of the quantities in (c) plus the molecular weight of the solute; (e) all of the quantities in (c) plus the weight of solvent.

24. In order to calculate the freezing point of a solution, one needs to know
    (a) only the molality of the solution.
    (b) only the freezing point depression constant of the solvent.
    (c) only the molecular weight of the solvent.
    (d) both (a) and (b) above.
    (e) more information is needed than is given by any combination of the above information.

25. Which of the following solutions would have the lowest freezing point if the solvent in all cases is water?
    (a) 1.00$m$ $AlCl_3$          (d) 2.00$m$ $CH_3OH$
    (b) 1.20$m$ NaOH          (e) 1.30$m$ $NH_4Cl$
    (c) 1.50$m$ NaCl

26. A solute added to a solvent raises the boiling point of the solution because
    (a) the temperature to cause boiling must be great enough to boil not only the solvent but also the solute.
    (b) the solute particles lower the solvent's vapor pressure thus requiring a higher temperature to cause boiling.
    (c) the solute particles raise the solvent's vapor pressure thus requiring a higher temperature to cause boiling.
    (d) the solute increases the volume of the solution, and an increase in volume requires an increase in temperature to reach the boiling point (from $PV = nRT$ relationship).
    (e) two of the above are correct.

27. By analysis, a solid organic compound is found to contain 40.0%C, 6.7%H, and 53.3%0. When a 0.6500g sample of this compound is dissolved in 27.80g of diphenyl ($K_f = 8.0$), the freezing point of diphenyl is lowered by 1.56°C. the molecular formula of this compound is
    (a) $C_2H_8O_2$              (d) $C_4H_6O_4$
    (b) $C_3H_7O_5$              (e) $C_4H_8O_4$
    (c) $C_3H_6O_3$

# GLOSSARY

**Absolute temperature** Temperature that is measured on a scale in which 273.15 °K is the freezing point of water and 373.15 °K is its boiling point. °K = °C + 273.15. Absolute zero is $-273.15$ °C.

**Absolute zero** The lowest possible temperature ($-273.15$ °C or $-459.67$ °F). Temperatures within a few thousandths of a degree of 0 °K have been attained. In the kinetic theory of gases, absolute zero is the temperature at which the kinetic energy of the molecules of an ideal gas is zero.

**Acid** A compound that gives rise to hydronium ions ($H_3O^+$) in an aqueous solution. Acids react with bases.

**Actinides** The fourteen elements following actinium (second inner transition series) in the Periodic Table.

**Allotropy** The existence of a free element in two or more forms in the same physical state. $O_2$ and $O_3$ (ozone) are the allotropic forms of free oxygen. Graphite and diamond, both crystalline solids, are allotropes of carbon.

**Amphoterism** The ability of a substance to act as either an acid or a base.

**Anion** A negative ion.

**Atomic mass unit** The unit in which the masses of individual atoms are expressed. One atom of fluorine has a mass of 19.0 amu.

**Atomic nucleus** The region at the center of an atom in which all the protons and neutrons are located. The diameter of the nucleus is 10,000 to 100,000 times smaller than the diameter of the atom, but it accounts for about 99.95% of the mass of the atom.

**Atomic number** The number of units of positive charge possessed by the nucleus of an atom. The atomic number is the same as the number of protons in the nucleus, and it determines the ordinal position of the element in the periodic table.

**Atomic spectrum** A pattern of sharply defined spectral lines, the energies of which correspond to changes in location of electrons from one energy level to another energy level.

**Atomic weight** The mass of an average atom of an element on the scale $^{12}C = 12$ amu exactly. The atomic weight is the weighted average of the isotopic weights.

**Aufbau order**    The atomic orbital energy ordering for writing the electronic configuration of all the atoms.

**Avogadro's number**    The number of atoms in a mole (i.e., a gram-mole) of atoms; the number of molecules in a mole of molecules; the number of ions in a mole of ions; the number of electrons in a faraday of electricity, or the number of whatever chemical units one may wish to designate in a gram-mole of such units. The number, $N$, is $6.02261 \times 10^{23}$.

**Avogadro's Principle**    Equal volumes of gases, under identical conditions of temperature and pressure, contain equal numbers of molecules.

**Balanced equation**    A chemical equation in which the numbers of atoms on both sides are equal.

**Barometer**    An instrument for measuring atmospheric pressure.

**Base**    A compound that gives rise to hydroxyl ions ($OH^-$) in an aqueous solution. Bases react with acids to form water and salts.

**Basic anhydride**    A basic oxide, designated as the anhydride of a specified base; e.g., we say that $CaO$ is a basic oxide, or that $CaO$ is the anhydride of the base calcium hydroxide, $Ca(OH)_2$.

**Boiling point**    The temperature at which a liquid boils (usually referring to the normal boiling point).

**Boyle's Law**    At constant temperature, the volume occupied by a gas varies inversely with the confining pressure. It can be written $PV = $ constant or $P_1V_1 = P_2V_2$.

**Buffer solution**    A solution capable of maintaining its $H^+$ concentration at a virtually constant level despite the addition of a small quantity of a strong acid or strong base.

**Calorie**    The quantity of heat required to raise the temperature of 1 g of water 1 °C.

**Cation**    A positive ion.

**Charles' Law**    The volume occupied by a fixed quantity of gas confined under constant pressure is directly proportional to the absolute temperature. It can be written $V = $ constant $\times T$ or $V_1/T_1 = V_2/T_2$, where $T$ is in °K.

**Chemical change**    A change in which new compounds are formed.

**Chemical equation**    A statement representing a chemical reaction, employing symbols and formulas instead of words.

**Chemical formula**    Any collection of symbols and subscripts used to represent a pure substance. Empirical formulas and molecular formulas are examples of chemical formulas.

**Combined gas law equation**    The equation that combines the Boyle's Law equation, the Charles' Law equation, and the effect of changes in $n$ into one expression. It can be written $PV/Tn = $ constant or $P_1V_1/n_1T_1 = P_2V_2/n_2T_2$.

**Combustion**    Any chemical process accompanied by the evolution of light and heat. Commonly, combustion involves union with oxygen.

**Compound**    Pure substance with a fixed set of properties, composed of two or more constituent elements chemically combined in definite proportions.

**Dalton's Law of Partial Pressures**    In a mixture of gases the molecules of each species exert the same pressure they would exert if they were present alone, so that the total pressure is the sum of these partial pressures exerted by the different gases in the mixture. It can be written $P_{\text{total}} = P_1 + P_2 + P_3 + \ldots$.

**Decomposition**    A chemical reaction in which one substance breaks down to form two or more simpler substances.

**Degenerate**    Equal in energy.

**Density**    The ratio of the mass of matter to its volume.

**Deuterium**    The hydrogen isotope of mass number 2 with 1 proton and 1 neutron in the nucleus; its symbol is D.

**Deuteron**    The nucleus of a deuterium atom.

**Diffusion**    The spontaneous spreading of a substance throughout the space available to it.

**Distillation**    The process of vaporizing a liquid by the application of heat and condensing its vapor by cooling.

**Electrolysis**    A chemical change brought about by electric current.

**Electrolyte**    A solute that produces ions when it dissolves. The resulting solution conducts electric current when ions are present.

**Electron**    A subatomic particle with a mass of $9.1 \times 10^{-28}$ g (which is 1/1837 of the mass of a complete hydrogen atom) and a negative charge of $1.60 \times 10^{-19}$ coulomb. On the atomic-weight scale the mass of an electron is 0.000548. The charge of an electron is the unit usually employed to express the charges of subatomic particles and ions.

**Electron affinity**    The energy released when an electron is added to a neutral, isolated atom, forming a negative ion.

**Electron configuration**    The particular arrangement of the electrons in the orbitals of an atom or ion.

**Electronegativity**    The tendency of a covalently bonded atom to attract the bonding electron pair.

**Electronic symbol**    The chemical symbol for an element with dots, small circles, or other suitable markings to indicate the number of electrons in the outermost shell; e.g., $:\ddot{\text{C}}\text{l}\cdot$,

$|\overline{\text{Cl}}\cdot$, or $\underset{\text{xx}}{\overset{\text{x}}{{}_{\text{x}}\text{Cl}_{\text{x}}}}$ for a chlorine atom and $:\ddot{\overline{\text{C}}\text{l}}:\text{,} \,\, \overset{\text{oo}}{{}_{\text{o}}\overline{\text{Cl}}{}_{\text{o}}^{-}},\overset{\text{xx}}{\underset{\text{xx}}{{}_{\text{x}}\text{Cl}_{\text{x}}^{-}}}$ or $|\overline{\text{Cl}}|$ for a chloride ion.

**Element**    A substance whose atoms all have the same atomic number.

**Empirical formula** (simplest formula)    The smallest whole-number ratio of symbols and subscripts used to represent the relative number of atoms of the constituent elements in a compound; e.g., the empirical formulas for hydrogen peroxide and benzene are HO and CH, respectively (but their molecular formulas are $H_2O_2$ and $C_6H_6$).

**Endothermic process**    Any process in which heat is absorbed from the surroundings, as in the melting of ice, the evaporation of a liquid, or the union of carbon and sulfur to form $CS_2$. Any chemical reaction in which heat is absorbed is an endothermic reaction.

**Energy**    The capacity to do work.

**Energy level (electronic)**    One of several sets of energy states in an atom that an electron may assume.

**Equilibrium constant**    A constant characteristic of a particular reaction in a state of chemical equilibrium at a particular temperature, found by calculating the ratio of the equilibrium concentrations of products to reactants, each raised to the appropriate power.

**Equilibrium mixture**    A system consisting of a mixture of substances, in which a state of equilibrium prevails.

**Excited state (electronic)**    Any state of an atom when at least one electron is in an energy level higher than the lowest possible.

**Exothermic process**    A process of any kind in which heat is evolved, as in the liquefaction of a gas, the freezing of a liquid, or the burning of a candle. Any chemical reaction in which heat is evolved is an exothermic reaction.

**Formula weight**    The sum of the atomic weights of the atoms in a formula. If the formula is the molecular formula of a substance, the formula weight is also its molecular weight.

**Fractional distillation**    A process by which the components of a liquid mixture are vaporized in the order of their boiling points, and the liquid condensates collected as separate fractions.

**Freezing (solidification, crystallization)**    The change from the liquid state to the solid (crystalline) state.

**Gaseous state**    The state of matter in which a substance takes the shape of its container and fills all parts of the container to the same degree.

**General gas law equation**    The equation that states the relationship of the volume of a gas to the pressure, the temperature, and the number of moles: $PV = nRT$.

**Gram-mole of atoms**    The quantity of an element, where the weight in grams is numerically equal to the atomic weight of the element; e.g., since the atomic weight of sodium is 22.9898 amu, a gram-mole of sodium atoms is 22.9898 g.

**Ground state**    The lowest energy state of an atom, i.e., the state in which each electron is in the lowest possible energy level.

**Group**    The set of chemical elements appearing in any one column of the periodic table (Group IA, Group IIA, Group IIIB, etc.).

**Half-reaction**    The half of an oxidation-reduction reaction corresponding to either oxidation or reduction.

**Heat**    The form of energy that passes from a body of higher temperature to a body of lower temperature.

**Heavy water (deuterium oxide)**    Water that is composed of deuterium (instead of ordinary H atoms) and oxygen. Its formula is $D_2O$.

**Hund's rule**    The statement that electrons must occupy equal energy orbitals one at a time with their spins parallel until they are forced to pair.

**Hydrate**   A crystalline substance that contains water.

**Hydride**   A binary compound in which hydrogen is combined with an atom less electronegative than itself. In all hydrides, hydrogen is in the oxidation state $-1$.

**Hydrocarbon**   A binary compound consisting of hydrogen and carbon.

**Hydrogenation**   A chemical reaction in which hydrogen is added to another compound.

**Hydrogen bond**   The bond between two molecules or a molecule and an ion linked together through a hydrogen atom, which serves as the bridge. Hydrogen bonding is common between polar molecules containing F—H, O—H, or N—H bonds. Hydrogen bonds are much weaker than ionic or covalent bonds.

**Hydrolysis of salts**   A reaction in which the water molecule is broken up into $H_3O^+$ or $OH^-$ ions.

**Hydroxy acid**   See **oxyacid.**

**Hygroscopic**   Having a tendency to absorb moisture from the air.

**Ideal behavior of a gas**   Perfect conformity with Boyle's Law and Charles' Law.

**Ideal gas**   An imaginary gas that behaves in perfect accord with Boyle's Law and Charles' Law over all conditions.

**Indicator**   A substance which exhibits different colors in aqueous solutions, depending on the degree of acidity or alkalinity of the solutions.

**Inner transition elements**   The elements in the sixth and seventh periods of the periodic table that have no counterparts in the fourth and fifth periods. The lanthanides (elements 58–71) constitute the first inner transition series; the actinides (elements 90–103) constitute the second series.

**Ionic bonding**   The type of chemical bonding involving electrostatic attraction between ions. Electrons have been transferred from atoms of low ionization potential to atoms of high electron affinity to form the positive and negative ions.

**Ionic equation, complete, total**   An equation, representing a reaction involving ionic compounds, in which all the individual ions, including spectator ions, are represented.

**Ionic equation, general**   Same as net ionic equation; so called because it represents all reactions of given type.

**Ionic solid**   A solid in which the lattice points are occupied by positive and negative ions. The electrostatic forces operating between the positive and negative charges hold an ionic crystal together.

**Ionization energy**   The energy required to remove an electron from an atom.

**Ions**   Charged particles, especially atoms or molecules, that have acquired electrical charges because the number of electrons and the number of protons are not the same.

**Isotopes**   Atoms of the same element containing different numbers of neutrons and thus having different masses.

**Isotopic weight**   The weight of particular isotope on the scale $^{12}C = 12$ exactly.

**Kindling temperature**   The temperature at which a substance bursts into flame.

**Kinetic energy**     The energy that a moving object possesses by virtue of its motion. The quantity of kinetic energy such an object possesses is equal to the work it is capable of performing in being brought to rest. This is expressed by the equation $E_k = \frac{1}{2}mv^2$, where $m$ is the mass of object and $v$ is its velocity.

**Lanthanides**     The fourteen elements following lanthanum (first inner transition series).

**Lewis structure**     Representation of the bonds and nonbonding electrons that exist in a molecule. Dots or $x$'s are used for electrons, or a pair of electrons can be represented by a line.

**Liquid state**     The state of matter in which a substance takes the shape of its container. The molecules are free to move among themselves but do not have the tendency to separate from one another as do gases.

**Mass**     A measure of the amount of matter in a substance.

**Mass number**     The integer that most nearly expresses the mass of an isotope on the atomic-weight scale. The mass number of an atom is the total number of protons and neutrons in its nucleus.

**Matter**     Something that occupies space, possesses mass, and exhibits inertia.

**Melting (fusion)**     The change from the solid to the liquid state.

**Melting point (freezing point)**     The temperature at which the solid and liquid phases of a substance can exist in equilibrium. At this point the solid and liquid phases have the same vapor pressure.

**Meniscus**     The curved upper surface of a liquid column in a container of small cross section (e.g., a burette, pipette, or capillary tube). The menicus may be either concave or convex, depending on whether or not the containing walls are wetted by the liquid.

**Metalloids**     Elements that are on the borderline between metals and nonmetals, e.g., boron, silicon, arsenic, and tellurium.

**Metals**     Chemical elements which, when not chemically combined with other elements, have a peculiar luster and are good conductors of heat and electricity. Every metal forms at least one basic oxide.

**Metathesis**     A reaction in which substances (usually two) react to produce new substances by simple exchange of the cations and anions.

**Miscibility**     The ability of two or more liquids to form a solution.

**Mixture**     A material composed of two or more ingredients not chemically combined. Some mixtures are homogeneous; some are heterogeneous.

**Molality**     Concentration of a solution expressed in the number of moles of solute per kilogram of solvent. Molality is usually designated by $m$.

**Molar gas constant**     The constant $R$ in the general gas law equation.

**Molarity**     Concentration of a solution expressed in the number of moles of solute per liter of solution. Molarity is usually designated by $M$.

**Molar volume**     The volume of 1 mole. Unless stated otherwise, the molar volume of a gas is the volume of 1 mole of the gas at standard conditions. The molar volume of an ideal gas is 22.414 liters.

**Mole**    A general term referring to $6.02 \times 10^{23}$ chemical units. A mole of atoms is $6.02 \times 10^{23}$ atoms. A mole of molecules is $6.02 \times 10^{23}$ molecules. A mole of ions is $6.02 \times 10^{23}$ ions. A mole of electrons is $6.02 \times 10^{23}$ electrons.

**Mole fraction (of a component of a mixture)**    The number of moles of a component of a mixture divided by the total number of moles of all components in the mixture.

**Mole of atoms**    An incomplete expression which should be taken to mean a gram-mole of atoms unless otherwise stated; e.g., a mole of sodium atoms in 22.9898 grams, not 22.9898 pounds, ounces, kilograms, etc.

**Molecular formula**    The combination of symbols and subscripts representing the actual number of atoms of each element in one molecule of a substance; e.g., the molecular formulas for elementary oxygen and for water are $O_2$ and $H_2O$, respectively.

**Molecular solid**    A crystalline substance consisting of molecules. The atoms within each molecule are held together by covalent bonds. If the molecules are nonpolar, the attractions between molecules are due to van der Waals forces. If the molecules are polar, the intermolecular binding is due to the attraction between the negative end of one molecule and the positive end of another.

**Molecular weight**    The weight of one molecule of a substance on the scale $^{12}C = 12$ exactly. The molecular weight is the sum of the atomic weights of the constituent elements, taking into account the number of atoms of each element in one molecule of the substance.

**Molecule**    A chemical combination of two or more atoms.

**Net ionic equation**    An equation, representing a reaction involving ionic compounds, from which spectator ions are omitted.

**Network solid (covalent solid or atomic crystal)**    A solid which consists of atoms united by covalent bonds into a network that extends throughout the crystal.

**Neutralization**    The process in which $H^+$ and $OH^-$ ions, brought together from separate sources, combine to form $H_2O$ molecules. The reaction between a base and an acid, producing water and a salt, is a typical neutralization reaction.

**Neutron**    A subatomic particle, having no electrical charge, with a mass of 1.0087 on the atomic-weight scale.

**Nonmetals**    Chemical elements which lack the luster and conductivity characteristic of metals. Most nonmetals form at least one acidic oxide.

**Normal boiling point**    The temperature at which a liquid boils when the pressure is 1 atmosphere.

**Organic chemistry**    The branch of chemistry that deals with the hydrocarbons and their derivatives; the chemistry of carbon compounds.

**Oxidation**    An increase in oxidation number. (A decrease in oxidation number is reduction.)

**Oxidation number**    An arbitrary number assigned to each atom in an ion or molecule so that the sum of the oxidation numbers of all the atoms is the charge of the ion (or is zero for a molecule).

**Oxidation state** A term used to indicate the oxidation number of each of an element's atoms. For example, each iron atom is in the same oxidation state ($+ 3$) in $Fe_2O_3$.

**Oxide** A compound containing oxygen and one other element.

**Oxyacid (hydroxy acid)** An acid which contains both hydrogen and oxygen, combined with a third element.

**Paramagnetic** Subject to being attracted into a magnetic field. (Substances subject to repulsion by magnetic field are diamagnetic.)

**Period** The set of chemical elements appearing in any one row of the periodic table (first period, second period, etc.).

**Periodic Law** If the elements are considered in the order of their atomic numbers, most elements with similar properties recur periodically. In brief, most of the properties of the elements are periodic functions of the atomic numbers.

**Periodic table** An arrangement of the chemical elements in rows and columns in the order of their atomic numbers, with similar elements in the same columns.

**Peroxides** Compounds containing oxygen in the oxidation state $- 1$.

**pH** A number used to designate the degree of acidity or alkalinity of a solution, defined as the negative logarithm of the hydrogen-ion concentration.

**Physical change** A change in the physical properties of a substance that occurs without a change in composition.

**Polymers** Compounds of high molecular weight which have been obtained by a large number of simple molecules reacting with one another.

**Polymorphism** The occurrence of a substance in more than one crystalline form.

**Potential energy** The energy that a body possesses by virtue of its position; e.g., if you lift this book above the desk you do work and thereby impart potential energy to the book.

**Pound-mole of atoms** The quantity of an element the weight of which in pounds is numerically equal to the atomic weight of the element; e.g., a pound-mole of sodium atoms is 22.9898 lb.

**Pressure** Force per unit area.

**Principal quantum numbers** The numbers (1,2,3, etc.) used to designate energy levels which an electron may occupy in an atom.

**Properties** The characteristics of a material that distinguish it from other materials. These characteristics are usually classified as physical and chemical properties.

**Protium** The hydrogen isotope of mass number 1; its symbol is H.

**Proton** A subatomic particle with a positive charge of $1.60 \times 10^{-19}$ coulomb and a mass of 1.0073 on the atomic-weight scale.

**Pyrolysis** Decomposition brought about by heat.

**Rare gas**    Any element with an $ns^2\,np^6$ electron configuration. ($n$ is the principal quantum number.)

**Reduction**    A downward change in oxidation state. (Reduction is the opposite of oxidation.)

**Resonance**    The existence of two or more reasonable Lewis structures that must be used to represent the actual molecular structure. The actual structure is an average of these Lewis structures, and the Lewis structures are then called resonance forms.

**Reversible reaction**    A reaction in which the products are able to interact to produce the starting materials.

**Salt**    An ionic compound consisting of the cation of a base and the anion of an acid.

**Saturated solution**    A solution of such concentration that if excess solute is present, equilibrium exists between the dissolved and undissolved solutes.

**Shell**    A term commonly used in referring to the electrons of a given energy level, e.g., $K$ shell, $L$ shell, etc.

**Significant figures**    All the reasonably reliable digits in a number.

**Solid state**    The state of matter in which a substance has no perceptible tendency to flow but has sufficient rigidity to maintain a definite shape independent of the shape of any container in which it is placed.

**Solubility**    The concentration of the saturated solution of a substance.

**Solutions**    Homogeneous mixtures.

**Solvation**    The clustering of solvent molecules around a solute.

**Solvent**    In a solution, the medium in which the solute is dissolved.

**Specific heat**    The quantity of heat (number of calories) that must be supplied to raise the temperature of 1 g of a substance 1 °C.

**Spectator ions**    The ions which are ''partners'' of the ions participating in a reaction but which do not take an actual part in the reaction themselves.

**Spontaneous combustion**    Combustion resulting from self-ignition, the heat evolved during slow oxidation being responsible for raising the temperature to the kindling temperature.

**Standard conditions**    Atmospheric pressure and 0 °C.

**Standard pressure**    The pressure exerted by a column of mercury 760 mm (29.9 in.) high, designated 1 atmosphere (1 atm), because it is the pressure exerted by the earth's atmosphere, or 760 torr.

**Standard temperature**    0 °C (32 °F).

**Strong acid**    An acid which gives rise to a high concentration of ions in its solutions, enabling the solutions to serve as good conductors of electricity.

**Strong base**    A base which gives rise to a high concentration of ions in solution, thus making a solution of a strong base a good conductor of electricity.

**Strong electrolyte**    Any electrolyte (acid, base, or salt) that is a good conductor of electricity in the dissolved state because of the high concentration of its ions.

**Superoxides**    Compounds of oxygen in which the oxidation state of oxygen is $-\frac{1}{2}$.

**Surface tension**    The inward pull, due to intermolecular attraction, that causes a liquid surface to become as small as possible.

**Symbol**    A letter or a pair of letters used to represent an element.

**Temperature**    Degree of hotness, measured on a suitable scale. The temperature of an object is not to be confused with the heat that it contains.

**Thermometer**    The instrument used for measuring temperature.

**Theory**    An explanation of a set of related observations.

**Titration**    The process of determining the volume of a solution needed to react with a given volume of another solution (or with a given weight of some material). An important example is the addition of an acid solution to a base solution (or vice versa) to determine the concentration of the base (or acid).

**Torr**    A unit of pressure (1 torr = 1 mm of Hg).

**Transition elements**    Those elements corresponding to a filling of the $d$ shells in the Aufbau procedure.

**Transmutation**    The conversion of one element into another. In ordinary physical and chemical processes, there is no transmutation of elements. Radioactivity involves transmutation.

**Tritium**    The hydrogen isotope of mass number 3; its symbol is T.

**Valence electrons**    Those electrons added after a noble gas electron configuration has been attained.

**Vapor**    The gaseous form of a substance at or below its critical temperature.

**Vaporization (evaporation)**    The change from the liquid to the gaseous (vapor) state.

**Vapor pressure**    The pressure that a vapor exerts when it is in equilibrium with its liquid.

**Viscosity**    The resistance of a fluid to flow.

**Volatility**    The tendency of a liquid to evaporate.

**Voltaic cell (galvanic cell)**    A device which produces electric current by means of an oxidation-reduction reaction.

**Weak acid**    An acid which gives rise to only a small concentration of ions in aqueous solution.

**Weak base**    A base which gives rise to a relatively small concentration of ions in aqueous solution.

**Weak electrolyte**    Any electrolyte that is only a fair or poor conductor of electricity in the dissolved state because the substance furnishes only a few ions in solution.

**Weight**   As commonly used in chemical practice, weight is a measure of the mass of a specimen of matter, as determined with a chemical balance. Technically, the weight of a body is the force with which it is attracted by gravity.

**Work**   Motion against an opposing force. Work has units of energy.

# ANSWERS TO THE TESTS

## Test 1–1

A. 1. The one significant figure to the right of the decimal point in 456.7 determines the number of significant figures in the answer.
   2. $456.7 - 18.23 = 438.5$
B. 1. The three significant figures in 4.92.
   2. 406
C. 1. 323
   2. $4.233 + 0.0013 = 4.234$

## Test 1–2

A. 1. $6.3477 \times 10^4$  2. $2.30 \times 10^{-4}$  3. $3.302 \times 10^3$
   4. $1.1 \times 10^{-2}$
B. 1. 65,400  2. 0.00555  3. 0.00003666
C. 1. $2.2 \times 10^{-2}$  2. $7.3 \times 10^{-10}$  3. $2.41 \times 10^{-9}$
   4. $6.82 \times 10^{-6}$

## Test 1–3

1. $a = by/x$    2. $b = ax/y$

## Test 1–4

A. 1. ? cm  2. 2 inches  3. inches to cm

   4. $2 \text{ in} \times \dfrac{2.54 \text{ cm}}{1 \text{ in}} = 5 \text{ cm}$

   5. yes
B. 1. ? meters  2. 10 yards  3. yards to feet, feet to inches, inches to cm, cm to m.

   4., 5. $10 \text{ yds} \times \dfrac{3 \text{ ft}}{1 \text{ yd}} \times \dfrac{12 \text{ in}}{1 \text{ ft}} \times \dfrac{2.54 \text{ cm}}{\text{in}} \times \dfrac{1 \text{ m}}{100 \text{ cm}} = 9.1 \text{ m}$

C. 1. ? pididdles  2. 7.00 daddles  3. daddles to pididdles

   4. $7.00 \text{ daddles} \times \dfrac{1 \text{ pididdle}}{3.33 \text{ daddles}} = 2.10 \text{ pididdles}$

   5. The number of pididdles in 1 daddle (or per daddle)

235

**Test 1–5**

A.   1. Parts uranium in 100 parts total.
2. 238 g U + 48 g O = 286 g total oxide

3. $\dfrac{238 \text{ g U}}{286 \text{ g total oxide}} \times 100 = 83.2\%$

B.   1. $\dfrac{238 \text{ g U}}{286 \text{ g total oxide}} \times 25.0 \text{ g oxide} = 20.8 \text{ g U}$

or 25.0 g × 0.832 g U/g total = 20.8 g U

C.   1. 500. g sample

2. $\dfrac{8.00 \text{ g UO}_2}{500 \text{ g total}} \times 100 = 1.60\% \text{ UO}_2$

3. $\dfrac{5.00 \text{ g UO}_3}{500 \text{ g total}} \times 100 = 1.00\% \text{ UO}_3$

4. g U in 5.00 g $UO_3$ is $5.00 \text{ g UO}_3 \times \dfrac{0.832 \text{ g U}}{1.00 \text{ g UO}_3} = 4.16 \text{ g U}$

$8.00 \text{ g UO}_2 \times \dfrac{0.881 \text{ g U}}{1.00 \text{ g UO}_2} = 7.05 \text{ g U}$

$\dfrac{11.2 \text{ g U}}{500 \text{ g total}} \times 100 = 2.24\% \text{ U}$

5. $48.0 \text{ g total} \times 0.0224 \dfrac{\text{g U}}{\text{g total}} = 1.08 \text{ g U}$

**Test 2–1**

A.   1. 2H + 4O + 1S = 2.016 + 64.00 + 32.06 = 98.08
2. 21C + 30H + 2O = 252.21 + 30.24 + 32.00 = 314.45
3. 1S + 2O = 32.06 + 32.00 = 64.06
B.   1.0 mole
C.   $6.02 \times 10^{23}$ molecules
D.   98 g
E.   98.08/64.06
F.   98.08 g
G.   Ratio of the masses of $SO_2$ to C is 64.06/12.01;

$\dfrac{64.06 \text{ g SO}_2}{12.01 \text{ g C}} \times 0.0066 \text{ g C} = 0.035 \text{ g SO}_2 \text{ g SO}_2$

**Test 2–2**

A.   $\dfrac{33.4 \text{ g}}{\text{mole}} \times 5.27 \text{ moles} = 176 \text{ g}$

B.   49.8 g mole$^{-1}$

C.   $\dfrac{13.3 \text{ g}}{55.5 \text{ g mole}^{-1}} = 0.240 \text{ mole}$

D.   $\dfrac{0.456 \text{ mole}}{84.3 \text{ g}} \times 17.5 \text{ g} = 0.0947 \text{ mole}$

E.    $$\frac{6.02 \times 10^{23} \text{ molecules mole}^{-1}}{185 \text{ g mole}^{-1}} \times 3.00 \times 10^{-6} \text{ g} = 9.76 \times 10^{15} \text{ molecules}$$

## Test 2-3

A.    1. 80 g/mole

2. $\frac{32 \text{ g}}{80 \text{ g}} \times 100\% = 40\%$

B.    1. 43.66 g P and 56.34 g O

2. $(18.00 \text{ g total})\left(\frac{(0.4366 \text{ g P})}{\text{g total}}\right) = 7.859 \text{ g P}$

3. $\frac{43.66 \text{ g}}{30.98 \text{ g mole}^{-1}} = 1.409 \text{ mole P}$

$\frac{56.34 \text{ g}}{16.00 \text{ g mole}^{-1}} = 3.521 \text{ mole O}$

4. $\frac{3.521}{1.409} = 2.499$

5. $P_2O_5$
6. $(2)(30.98) + 5(16.00) = 141.96$

$\frac{284}{141.96} = 2$; The molecular formula is $P_4O_{10}$

## Test 2-4

A.    MW of AgCl = 107.87 + 35.45 = 143.32

$\frac{35.45 \text{ g Cl}}{143.32 \text{ g AgCl}} \times 100 = 24.73\% \text{ Cl}$

B.    23.48 g AgCl $\times \frac{0.2473 \text{ g Cl}}{1 \text{ g AgCl}} = 5.808 \text{ g Cl}$

C.    5.808 g

D.    $\frac{5.808 \text{ g Cl}}{7.500 \text{ g unknown}} \times 100 = 77.44\%$

## Test 3-1

A.    1. $CH_4 + O_2 \rightarrow CO_2 + 2H_2O$
2. No. $CH_4 + 2O_2 \rightarrow CO_2 + 2H_2O$
3. Yes.
B.    1. $C_4H_{10} + O_2 \rightarrow CO_2 + 5H_2O$
2. No. $C_4H_{10} + O_2 \rightarrow 4CO_2 + 5H_2O$
3. No. Would need 6½ $O_2$ molecules, so
$2C_4H_{10} + 13O_2 \rightarrow 8CO_2 + 10H_2O$.
4. We have the simplest whole number set.

## Test 3-2

A.    1. Balance the equation. $N_2 + 3H_2 \rightarrow 2NH_3$
2. ? moles of $H_2$

3. 0.889 mole $NH_3$

4. 3 moles $H_2$/2 moles $NH_3$

5. ? moles $H_2$ = 0.889 mole $NH_3 \times \dfrac{3 \text{ moles } H_2}{2 \text{ moles } NH_3} = 1.33$ moles $H_2$

B. 1. ? moles $NH_3$ = 0.369 mole $N_2 \times \dfrac{2 \text{ moles } NH_3}{1 \text{ mole } N_2} = 0.738$ mole $NH_3$

C. ? moles $N_2$ = 0.577 mole $H_2 \times \dfrac{1 \text{ mole } N_2}{3 \text{ moles } H_2} = 0.192$ mole $N_2$

## Test 3–3

A. $N_2 + 3H_2 \rightarrow 2NH_3$

? g $NH_3$ = 0.267 mole $N_2 \times \dfrac{2 \text{ moles } NH_3}{1 \text{ mole } N_2} \times \dfrac{17.03 \text{ g } NH_3}{1 \text{ mole } NH_3} = 9.09$ g $NH_3$

B. 1. We shall convert moles of $NH_3$ (begin with) to moles of $H_2$ and then moles of $H_2$ to grams of $H_2$.

2. ? g $H_2$ = 0.275 mole $NH_3 \times \dfrac{3 \text{ moles } H_2}{2 \text{ moles } NH_3} \times \dfrac{2.02 \text{ g } H_2}{1 \text{ mole } H_2} = 0.833$ g $H_2$

C. ? moles $H_2$ = 1000 g $NH_3 \times \dfrac{1 \text{ mole } NH_3}{17.03 \text{ g } NH_3} \times \dfrac{3 \text{ moles } H_2}{2 \text{ moles } NH_3} = 88.1$ moles

D. $N_2 + 3H_2 \rightarrow 2NH_3$

28.01 g $N_2$ + 6.05 g $H_2 \rightarrow$ 34.06 g $NH_3$

E. Using the data in part D:

? g $NH_3$ = 66.6 g $H_2 \times \dfrac{34.06 \text{ g } NH_3}{6.05 \text{ g } H_2} = 375$ g $NH_3$

F. ? g $H_2$ = 88.8 g $N_2 \times \dfrac{6.05 \text{ g } H_2}{28.01 \text{ g } N_2} = 19.2$ g $H_2$

## Test 3–4

A. 1. ? moles $H_2$ = 0.333 mole $HCl \times \dfrac{1 \text{ mole } H_2}{2 \text{ moles } HCl} = 0.167$ mole $H_2$

2. 65.38 g Zn + 72.92 g HCl $\rightarrow$ 136.28 g $ZnCl_2$ + 2.02 g $H_2$

3. $\dfrac{72.92 \text{ g HCl}}{65.38 \text{ g Zn}} = 1.115$

Given: $\dfrac{25.0 \text{ g HCl}}{30.0 \text{ g Zn}} = 0.833$

Therefore, zinc is in excess.

4. 25.0 g of HCl.

5. 25.0 g of HCl.

6. Theoretical amount:

? g $ZnCl_2$ = 25.0 g $HCl \times \dfrac{136.3 \text{ g } ZnCl_2}{72.92 \text{ g HCl}} = 46.7$ g $ZnCl_2$

$$\frac{\text{actual}}{\text{theoretical}} \times 100 = \frac{35.0}{46.7} \times 100 = 75.0\%$$

**Test 4–1**

A. 1. 53  2. 126.9  3. 127
   4. 53  5. 74  6. 53
   7. It has 54 electrons. Everything else is the same.
B. 1. A pair of bonding electrons shared by H and I.
   2. An ionic bond
   3. A pair of bonding electrons is attracted by both the H and I positive nuclei in H-I. The positive $Na^+$ electrostatically attracts many negative iodide ions ($I^-$) in $Na^+I^-$
C. 1. ionic  2. covalent  3. covalent
   4. ionic  5. ionic  6. covalent

**Test 4–2**

A. fluoride and iodide
B. 1. sodium iodide  2. ammonium bromide  3. calcium fluoride
C. Because the only fluoride formed by calcium is $CaF_2$, so there is no ambiguity in simply naming it calcium fluoride.
D. 1. MgS, Rules 1a, 1c, 2
   2. $CS_2$, Rules 3, 4
   3. NaH, Rules 1a, 1c, 3
   4. $(NH_4)_2SO_4$, Rules 1b, 1d, 2
E. Rules 3, 6
F. 1. $NH_3$, $PH_3$, $AsH_3$, $SbH_3$, $BiH_3$
   2. $NCl_3$, $PCl_3$, $AsCl_3$, $SbCl_3$, $BiCl_3$ or $NF_3$, $NCl_3$, $NBr_3$, $NI_3$, $NAt_3$
   3. $CCl_4$, $SiCl_4$, $GeCl_4$, $SnCl_4$, $PbCl_4$, or $CF_4$, $CCl_4$, $CBr_4$, $CI_4$, $CAt_4$

**Test 5–1**

A. 1. $m = \dfrac{\text{moles}}{\text{kg solvent}}$  (equation 5-2)

   2. $m$ can convert moles to kg of solvent or kg of solvent to moles.
   3.a.  ? $m$
     b.  0.224 mole = 5.75 g solvent
     c.
       $$m = \frac{0.224 \text{ mole}}{575 \text{ g solvent}} \times \frac{1000 \text{ g solvent}}{1 \text{ kg solvent}} = 0.390 \frac{\text{mole}}{\text{kg solvent}}$$

   4. a.  ? kg $H_2O$
      b.  ? kg = 3.75 moles $\times \dfrac{1 \text{ kg}}{1.66 \text{ moles}}$ = 2.26 kg $H_2O$

   5. a.  ? g $H_2O$
      b.  g $C_2H_5OH$ to moles, then moles $C_2H_5OH$ to kg $H_2O$
      c.  ? moles $C_2H_5OH$ = 11.5 g $C_2H_5OH \times \dfrac{1 \text{ mole } C_2H_5OH}{46.07 \text{ g}}$

       = 0.250 moles $C_2H_5OH$

$$? \text{ g H}_2\text{O} = 0.250 \text{ moles C}_2\text{H}_5\text{OH} \times \frac{1 \text{ kg}}{0.336 \text{ moles}} \times \frac{1000 \text{g}}{\text{kg}} = 744 \text{ g H}_2\text{O}$$

B.  1. Determine the number of moles contained in 675 ml of 0.222 M solution of NaOH. Determine the number of ml of 2.00 M solution needed to obtain the required number of moles. Dilute the 2.00 M solution to 675 ml of solution.

2. $0.222 \dfrac{\text{moles}}{\text{liter}} \times 0.675 \text{ liter} = 0.150 \text{ mole}$

3. $0.150 \text{ mole} \times \dfrac{1 \text{ liter}}{2.00 \text{ moles}} = 0.0750 \text{ liter} = 75.0 \text{ ml}$

4. Dilute 0.075 liters (75.0 ml) of 2.00 M NaOH solution with water to 675 ml of solution.

## Test 5–2

A.  1. $Zn^{2+}(aq) + 2NO_3^-(aq)$     9. $2Na^+(aq) + CO_3^{2-}(aq)$
2. $PbCl_2(s)$     10. $Cs^+(aq) + OH^-(aq)$
3. $Sr^{2+}(aq) + 2OH^-(aq)$     11. $H_3BO_3(aq)$
4. $CH_3CO_2H(aq)$     12. $CaF_2(s)$
5. $H^+(aq) + Br^-(aq)$     13. $Pb^{2+}(aq) + 2NO_3^-(aq)$
6. $C_2H_5OH(aq)$     14. $2Na^+(aq) + SO_4^{2-}(aq)$
7. $NH_4^+(aq) + Cl^-(aq)$     15. $2NH_4^+(aq) + SO_4^{2-}(aq)$
8. $PbSO_4(s)$

B.  1. It must be a weak acid because we drink soda pop.
2. $2H^+(aq) + CO_3^{2-}(aq) \rightarrow H_2CO_3(aq) \rightarrow H_2O(l) + CO_2(g)$

C.  Total ionic equation:
$2H^+(aq) + 2Cl^-(aq) + 2Na^+(aq) + CO_3^{2-}(aq) \rightarrow 2Cl^-(aq)$
$+ H_2CO_3(aq) + 2Na^+(aq) \rightarrow 2Cl^-(aq) + 2Na^+(aq)$
$+ H_2O(l) + CO_2(g)$
Net ionic equation:
$2H^+(aq) + CO_3^{2-}(aq) \rightarrow H_2CO_3(aq) \rightarrow H_2O(l) + CO_2(g)$

D.  1. Yes. $Na^+Cl^-$ is a soluble ionic solid.
2. No. $H^+$ and $OH^-$ combine to form the poorly ionized compound water.
3. No. $H^+$ and $CN^-$ combine to form the weak acid HCN.
4. No. $Ag^+$ and $Cl^-$ combine to form the insoluble solid $Ag^+Cl^-(s)$.
5. No. $H^+$ and $CO_3^{2-}$ combine as shown in part C.

## Test 6–1

A.  1. $E_k = \frac{1}{2} mv^2$
2. It is increased by a factor of four ($2^2$). When $v$ of the above equation is doubled
$E_k = \frac{1}{2} m (2v)^2 = 4 \times \frac{1}{2} mv^2$

3. $? \text{ kJ} = 88.6 \dfrac{\text{kcal}}{\text{mole}} \times \dfrac{4.184 \text{ kJ}}{1 \text{ kcal}} = 371 \text{ kJ mole}^{-1}$

B. 1. A solid (s) is converted to a gas (g).

2. The gas.
3. The gas.
4. $\Delta$ = final − initial; $\Delta H = H_{(g)} - H_{(s)}$.
Since $H_{(g)} > H_{(s)}$, $\Delta H$ is positive. The process is endothermic.
5. The same magnitude but negative. The process is exothermic.

## Test 6–2

A. 1. $\Delta H = \Sigma H$ (products) − $\Sigma H$ (reactants)
2. $2H$ (HNO$_3$) = $2\Delta H_f$ HNO$_3$(aq) = −414 kJ
$H$(NO) ≡ $\Delta H_f$ NO(g) = 90.37 kJ
$\Sigma H_p$ = −324 kJ
3. $3H$(NO$_2$) ≡ $3\Delta H_f$ NO$_2$(g) = 101.6 kJ
$H$(H$_2$O) ≡ $\Delta H_f$ H$_2$O(l) = −285.8 kJ
$\Sigma H_r$ = −184 kJ
4. $\Delta H = \Sigma H_p - \Sigma H_r$ = − 324 kJ − (−184 kJ) = −140 kJ
5. exothermic
6. +140 kJ
7. −70 kJ mole$^{-1}$ HNO$_3$

8.

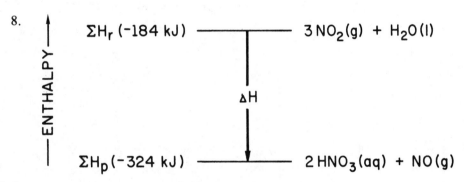

## Test 6–3

A. 1. ZnS(s) + 3O$_2$(g) → 2ZnO(s) + 2SO$_2$(g)
2. $\Delta H = \Sigma H_p - \Sigma H_r$
3. $2\Delta H_f$ZnO = 2(−83.2)    = −166.4 kJ

   $2\Delta H_f$SO$_2$ = 2(−296.9) = $\underline{−593.8 \text{ kJ}}$
                                          −760.2 kJ

4. Zero. It is an element in its standard state.
5. $2\Delta H_f$ZnS = 2(−48.5) = −97.0 kJ
6. $\Delta H$ = −760.2 − (−97.0) = −663.2 kJ.
7. Exothermic
8. (a) −331.6 kJ/mole ZnS
   (b) −331.6 kJ
9. The products are at a lower potential energy and thus are more stable.
10.   2SO$_2$(g) + O$_2$(g) → 2SO$_3$(g)
      $\Delta H = 2(\Delta H_f SO_3) - [2(\Delta H_f SO_2) + \Delta H_f O_2]$ =
      2(−395.2 kJ) − [2(−296.9 kJ) + 0] = −196.6 kJ

11.  The $\Delta H$ for $ZnS + 2O_2 \rightarrow ZnO + SO_3$ would be the sum of:

$$ZnS + \frac{3}{2}O_2 \rightarrow ZnO + SO_2 \qquad \Delta H = -331.6 \text{ kJ}$$

$$SO_2 + \frac{1}{2}O_2 \rightarrow SO_3 \qquad \Delta H = -98.3 \text{ kJ}$$

Or one half the sum of:
$$2ZnS + 3O_2 \rightarrow 2ZnO + 2SO_2 \qquad \Delta H = -663.2 \text{ kJ}$$
$$2SO_2 + O_2 \rightarrow 2SO_3 \qquad \Delta H = -196.6 \text{ kJ}$$

12.

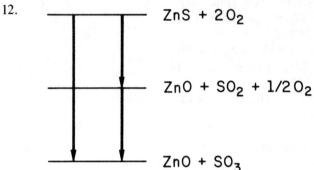

13.

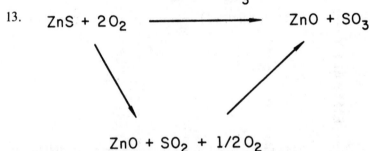

An equally valid cycle would result without a $\frac{1}{2}O_2$ if all coefficients were multiplied by two.

**Test 7–1**

A.  1. $P_2V_2$
    2. decreases, smaller
    3. inversely
    4. greater
    5. less, decreased
    6. 700 torr

B.  1. $\dfrac{V_1}{T_1} = \dfrac{V_2}{T_2}$

    2. $\dfrac{T_1}{T_2}$

    3. increase
    4. 54.5 ml (Be sure to use °K in the calculation.)
    5. increase, increase, decrease, increase

C.  1.  $$\frac{50 \text{ ml}}{(2.0 \text{ mole}) (373 °K)} = \frac{x \text{ ml}}{(3.0 \text{ mole}) (423 °K)}; x = 85 \text{ ml}$$

2.  increase
3.  decrease

D.  1.  one sample is described by signalling $PV = nRT$
2.  one, $n$
3.  $n = PV/RT$
4.  changing 700 torr to atm:

$$700 \text{ torr} \times \frac{1 \text{ atm}}{760 \text{ torr}} = 0.921 \text{ atm}$$

$$\frac{(0.921 \text{ atm})(500 \text{ ml})}{(82.05 \text{ ml atm } °K^{-1})(303 °K)} = 0.0185 \text{ mole}$$

## Test 7–2

A.  1.  $PV = nRT$ and $n = $ g/GMW

$$PV = \frac{\text{g}}{\text{GMW}} RT$$

Multiplying both sides by GMW and dividing both by $PV$ produces:
GMW $= $ g$RT/PV$

2.  11.5 g and 1.00 liter
3.  0.08205 liter atm mole$^{-1}$ $°K^{-1}$

4.  GMW $= \dfrac{(11.5 \text{ g}) (0.08205 \text{ liter atm mole }^{-1} °K^{-1}) (373 °K)}{(1.00 \text{ atm})(1.00 \text{ liter})} = 352 \text{ g}$

5.  352 amu

B.  GMW $= \dfrac{(0.495 \text{ g}) (0.08205 \text{ liter atm mole}^{-1} °K^{-1}) (371 °K)}{\left(\dfrac{754 \text{ atm}}{760}\right) (0.127 \text{ liter})} = 120 \text{ g}$

MW $= 120$ amu

C.  $PV = \dfrac{\text{g}}{(\text{GMW})} RT$

$(\text{GMW})PV = \text{g} RT$

$\dfrac{(\text{GMW})PV}{RT} = \text{g}$

$\dfrac{(\text{GMW})P}{RT} = \dfrac{\text{g}}{V} = \text{d}$

## Test 8–1

A.  1.  37 electrons
2.  52 electrons
3.  27 electrons

B.  1s, 2s, 2p, 3s, 3p, 4s, 3d, 4p

C.  1.  $1s^2\,2s^2\,2p^6\,3s^2\,3p^3$
    2.  $1s^2\,2s^2\,2p^6\,3s^2\,3p^6\,4s^2\,3d^{10}\,4p^3$
    3.  $1s^2\,2s^2\,2p^6\,3s^2\,3p^6\,4s^2\,3d^6$
    4.  $1s^2\,2s^2\,2p^6\,3s^2\,3p^6\,4s^2$
    5.  $1s^2\,2s^2\,2p^6\,3s^2\,3p^6\,4s^2\,3d^{10}\,4p^4$

D.  1.  C, Si, Ge, Sn, Pb
    2.  H, Li, Na, K, Rb, Cs, Fr
    3.  Ne, Ar, Kr, Xe, Rn

E.  1.  $1s^2\,2s^2\,2p^6\,3s^2\,3p^6\,4s^2\,3d^{10}\,4p^6\,5s^2\,4d^3$
    2.  $1s^2\,2s^2\,2p^6\,3s^2\,3p^6\,4s^2\,3d^{10}\,4p^6\,5s^2\,4d^{10}\,5p^6\,6s^2\,4f^{14}\,5d^5$
    3.  $1s^2\,2s^2\,2p^6\,3s^2\,3p^6\,4s^2\,3d^{10}\,4p^6\,5s^2\,4d^{10}\,5p^6\,6s^2\,4f^4$

F.

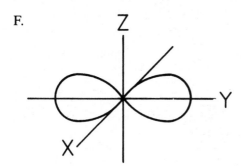

**Test 8–2**

A.  1.

4s
| 1↓ |

4p
| 1↓ | 1↓ | 1 |

2.

6s
| 1↓ |

3.

3d
| 1 | 1 | 1 | 1 |  |

4s
| 1↓ |

4.

3d
| 1 | 1 | 1 | 1 | 1 |

4s
|  |

5.

5s
| 1↓ |

5p
|  |  |  |

6.

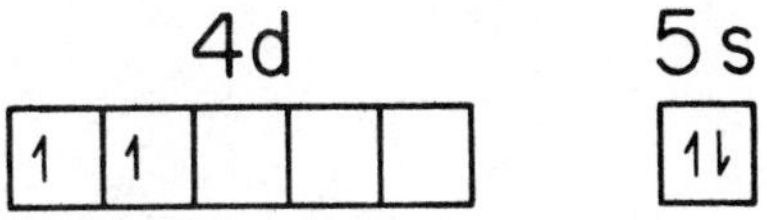

**Test 8–3**

A.  1. H—O—O—H
    2. 14 valence electrons
    3. 14 − 6 = 8 electrons
    4. H—$\overline{\text{O}}$—$\overline{\text{O}}$—H
    5. All atoms are satisfied.

B.  1. Ten valence electrons
    2. 10 − 6 = 4
    3. H—$\overline{\text{C}}$—$\overline{\text{C}}$—H (one of several possible ways)
    4. Four
    5. H—C≡C—H

C.      Cl
        |
    Cl—B—Cl; 24 electrons

    24 − 6 = 18 remaining electrons

          $|\overline{\text{Cl}}|$
          |
    $|\overline{\text{Cl}}$ — B — $\overline{\text{Cl}}|$

D.
          $|\overline{\text{Cl}}|$
          |
    $|\overline{\text{Cl}}$ — B — $\overline{\text{Cl}}|$
          |
          $|\overline{\text{Cl}}|$

**Test 8–4**

A.  1. O—N—O⁻

    2. 18 electrons

    3. 18 − 4 = 14 electrons

    4. $|\overline{\text{O}}$—$\overline{\text{N}}$—$\overline{\text{O}}|$ (one of several possible ways)

    5. Yes. $|\overline{\text{O}}$=$\overline{\text{N}}$—$\overline{\text{O}}|$

    6. Yes. $|\overline{\text{O}}$=$\overline{\text{N}}$—$\overline{\text{O}}|$ ↔ $|\overline{\text{O}}$—$\overline{\text{N}}$=$\overline{\text{O}}|$

    7. 1.5

B.  1. O—Cl—O

    2. 19 electrons

    3. 19 − 4 = 15 electrons

    4. $|\overline{\text{O}}$—$\overline{\text{Cl}}$—$\overline{\text{O}}|$

    5. No.

    6. Yes. $|\overset{.}{\overline{\text{O}}}$—$\overline{\text{Cl}}$—$\overline{\text{O}}|$ ↔ $|\overline{\text{O}}$—$\overset{.}{\overline{\text{Cl}}}$—$\overline{\text{O}}|$ ↔ $|\overline{\text{O}}$—$\overline{\text{Cl}}$—$\overset{.}{\overline{\text{O}}}|$

C.  1.  N—N
    2.  10 electrons
    3.  $10 - 2 = 8$ electrons
    4.  |N̅—N̅|
    5.  |N≡N|

D.  1.  22 electrons
    2.  $22 - 14 = 8$ electrons
    3. 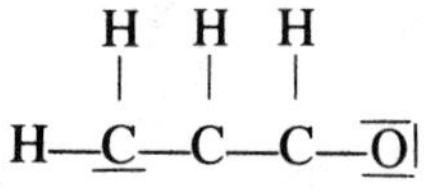
$$\begin{array}{ccc} H & H & H \\ | & | & | \end{array}$$
H—C—C—C—O̅|(one of several posibilities)

    4. 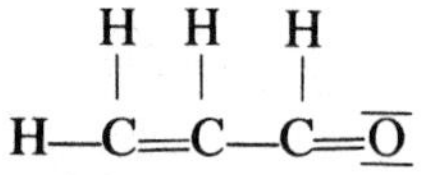
$$\begin{array}{ccc} H & H & H \\ | & | & | \end{array}$$
H—C=C—C=O̅

E.  1.  24 electrons
    2.  $24 - 6 = 18$ electrons

    3. 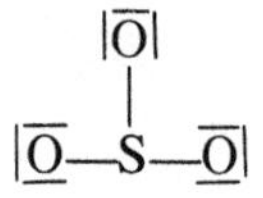
|O̅|
|
|O̅—S—O̅|

    4. 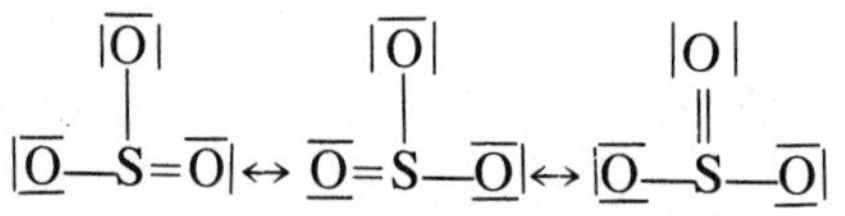
|O̅|          |O̅|          |O|
|            |            ‖
|O̅—S=O̅|↔ O̅=S—O̅|↔ |O̅—S—O̅|

## Test 9–1

A.  1.  O $= -2$, Na$= +1$
    2.  $-14$ for seven O and $+2$ for two Na $= -12$
    3.  $+12$ to make $Na_2Cr_2O_7$ neutral
    4.  $+6$
B.  1.  two O $= -4$
    2.  ion charge $-1$
    3.  $+3$ ($-4 + 3 = -1$ charge on ion)
C.  zero
D.  $3H = +3$, one Cl $= -1$, so C $= -2$
E.  1.$+2$   2.$-2$   3.$-1$

## Test 9–2

A.  1.  iron(III) chloride
    2.  iron(II) chloride
    3.  phosphorus(V) oxide
    4.  phosphorus(III) oxide
    5.  chlorine(VII) oxide
    6.  copper(I) oxide
B.  1.  $+5$
    2.  $+5$
    3.  phosphoric
    4.  $+3$ and phosphorous
    5.  phosphate ion
C.  sulfurous acid and sulfite ion

**Test 9-3**

A.  1.  Write the net ionic equation:

$$Cr_2O_7^{2-}(aq) + H^+(aq) + Cl^-(aq) \rightarrow Cr^{3+}(aq) + Cl_2(g)$$

2.  Pick out the half-reactions:

$$Cl^- \rightarrow Cl_2$$
$$Cr_2O_7^{2-} \rightarrow Cr^{3+}$$

3.  Balance chemically (acid solution):

$$2Cl^- \rightarrow Cl_2$$
$$14H^+ + Cr_2O_7^{2-} \rightarrow 2Cr^{3+} + 7H_2O$$

4.  Balance the charge: $2Cl^- \rightarrow Cl_2 + 2e^-$

$$6e^- + 14H^+ + Cr_2O_7^{2-} \rightarrow 2Cr^{3+} + 7H_2O$$

5.  Cancel electrons and total.

$$6Cl^- \rightarrow 3Cl_2 + 6e^-$$
$$\underline{6e^- + 14H^+ + Cr_2O_7^{2-} \rightarrow 2Cr^{3+} + 7H_2O}$$
$$14H^+ + 6Cl^- + Cr_2O_7^{2-} \rightarrow 3Cl_2 + 2Cr^{3+} + 7H_2O$$

6.  We have the lowest common denominator of coefficients, so we convert to the molecular equation. We need two $K^+$ for $Cr_2O_7^{2-}$ and $3Cl^-$ for each $Cr^{3+}$.

Adding $2K^+$ and $6Cl^-$ to each side we obtain:

$$6Cl^- + 8H^+ + 6HCl + K_2Cr_2O_7 \rightarrow 3Cl_2 + 2CrCl_3 + 7H_2O + 2K^+$$

Adding $2Cl^-$ to each side:

$$12HCl + K_2Cr_2O_7 \rightarrow 3Cl_2 + 2CrCl_3 + 7H_2O + 2KCl$$

B.  1.  $Cl^-$
    2.  $Cr_2O_7^{2-}$

**Test 10-1**

A.  1.  $m$
2.  From Table 10-1, $CCl_4$ freezes at $-22.3\ °C$, so $-25.0 - (-22.3)$ $= -2.7\ °C$
3.  $-29.8\ °C\,m^{-1}$

$$4 \quad m = \frac{\Delta T_{fp}}{k_{fp}} = \frac{-2.7\ °C}{-29.8\ °C\,m^{-1}} = 0.0906\ m$$

5.  $$\frac{3.66\ g}{86.7\ g\ CCl_4} \times \frac{1000\ g}{1\ kg} = 42.2\ g\ solute/kg\ CCl_4$$

6.  $42.2\ g = 0.0906$ moles ($42.2\ g/kg = 0.0906\ m$)

7.  $$\frac{42.2\ g}{0.0906\ moles} = 466\ g/mole$$

MW $= 466$ amu

# ANSWERS TO EXERCISES

## Chapter 1

1. (a) 464 miles
   (b) 1.40 hours
   (c) 22.3 pididdles
   (d) 1.62 daddles
2. (a) four
   (b) five
   (c) two
   (d) three
   (e) four
3. (a) 343.2
   (b) 0.0164
   (c) 222.06
   (d) 5.8
   (e) 2.2
   (f) 0.94389
   (g) 5.4
   (h) 17.8
4. (a) 0.250 g S
   (b) 4.00 g Cu
   (c) 128 g Cu
   (d) The answers to part (a)
       converts g Cu to g S,
       while the answer to
       part (b) converts
       g S to g Cu.
5. (a) $9.1 \times 10^2$ cm
   (b) 12 in
   (c) 2.0 m
   (d) 23 kg
   (e) 2.993 lb
   (f) 4.20 liters
   (g) 30. ml
6. (a) $1.00 \times 10^2$
   (b) $3.56000 \times 10^5$
   (c) $3.30 \times 10^{-1}$
   (d) $1.2158 \times 10^4$

(e) $2.56 \times 10^{-2}$
(f) $3.2 \times 10^{-7}$
(g) $6.87 \times 10^{-3}$
(h) $9.5543 \times 10^2$

7. (a) 1440
   (b) 0.000633
   (c) 255.6
   (d) 0.000000000555
8. (a) $2.5 \times 10^{10}$
   (b) $1.4 \times 10^2$
   (c) $2.55 \times 10^{-6}$
   (d) $2.38 \times 10^{-2}$
   (e) $1.5 \times 10^{-9}$
   (f) $3.97 \times 10^{-4}$
   (g) $7.290 \times 10^5$
   (h) $1.00 \times 10^{12}$
   (i) $43 \times 10^{18}$
9. (a) $g = rx/y$
   (b) $r = gy/x$
   (c) $x = gy/r$
   (d) $y = xr/g$
10. (a) $a = bcd/ex^2$
    (b) $d = aex^2/cb$
    (c) $e = bcd/ax^2$
    (d) $x = (bcd/ae)^{\frac{1}{2}}$
11. (a) $a = cd/bef$
    (b) $c = abefd$
    (c) $f = cd/abe$
12. 8.92 g/ml
13. 18.9 ml
14. 4.04 ml
15. 77.5 g
16. 40.0% calcium
    12.0% carbon
    48.0% oxygen

17. 23.3 g Fe
18. 24.9% increase
19. 30.8%

20. 107 g iron oxide
21. 69.0% Cr
    31.0% O

22. The answers to all these questions can be found in the text. Check your written statement against what is given there.

23. 100 yards = 91.4 meters
    Increase is $100 - 91.4 = 8.6$ meters

$$\% \text{ increase} = \frac{8.56 \text{ m}}{91.4 \text{ m}} \times 100 = 9.37\%$$

Salary desired
$88,000 + 8,246 = \$96,246$

24. $11.3 \text{ g/ml} \times \dfrac{1 \text{ lb}}{454 \text{ g}} \times \dfrac{1000 \text{ ml}}{1 \text{ liter}} \times \dfrac{0.946 \text{ liter}}{1 \text{ qt}} \times \dfrac{4 \text{ qt}}{\text{gallon}} = 94.2 \text{ lb/gal}$

25. Cost of 1 g of U

$$\frac{0.50\cancel{c}}{1 \text{ g UF}_6} \times \frac{1 \text{ g UF}_6}{0.58 \text{ g U}} = 0.86\cancel{c}/\text{g U}$$

$0.86\cancel{c} + 0.47\cancel{c} = \$1.33 \text{ per g U}$

26. Let $x$ be the fraction $UO_2$ and $1-x$ the fraction $UO_3$.
    $0.845 = x(0.881) + (1-x)(0.832)$
    $0.845 = 0.881x + 0.832 - 0.832x$
    $0.013 = 0.049x$
    $x = 0.265$
    so have 26.5% $UO_2$ and 73.5% $UO_3$

## Chapter 2

1. (a) compound
   (b) element
   (c) mixture
   (d) mixture
   (e) compound
2. (a) physical; change of state
   (b) chemical
   (c) chemical
   (d) physical; heating a filament
   so it glows
   (e) chemical
3. (a) 58.100 amu
   (b) 53.492 amu
   (c) 132.138 amu
   (d) 202.58 amu
   (e) 486.01 amu
   (f) 60.05 amu
4. (a) 0.43 mole
   (b) 0.56 mole

   (c) 0.16 mole
   (d) 25.5 mole
5. (a) 43.6 g
   (b) 160 g
   (c) 20.3 g
6. 71 g mole$^{-1}$
7. 86.8 g mole$^{-1}$
8. (a) $9.27 \times 10^{22}$ molecules
   (b) $1.30 \times 10^{-19}$ g
   (c) $6.0 \times 10^{19}$
   (d) 25.0 g $CO_2$
9. 4.8 g $C_2H_6$
10. 26.8 g $C_6H_6$
11. 5.927% H
12. 47.26% Cu
13. NO
14. 34.998% N
15. $N_2O_4$
16. $H_4P_2O_7$

17. $C_2H_4$
18. $SO_3$
19. $Ag_2O$
20. 79.1 g P
21. SnO
22. 20.26%

23. $CH_2$
24. $ClO_2$
25. 51.9 amu
26. $x = 7$
27. 0.314 moles
28. See text.

## Chapter 3

1. (a) $2KClO_3 \rightarrow 2KCl + 3O_2$
   (b) 2 moles $KClO_3 \rightarrow$ 2 moles KCl + 3 moles $O_2$
   2 molecules $KClO_3 \rightarrow$ 2 molecules KCl + 3 molecules $O_2$
   245.10 g $KClO_3 \rightarrow$ 149.10 g KCl + 96.00 g $O_2$
2. (a) $2H_2O_2 \rightarrow 2H_2O + O_2$
   (b) 2 molecules $H_2O_2 \rightarrow$ 2 molecules $H_2O$ + 1 molecule $O_2$
   2 moles $H_2O_2 \rightarrow$ 2 moles $H_2O$ + 1 mole $O_2$
   68.04 g $H_2O_2 \rightarrow$ 36.04 g $H_2O$ + 32.00 g $O_2$
3. (a) $2Al + N_2 \rightarrow 2AlN$
   (b) $3Fe + 2O_2 \rightarrow Fe_3O_4$
   (c) It is balanced.
   (d) $NH_4NO_3 \rightarrow N_2O + 2H_2O$
   (e) $2KI + Cl_2 \rightarrow 2KCl + I_2$
   (f) $Pb(NO_3)_2 + 2HCl \rightarrow PbCl_2 + 2HNO_3$
   (g) $2BaO_2 \rightarrow 2BaO + O_2$
   (h) $2Al + 3H_2SO_4 \rightarrow Al_2(SO_4)_3 + 3H_2$
   (i) $CH_4 + 3Cl_2 \rightarrow CHCl_3 + 3HCl$
   (j) $MgCl_2 + 2NaOH \rightarrow Mg(OH)_2 + 2NaCl$
   (k) $2AgNO_3 + CuCl_2 \rightarrow 2AgCl + Cu(NO_3)_2$
   (l) $2ZnS + 3O_2 \rightarrow 2ZnO + 2SO_2$
   (m) $2Na + 2H_2O \rightarrow 2NaOH + H_2$
   (n) $BaCl_2 + (NH_4)_2CO_3 \rightarrow BaCO_3 + 2NH_4Cl$
4. (a) ½ mole $Al_2O_3$
   (b) 12 moles Al
   (c) 9 moles $O_2$
   (d) 96.0 g $O_2$ and 204 g $Al_2O_3$
5. (a) 4.00 g $SO_2$
   (b) 2.00 g $O_2$
   (c) 10.0 g
   (d) 9.98 g $O_2$
6. (a) 169 g $I_2$
7. (a) 41 g $Cl_2$
   (b) 44 g of $MnCl_2$
8. (a) 31.20 moles
   (b) 156 moles
   (c) 602 g $H_2O$
   (d) 2124 g $H_2O_2$
9. (a) 869 g $CO_2$
   (b) 632 g $O_2$
10. (a) 346 g Cu

    (b) 698 g $SO_2$
11. 364 g $O_2$
12. (a) 608 g $KClO_3$
    (b) 370 grams KCl
13. (a) $H_2O_2$ is limiting, 32.1 g $H_2O$
    (b) 90.4%
    (c) 19.2 g of $N_2H_4$ excess
14. (a) 1.53 kg $H_2SO_4$
    (b) 33.4%
15. 26.1 g of $SO_2$
16. 33.3 g $C_6H_{12}O_6$
17. 76.0%
18. (a) The Al is limiting; 10.3 g Fe
    (b) 0.001 mole $Fe_2O_3$
    (c) 100%
19. (a) 14.6 g $NH_3$
    (b) 1.42 g $H_2$
20. Check your answers against the text.

21. (a) 163 g $HNO_3$
    (b) 30.0 g $NH_3$
22. 0.106 mole $P_4$
23. 110 g

24. $1.1 \times 10^3$ g air
25. (a) 71.9%
    (b) 69.2 g Fe

## Chapter 4

1. (a) 30, 35, 30
   (b) 49, 66, 49
   (c) 26, 30, 23
   (d) 1, 0, 0
   (e) 16, 16, 18
   (f) 92, 146, 92

2. (a) covalent     (e) ionic
   (b) covalent     (f) covalent
   (c) covalent     (g) covalent
   (d) covalent     (h) ionic

   (i) $NH_4^+Br^-$, ionic, N—H covalent
   (j) $Na^+NO_3^-$ ionic, N—O covalent
   (k) $2K^+ + CO_3^{2-}$ ionic, C—O covalent
   (l) $NH_4^+NO_3^-$ ionic, N—O covalent

3. (a) $(NH_4)_2S$     (d) $SO_2$
   (b) CaO            (e) $SiO_2$
   (c) $Mg(OH)_2$     (f) $(NH_4)_2SO_4$
   (g) $BeH_2$        (j) $BaSO_4$
   (h) $Na_3PO_4$     (k) $BaSO_3$
   (i) $Mg_3(PO_4)_2$  (l) $NaHCO_3$

4. (a) hydrogen iodide
   (b) strontium bromide
   (c) silicon tetrachloride
   (d) nitrogen dioxide
   (e) rubidium oxide
   (f) methane (a common name)
   (g) hydrogen telluride
   (h) strontium sulfide
   (i) ammonium bromide
   (j) sodium nitrate
   (k) potassium carbonate
   (l) ammonium nitrate

5. (a) $2NaOH + CO_2 \rightarrow Na_2CO_3 + H_2O$
   (b) $Mg(NO_3)_2 + K_2SO_4 \rightarrow MgSO_4 + 2KNO_3$
   (c) $K_2SO_3 + Ba(NO_3)_2 \rightarrow BaSO_3 + 2KNO_3$
6. Check your answers against the text.

## Chapter 5

1. Weigh out 39.2 g of $Ba(OH)_2$ and dissolve in enough water to make 350 ml of solution.
2. 18.6 g $Ca(NO_3)_2$     is diluted to 325 ml
3. 0.686 M
4. 0.121 M
5. 826 ml
6. 554 ml
7. 564 ml
8. 0.219 mole
9. (a) 0.692 M
   (b) 0.0519 mole
   (c) 663 ml
10. 1.80 M
11. 93.4 ml of 2.00 M solution
12. 11.4 M
13. 0.500 M
14. 0.424 M
15. 1.11 m
16. Add 23.2 g $H_2O$ to give 93.1 g
17. 3.44 g glucose
18. 0.10 ppm
19. (a) 0.0206
    (b) 0.167
20. $1.17 \times 10^3$ g of fish

21.  (a) $Zn^{2+} + 2Cl^- + H_2S \rightarrow ZnS(s) + 2H^+ + 2Cl^-$
$Zn^{2+} + H_2S \rightarrow ZnS(s) + 2H^+$

Rules 2 and 7

(b) $Ag^+ + NO_3^- + H^+ + Br^- \rightarrow AgBr(s) + H^+ + NO_3^-$
$Ag^+ + Br^- \rightarrow AgBr(s)$

Rules 1 and 3

(c) $Ba^{2+} + 2OH^- + 2H^+ + 2Cl^- \rightarrow 2H_2O + Ba^{2+} + 2Cl^-$
$H^+ + OH^- \rightarrow H_2O$

Rules 2 and 6

(d) $Na^+ + CH_3CO_2^- + H^+ + Br^- \rightarrow Na^+ + Br^- + CH_3CO_2H$
$H^+ + CH_3CO_2^- \rightarrow CH_3CO_2H$

Rule 8

(e) $HCN + Na^+ + OH^- \rightarrow H_2O + Na^+ + CN^-$
$HCN + OH^- \rightarrow H_2O + CN^-$

Rule 8

(f) $Pb^{2+} + 2NO_3^- + 2Na^+ + 2Cl^- \rightarrow PbCl_2(s) + 2Na^+ + 2NO_3^-$
$Pb^{2+} + 2Cl^- \rightarrow PbCl_2(s)$

Rules 1, 2 and 8.

(g) $Cu(s) + 2Ag^+ + 2NO_3^- \rightarrow Cu^{2+} + 2NO_3^- + 2Ag(s)$
$Cu(s) + 2Ag^+ \rightarrow Cu^{2+} + 2Ag(s)$

Rule 1

(h) $Mg^{2+} + 2NO_3^- + 2K^+ + 2OH^- \rightarrow Mg(OH)_2(s) + 2K^+ + 2NO_3^-$
$Mg^{2+} + 2OH^- \rightarrow Mg(OH)_2(s)$

Rules 1 and 6

(i) $Pb^{2+} + 2NO_3^- + 2Na^+ + SO_4^{2-} \rightarrow PbSO_4(s) + 2Na^+ + 2NO_3^-$
$Pb^{2+} + SO_4^{2-} \rightarrow PbSO_4(s)$

Rules 1 and 5.

(j) $Mg(OH)_2(s) + 2H^+ + 2Cl^- \rightarrow Mg^{2+} + 2H_2O + 2Cl^-$
$Mg(OH)_2(s) + 2H^+ \rightarrow Mg^{2+} + 2H_2O$

Rules 6 and 2.

(k) $2NH_4^+ + CO_3^{2-} + Ba^{2+} + 2NO_3^- \rightarrow BaCO_3(s) + 2NH_4^+ + 2NO_3^-$
$Ba^{2+} + CO_3^{2-} \rightarrow BaCO_3(s)$

Rules 7 and 1.

(l) $2K^+ + CO_3^{2-} + 2H^+ + 2Cl^- \rightarrow H_2O + CO_2 + 2K^+ + 2Cl^-$
$CO_3^{2-} + 2H^+ \rightarrow H_2O + CO_2$

22.  Strong acids: $HNO_3$, $HCl$, $H_2SO_4$
Weak acids: $HCN$, $CH_3CO_2H$, $H_2CO_3$

$$HNO_3 + H_2O \rightarrow H^+(aq) + NO_3^-$$
$$CH_3CO_2H + H_2O \rightarrow H^+(aq) + CH_3CO_2^-$$

23. $H^+ + NO_3^- + Na^+ + OH^- \rightarrow H_2O + Na^+ + NO_3^-$
    $CH_3CO_2H + Na^+ + OH^- \rightarrow H_2O + CH_3CO_2^- + Na^+$

24. (a) No. They combine to form the weak electrolyte $CH_3CO_2H$ (acetic acid).
    (b) No. They form insoluble $BaSO_4$ (Rule 5).
    (c) Yes. This is a soluble compound (Rule 1).
    (d) No. Insoluble $PbCl_2$ forms (rule 2).
    (e) Yes. This is a soluble compound (Rule 5).
    (f) Yes. HCl is a strong acid.
    (g) Yes. This is a soluble compound and a strong base (Rule 6).

25. (a) 1.68 liters or $1.68 \times 10^3$ ml
    (b) 95.9 ml
26. 0.259 M
27. (a) 598 ml
    (b) 3.81 M
28. 0.100
29. 0.0560 M $Ba^{2+}$
    0.0620 M $OH^-$
    0.0500 M $Cl^-$
30. (a) 121 amu
    (b) 363 amu
    (c) 0.916 N
31. 29.1

32. 0.0170 mole HCl and 0.00850 mole $H_2SO_4$
33. 1.00 N
34. (a) 142 ml
    (b) 284 ml
35. Check your answers against the text.
36. (a) 0.308 M
    (b) 0.317 m
    (c) 0.00568
37. (a) 2.9 M
    (b) 3.3 m
    (c) 0.056
38. ml of A $\times M_A$ = 2 ml of B $\times M_B$
    ml of A $\times N_A$ = ml of A $\times N_B$

## Chapter 6

1. There are many possible answers, including: a stove, a light bulb, a nuclear reactor, and most machines.
2. Food, gasoline, and a battery are a few of many possible answers.
3. (a) kinetic
   (b) kinetic
   (c) potential
4. KE = $\frac{1}{2} mv^2$; 0.5 kg $\times$ (50 km/hr)$^2$ is a larger number than 1 kg $\times$ (25 km/hr)$^2$
5. 17.9 kcal
6. (a) solid $\rightarrow$ gas
   (b) melting of a solid; solid to liquid
   (c) liquid to gas (includes boiling)
   (d) freezing of a gas on cooling it down; reverse of the sublimation process
   (e) the heat that must be supplied to one mole of a solid material at its sublimation temperature to convert it to a gas
7. 59.9 kJ mole$^{-1}$
8. 42.5 kJ mole$^{-1}$

9. (a) $-4762$ kJ ($-$ sign for heat evolved)
   (b) 10.5 g
10. 10.0 g of Fe gives 14.3 g of $Fe_2O_3$ and 73.6 kJ of heat
11. (a) $-1644$ kJ ($-$ sign for heat evolved)
    (b) products
    (c)

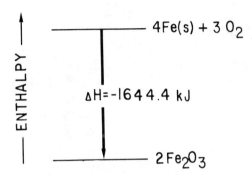

(d) $+411$ kJ mole$^{-1}$ Fe
(e) The enthalpy change for that part of the process represented by $2Fe_2O_3 \rightarrow 4Fe + 3O_2$ would be the same, but the enthalpy change for the entire reaction would differ for

$Fe_2O_3 + 3H_2 \rightarrow 2Fe + 3H_2O$ and
$Fe_2O_3 + 3C \rightarrow 2Fe + 3CO$

12. $-167$ kJ mole$^{-1}$
13. $-226.5$ kJ
14. $-166$ kJ mole$^{-1}$
15. (a) $-904$ kJ

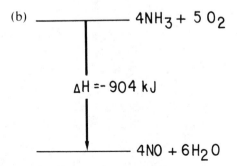

16. (a) $HF(g) \rightarrow H\cdot(g) + F\cdot(g)$
    (b)

    | | | |
    |---|---|---|
    | $2HF \rightarrow H_2 + F_2$ | + 518 kJ |
    | $F_2 \rightarrow 2F\cdot$ | + 151 kJ |
    | $H_2 \rightarrow 2H\cdot$ | + 435 kJ |
    | $2HF \rightarrow 2F\cdot + 2H\cdot$ | +1104 kJ |

    $\Delta H_D = 552$ kJ mole$^{-1}$

(c)

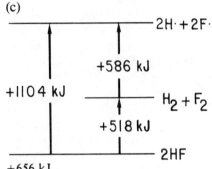

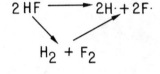

17. +656 kJ
18. −425 kJ mole$^{-1}$

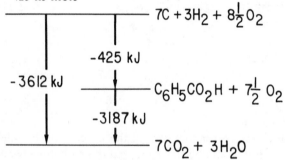

19. +178 kJ

**Chapter 7**

1. (a) −3.0°C
   (b) 152°F
   (c) 279.83°K
   (d) 244.6°K
   (e) −380°F
   (f) −5.98°F

2. 347 ml
3. Use $PV = nRT$ for 5 moles. 112 liters (All original conditions are superfluous information except for $n$.)
4. 1.58 g
5. 170 °C
6. 0.0350 torr
7. 22.3 liter
8. 1.05 g
9. 154 °C
10. $2.97 \times 10^{-3}$ mole
11. 26.2 atm. The tank should not burst.
12. 105 ml
13. $4.71 \times 10^{-3}$ moles
14. 729 torr
15. 50.9 ml
16. 264 ml $H_2$
17. For $PV = nRT$ to be valid, $n$ must be doubled for constant $T$ and $P$.
18. 22.6 liters
19. 145 g mole$^{-1}$
20. 196 g mole$^{-1}$
21. 2.858 g liter$^{-1}$
22. 81.6 g mole$^{-1}$
23. 52.4 liters $SO_2$
24. 23 liters CO
25. 4.76 liters $H_2$
26. 14.6 g Zn
27. 2.646 g liter$^{-1}$
28. 90.4 amu
29. 28.010 amu
30. 45.8 liters
31. Check your answers against the text.
32. 140 ml
33. 0.0891 g Al and 0.0609 g Zn; 59.5% Al
34. 58.5% C

## Chapter 8

1. (a) $1s^2\, 2s^2\, 2p^6\, 3s^2\, 3p^6\, 4s^2\, 3d^5$
   (b) $1s^2\, 2s^2\, 2p^6\, 3s^2\, 3p^6\, 4s^2\, 3d^{10}\, 4p^5$
   (c) $1s^2\, 2s^2\, 2p^6\, 3s^1$
   (d) $1s^2\, 2s^2\, 2p^6\, 3s^2\, 3p^6\, 4s^2\, 3d^{10}\, 4p^4$
   (e) $1s^2\, 2s^2\, 2p^6\, 3s^2\, 3p^6\, 4s^2\, 3d^6$
   (f) $1s^2\, 2s^2\, 2p^6\, 3s^2\, 3p^6\, 4s^2\, 3d^{10}\, 4p^6$
   (g) $1s^2\, 2s^2\, 2p^6\, 3s^2\, 3p^6\, 4s^2\, 3d^{10}\, 4p^6\, 5s^2\, 4d^{10}\, 5p^6\, 6s^2\, 4f^{14}\, 5d^7$
   (h) $1s^2\, 2s^2\, 2p^6\, 3s^2\, 3p^6\, 4s^2\, 3d^4$
2. (a) $1s^2\, 2s^2\, 2p^6\, 3s^2\, 3p^6\, 4s^2\, 3d^{10}\, 4p^6$
   (b) $1s^2\, 2s^2\, 2p^6$
   (c) $1s^2\, 2s^2\, 2p^6\, 3s^2\, 3p^6\, 3d^4$
   (d) $1s^2\, 2s^2\, 2p^6\, 3s^2\, 3p^6\, 3d^3$
   (e) $1s^2\, 2s^2\, 2p^6\, 3s^2\, 3p^6\, 4s^2\, 3d^{10}\, 4p^6\, 5s^2\, 4d^{10}$
   (f) $1s^2\, 2s^2\, 2p^6\, 3s^2\, 3p^6\, 4s^2\, 3d^{10}\, 4p^6\, 5s^2\, 4d^{10}\, 5p^6\, 6s^2\, 4f^{14}\, 5d^{10}$
   (g) $1s^2\, 2s^2\, 2p^6\, 3s^2\, 3p^6\, 3d^6$

3.
   (a)

   3s  3p
   [↿⇂] [↿][ ][ ]

   (b)

   5s  5p
   [↿⇂] [↿⇂][↿][↿]

   (c)

   3d                4s
   [↿⇂][↿⇂][↿⇂][↿][↿]  [↿⇂]

   (d)

   6s
   [↿⇂]

(e)
|3d| | | | | | |4s|
|↑↓|↑|↑|↑|↑| |↑↓|

(f)
|4f| | | | | | | |6s|
|↑|↑| | | | | | |↑↓|

(g)
|4d| | | | | |5s|
|↑|↑|↑|↑|↑| |↑↓|

(h)
|5d| | | | |6s|
|↑|↑|↑|↑| |↑↓|

(i)
|3d| | | | |4s|
|↑|↑|↑| | |↑↓|

4.

(a)
|4s| |4p| | |
|↑↓| |↑|↑|↑|

(e)
|5s|
|↑↓|

(b)
|3d| | | | | |
|↑↓|↑|↑|↑|↑|

(f)
|3d| | | | |
|↑|↑|↑| | |

(c)
|3d| | | | | |
|↑↓|↑↓|↑↓|↑|↑|

(g)
|3d| | | | |
|↑| | | | |

(d)
|3d| | | | |
|↑|↑|↑|↑|↑|

5.  $2s$ $2p$ $3p$ $4s$ $3d$ $5p$ $6s$ $4f$
6.  $2d$, $3f$
7.  (a) 10 electrons
    (b) 14 electrons
    (c) 6 electrons
8.  (a) phosphorus
    (b) manganese
    (c) O, S, Se, Te, Po
9.  (a) Ca
    (b) O
    (c) V
10. (a) As
    (b) V
    (c) Zr
    (d) Rb

11. (a)

$$\overline{|Br|}$$
$$|\overline{Br}-Si-\overline{Br}| \text{ (polar covalent)}$$
$$|\overline{Br}|$$

(b)

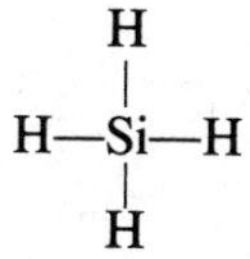

H—Si—H    (polar covalent)

(c) $|N{\equiv}O|^+$ (polar covalent)

(d) $|\overline{N}{=}\overline{O}|^-$ (polar covalent)

(e) $|\overline{F}{-}\overline{N}{=}\overline{N}{-}\overline{F}|$ (N—N pure covalent, N—F polar covalent)

(f)

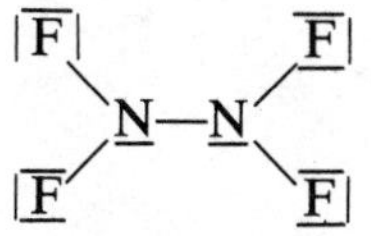

(N—N pure covalent, N—F polar covalent)

(g) H—C≡C—H    (C—C pure covalent, C—H polar covalent)

(h)

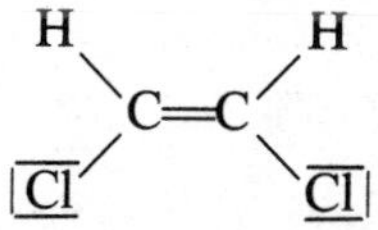

(C—C pure covalent, C—H and C—Cl polar covalent)

(i)

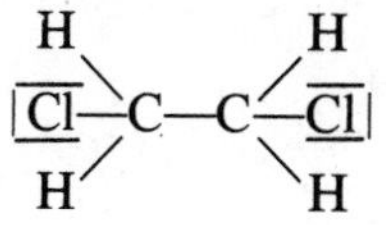

(same as (h))

(j)

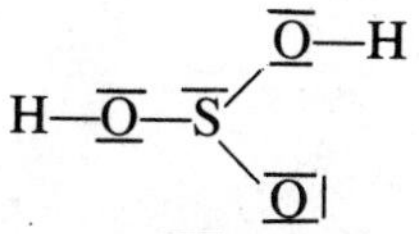

(polar covalent)

(k) $2Rb^+ + |\overline{O}|^{2-}$ (ionic)

12.  (a)

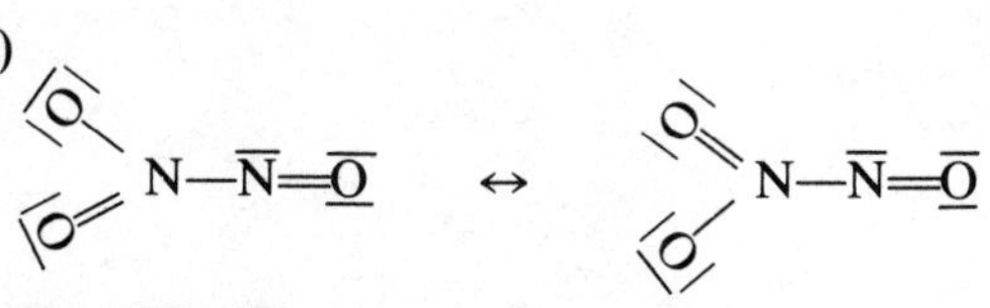

(b) $|\overline{O}{-}\overline{Cl}{-}\overline{O}|^-$

(c)

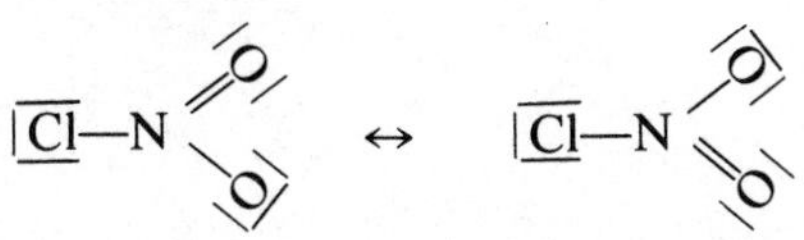

(d) $\overline{O}{=}C{=}\overline{O}$  ↔  $|\overline{O}{-}C{\equiv}O|$  ↔  $|O{\equiv}C{-}\overline{O}|$

(e) $|C{\equiv}O|$

(f) $|\overline{O}{-}\overline{O}{=}\overline{O}|$  ↔  $|\overline{O}{=}\overline{O}{-}\overline{O}|$

(g)

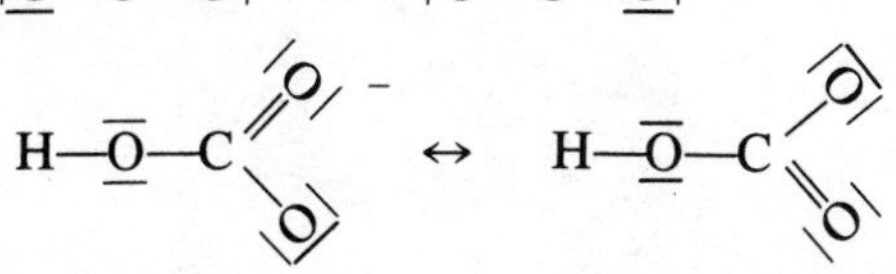

(h)

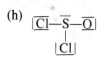

$$\overline{Cl}-\overset{\bullet}{S}-\overline{O}|$$
$$|\ \ \ |$$
$$\ \ \ |\underline{Cl}|$$

(i)

$$\overset{|\overline{O}|}{\underset{|}{}} \quad ^{2-}$$
$$|\overline{O}-\overset{|}{S}-\overline{O}|$$

(j)

$$\overline{F}\ \ |\overline{F}|\ \ \overline{F}|$$
$$\underset{|}{\diagdown}\ \underset{|}{|}\ \diagup$$
$$S$$
$$\diagup\ |\ \diagdown$$
$$\overline{F}\ \ |\underline{F}|\ \ \overline{F}|$$

(k)

$$|\overline{F}|\ \ \overline{F}|$$
$$\underset{|}{|}\ \diagup$$
$$|\overline{F}-P$$
$$\diagup\ \underset{|}{|}\ \diagdown$$
$$|\underline{F}|\ \ \overline{F}|$$

(l) $\overline{O}=\overset{\bullet}{N}-\overline{O}| \ \leftrightarrow\ |\overline{O}-N=\overline{O}\ \leftrightarrow\ \overset{\bullet}{\overline{O}}=\underset{}{N}-\overline{O}|\ \leftrightarrow\ |\overline{O}-N-\underset{\bullet}{\overline{O}}|$

13. (a) $|\overline{F}-\overset{\frown}{Xe}-\overline{F}|$

(b)

$$|\overline{F} \qquad \overline{F}|$$
$$\diagdown\ \diagup$$
$$\overline{Xe}$$
$$\diagup\ \diagdown$$
$$|\underline{F}|\ \ \ \ \ \ \overline{F}|$$

(c)

$$\overline{F}\ \ |\overline{F}|\ \ \overline{F}|$$
$$\diagdown\ |\ \diagup$$
$$|\overline{F}-\overset{|}{Xe}-\overline{F}|$$
$$|$$
$$|\underline{F}|$$

(d) $|\overline{Cl}-\overline{O}|^{-}$

(e) $|\overline{O}-\overline{Cl}-\overline{O}|^{-}$

(f)

$$|\overline{O}-\overset{\overline{\phantom{Cl}}}{Cl}-\overline{O}|^{-}$$
$$|$$
$$|\underline{O}|$$

(g)

$$|\overline{O}|$$
$$|$$
$$|\overline{O}-Cl-\overline{O}|$$
$$|$$
$$|\underline{O}|$$

(h) $Na^{+} + Cl^{-}$

(i)

$$\overset{H}{\diagdown}$$
$$C=\overline{O}$$
$$\diagup$$
$$H$$

(j) $H-C\equiv N|$

14. 11c, triple; 11d, double; 12a, N—O of $NO_2$ part 1.5, other N—O 2.0, N—N single, 12f, 1.5; 12g, O—H single, O—C of HOC single, C—O 1.5; 12k, single

15. (a) Bond order of C—O and one C—C is 2.0; all others are 1.0.

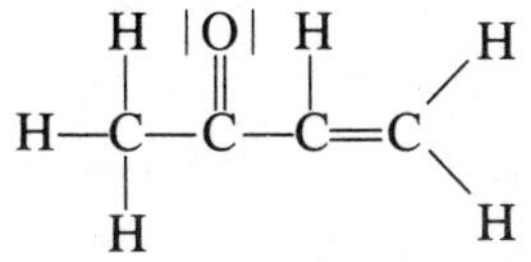

    (b) Bond order of N—O is 1.5, all others 1.0.

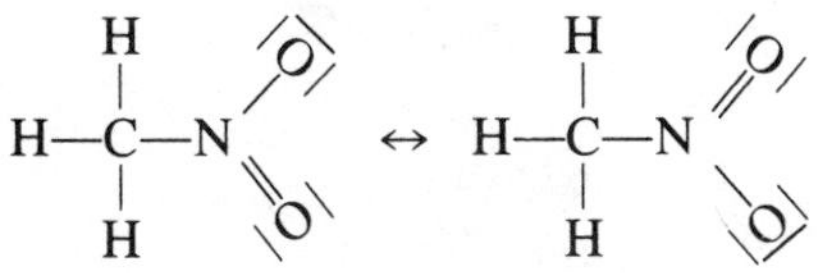

    (c) Bond order of C—O is 1.5; C—N is 1.5; all others 1.0.

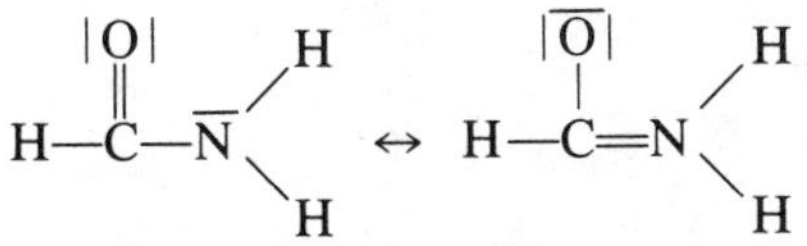

    (d) 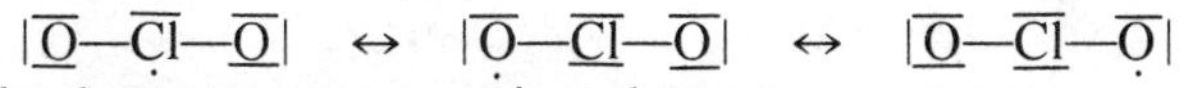 $|\overline{O}-\overline{\underset{.}{Cl}}-\overline{O}|$ ↔ $|\overline{O}-\overline{Cl}-\overline{O}|$ ↔ $|\overline{O}-\overline{Cl}-\overline{O}|$

16. Check your answers against the text.

## Chapter 9

1.  (a) N = −2, H = +1       (f) O = −2, Mo = +6
    (b) H = +1, Cl = −1, N = −1   (g) O = −2, Cr = +6
    (c) N = +3, Cl = −1         (h) O = −2, S = +6
    (d) O = −2, N = +4        (i) K = +1, O = −2, Mn = +6
    (e) H = +1, O = −2, N = +5   (j) H = +1, O = −2, P = +5

2.  (a) Cu
    (b) $NO_3^-$
    (c) Cu
    (d) $NO_3^-$

3.  (a) $MnO_4^-$
    (b) $SO_3^{2-}$
    (c) $MnO_4^-$
    (d) $SO_3^{2-}$

4.  (a) sulfur (VI) oxide         (i) phosphoric acid
    (b) chromium (III) oxide     (j) sodium phosphate
    (c) selenium (IV) oxide      (k) phosphorous acid
    (d) titanium (III) chloride    (l) sulfuric acid
    (e) copper (II) chloride      (m) sufurous acid
    (f) silver (II) oxide          (n) sodium sulfate
    (g) lead (IV) oxide          (o) sodium hydrogen sulfate
    (h) nitrogen (III) chloride    (p) potassium sulfite

5. hydrogen sulfide plus nitric acid yields sulfur plus nitrogen (II) oxide plus water (the coefficients could be mentioned if desired).

6. (a) +7
   (b) +5
   (c) +6
   (d) +5
   (e) +4
   (f) +4
   (g) +2
   (h) +5
   (i) +3

7. (a) −1
   (b) −3
   (c) −2
   (d) −4
   (e) −4
   (f) −2

8. (a) $SiO_2$
   (b) $TiS_2$
   (c) $Cl_2O_7$
   (d) $Ba_2C$
   (e) $GaS_2$
   (f) $As_2S_5$

9. (a) $2H^+ + 2NO_3^- + 3H_2S \rightarrow 3S + 2NO + 4H_2O$
   (b) $Pb + PbO_2 + 2H_2SO_4 \rightarrow 2PbSO_4 + 2H_2O$
   (c) $3H_2SO_4 + 6FeSO_4 + KClO_3 \rightarrow 3Fe_2(SO)_4 + KCl + 3H_2O$
   (d) $H_2O + 2MnO_4^- + 3CN^- \rightarrow 2MnO_2 + 2OH^- + 3CNO^-$
   (e) $4H^+ + 4NO_3^- + 3Se \rightarrow 3SeO_2 + 4NO + 2H_2O$
   (f) $4H_2O + 6S_2O_3^{2-} + 2MnO_4^- \rightarrow 3S_4O_6^{2-} + 2MnO_2 + 8OH^-$
   (g) $2H^+ + 3SO_2 + Cr_2O_7^{2-} \rightarrow 3SO_4^{2-} + 2Cr^{3+} + H_2O$
   (h) $C_2O_4^{2-} + MnO_4^{2-} \rightarrow 2CO_3^{2-} + MnO_2$
   (i) $2KOH + Cl_2 \rightarrow KCl + KClO + H_2O$
   (j) $5PbO_2 + 3H_2SO_4 + 2MnSO_4 \rightarrow 5PbSO_4 + 2H_2O + 2HMnO_4$
   (k) $2OH^- + 2CrO_2^- + 3ClO^- \rightarrow 2CrO_4^{2-} + H_2O + 3Cl^-$
   (l) $H_3AsO_4 + 4Zn + 8HNO_3 \rightarrow AsH_3 + 4Zn(NO_3)_2 + 4H_2O$
   (m) $K_2Cr_2O_7 + 14HCl \rightarrow 2CrCl_3 + 3Cl_2 + 7H_2O + 2KCl$
   (n) $CH_3OH + 2MnO_4^- \rightarrow 2MnO_2 + CO_2 + 2OH^- + H_2O$
   (o) $3H_2O + 3OH^- + P_4 \rightarrow PH_3 + 3H_2PO_2^-$
   (p) $4Fe(OH)_2 + 2H_2O + O_2 \rightarrow 4Fe(OH)_3$

10. Check your answers against the text.

## Chapter 10

1. −1.11 °C
2. 131 amu
3. 82.2 °C
4. 159 amu

5.  0.10 m ethylene glycol, 0.07 m NaCl, 0.05 m CaBr$_2$, 0.10 m NaCl
6.  52.2 amu
7.  $-66.6\,°C$
8.  89.6 °C
9.  $-3.51\,°C$ freezing point, 100.97 °C boiling point
10.  $-8.66\,°C$
11.  0.594 °C molal$^{-1}$
12. to 14.   Check your answer against the text.
15.  0.097 mole of HF and 0.003 mole H$^+$ and 0.003 mole F$^-$
16.  6.70 kg or 5.97 liters